S. V. Gupta

Units of Measurement

History, Fundamentals and Redefining the SI Base Units

Second Edition

S. V. Gupta
National Physical Laboratory
New Delhi, India

ISSN 0933-033X   ISSN 2196-2812   (electronic)
Springer Series in Materials Science
ISBN 978-3-030-43968-2   ISBN 978-3-030-43969-9   (eBook)
https://doi.org/10.1007/978-3-030-43969-9

This Springer imprint is published by the registered company Springer Nature Switzerland AG
The registered company address is: Gewerbestrasse 11, 6330 Cham, Switzerland

In loving memory of my wife Mrs. Prem Gupta

Preface to the Second Edition

Doing well in the first edition of the book has inspired me to write the second edition. The necessity and urgency arose due to redefining the SI base units in terms of fundamental constants and realization of the base units in terms of the defining constants. Each of the SI base units has been redefined in terms of a fundamental constant. Some of the units like second and metre were derived from the fundamental constants. Like the second was the duration of 9 192 631 770 periods of the radiation corresponding to the transition between the two hyperfine levels of the ground state of the cesium-133 atom. Now only the wording has changed. Same was the case of the base unit of length—metre, it was the distance travelled by light in vacuum during the interval of 1/299 792 458 of a second. Now the second is such that velocity of light is 299 792 458 ms^{-1}. In case of base units of mass, electric current and temperature, there are drastic changes. The unit of mass—kilogram—is such that Planck's constant has a predefined value. Similarly unit of electric current—ampere—is such that electronic charge is 1.602 176 634 $\times 10^{-19}$ C. Boltzmann constant is used to define kelvin—the unit of temperature.

Realization of kilogram is drastically changed. The two methods, namely, electromechanical method through Kibble balance and XRCD (X-ray-crystal-density) method, have been described. Basics of Boltzmann constant and its determination by various methods have been described. Any of the methods preferably acoustic gas thermometry may be used to establish kelvin in terms of Boltzmann. On taking Planck's constant and electronic charge as redefining constants, i.e. each has a fixed value in SI units with zero uncertainty, Josephson constant and quantum Hall resistance have also become constant, so can be used to define as other electrical SI units.

I wish to thank Dr. D. K. Aswal, Director of National Physical Laboratory and President of the Metrology Society of India, New Delhi, who agreed to bring out this book.

Delhi   S. V. Gupta
January 2020

Preface to the First Edition

Professor A. R. Verma, former Director National Physical Laboratory, New Delhi inspired me for writing about the units of measurements as a chapter in my forthcoming book on Practical mass measurement. While travelling through India I have found excellent examples of metrology in our historical monuments and old temples. In Tiruchirappalli, I visited a temple which was in the centre of the city and had several identical big arch-shaped gates. The pathways were perpendicular to each other and all the gates along the road were exactly in one straight line. Inside the innermost sanctuary where the main deity was placed there was a small opening in the roof. The opening was positioned in such a way that every morning when the sun rose its first ray would pass through this opening and fall on the deity round the year. This made me think about the metrology in ancient times. So I wrote a chapter on metrology in olden days and its development in brief up to the present.

The International System of Units of measurement adopted in 1962 has seven base units as well as a host of derived and dimensionless units. The International Bureau of Weights and Measures occasionally publishes a booklet, which is an authentic document. Most of the National Measurement Laboratories like those in the USA and the UK strictly copy it and, in some cases, translate the document in their national languages. To make it clear that the number of base units need not be seven all the time, I discussed various three- and four-dimensional measuring systems. I established that minimum four base units are required in terms of which all other units of measurements can be expressed.

I have also attempted to provide a brief history of CGS and FPS systems. It has been found that FPS system is a few hundred years older that CGS or metric systems. Most of the national laboratories have strictly followed the latest available BIPM document. I have also followed the BIPM document on SI units 8th Edition of 2006. In this edition, a chapter on quantities, units and dimensions along with units used in specialized fields of health, biology and human health have been included. I have included them as such with all their notes and explanations. The new elements that I have added are the reasoning to arrive at the derived units, the explanation of base unit of ampere and the intensity of illumination, and the unification of electrostatic and electromagnetic units. Chapter 8 of the book deals with the future definitions of base units and their effects. One of the chapters also gives the brief life history of scientists who have been honoured by assigning their name to a unit.

The book is written in such a way that it caters to the need of one and all. Students of class X and above can profitably use Chapters 1 to 8 barring certain portions of Chapter 1, 2, 3 and 5. Biographies of the scientists associated with units of measurements will definitely be inspiring to young students and metrologists. The last two chapters are for specialists who are interested in redefining the units of measurements or in the evolution of a new measurement system based on fundamental constants. Metrologists at all levels will be delighted to know the origin of the names for base units and derived units.

I acknowledge the great help which I received from Dr. R. S. Davis, Head of Mass BIPM, Professor A. J. Wallard, Director BIPM, and Dr. Claudine Thomas, Secretary Consultative Committee of Units (CCU) at BIPM. They explained to me the meaning of the redefinition of the unit, keeping the same name and effect as the old unit. I wish to thank Dr. Vikram Kumar, Director National Physical Laboratory and President of the Metrology Society of India, New Delhi, who agreed to bring out this document. I will fail in my duty if I do not express my most sincere thanks to the referees to whom manuscript was sent. Each of them has gone into minute details and offered editorial suggestions. My thanks are also due to my daughter Mrs. Reeta Gupta, Scientist, National Physical Laboratory, New Delhi.

Delhi   S. V. Gupta
June 2009

Contents

Acronyms

Acronyms for International Organizations

BAAS	British Association for the Advancement of Science
BIH	Bureau International de l'Heure
CARICOM	Caribbean Community
CIE	International Commission on Illumination/Commission Internationale de l'Éclairage
IAU	International Astronomical Union
ICRP	International Commission on Radiological Protection
ICRU	International Commission on Radiation Units and Measurements
IEC	International Electrotechnical Commission/Commission Électrotechnique Internationale
IERS	International Earth Rotation and Reference Systems Service
ISO	International Organization for Standardization
IUPAC	International Union of Pure and Applied Chemistry
IUPAP	International Union of Pure and Applied Physics
OIML	International Organization of Legal Metrology/Organisation Internationale de Métrologie Légale
SUNAMCO	Commission for Symbols, Units, Nomenclature, Atomic Masses and Fundamental Constants, IUPAP
TAI	International Atomic Time/Temps Atomique International
WHO	World Health Organization

Acronyms for Metre Convention and Associated Organizations

BIPM	International Bureau of Weights and Measures/Bureau International des Poids et Mesures
CCAUV	Consultative Committee for Acoustics, Ultrasound and Vibration/ Comité Consultatif de l'Acoustique, des Ultrasons et des Vibrations

CCDS*	Consultative Committee for the Definition of the Second/Comité Consultatif pour la définition de la Seconde, see CCTF
CCE*	Consultative Committee for Electricity/Comité Consultatif d'Électricité, see CCEM
CCEM	(formerly the CCE) Consultative Committee for Electricity and Magnetism/Comité Consultatif d'Électricité et Magnétisme
CCL	Consultative Committee for Length/Comité Consultatif des Longueurs
CCM	Consultative Committee for Mass and Related Quantities/Comité Consultatif pour la Masse et les Grandeurs Apparentées
CCPR	Consultative Committee for Photometry and Radiometry/Comité Consultatif de Photométrie et Radiométrie
CCQM	Consultative Committee for Amount of Substance: Metrology in Chemistry/Comité Consultatif pour la Quantité de Matière : Métrologie en Chimie
CCRI	Consultative Committee for Ionizing Radiation/Comité Consultatif des Rayonnements Ionisants
CCT	Consultative Committee for Thermometry/Comité Consultatif de Thermométrie
CCTF	(formerly the CCDS) Consultative Committee for Time and Frequency/Comité Consultatif du Temps et des Fréquences
CCU	Consultative Committee for Units/Comité Consultatif des Unités
CGPM	General Conference on Weights and Measures/Conférence Générale des Poids et Mesures
CIPM	International Committee for Weights and Measures/Comité International des Poids et Mesures
CODATA	Committee on Data for Science and Technology IAU
CR	Comptes Rendus of the Conférence Générale des Poids et Mesures, CGPM
PV	Procès-Verbaux of the Comité International des Poids et Mesures, CIPM

Note: * Organizations marked with an asterisk either no longer exist or operate under a different acronym.

Acronyms for Scientific Terms

CGS	Three-dimensional coherent system of units based on the three
EPT-76	Provisional Low Temperature Scale of 1976/Échelle provisoire de température de 1976
IPTS-68	International Practical Temperature Scale of 1968
ITS-90	International Temperature Scale of 1990 mechanical units centimetre, gram and second

MKS	System of units based on the three mechanical units metre, kilogram and second
MKSA	Four-dimensional system of units based on the metre, kilogram, second and the ampere
SI	International System of Units/Système International d'Unités
TCG	Geocentric Coordinated Time/Temps-coordonnée Géocentrique
TT	Terrestrial Time
UTC	Coordinated Universal Time
VSMOW	Vienna Standard Mean Ocean Water

Chapter 1
Old Units of Measurement in India

The examples of old units of measurement have been divided into three parts, namely, Sect. 1.1 is for time intervals, Sect. 1.2 is for length intervals and Sect. 1.3 is for weight and volume.

1.1 Time Intervals

1.1.1 Introduction

1.1.1.1 Source of Information

Religious activities and scientific activities are also made part of the religious routine. Hindu religion is basically the way of living through various faiths. All literature regarding measurement is also hidden in the old religious books. There are 4 *Veda* and 18 *puran*s like *Srimad Bhagwad Puran, Bhavishya Puran, Agni Puran, Narad Puran, Vishnu Puran, Harivans Puran* and so on. *Srimad Bhagwad Gita, Mahabharat* and *Ramayan* are the other scriptures where knowledge is hidden under slokas (verses). Many Sastras like *Surya Siddhant* need to be mentioned.

Astronomy was the most advanced field out of the best of six sciences enunciated in *Vedas* [1]. So measurement of time and length was of paramount importance to ancient Indians.

1.1.1.2 Concept of Time

According to *Surya Siddhant* [2], the time is of two kinds. The former is continuous endless cycle with no origin or end, which destroys all (animates and

© Springer Nature Switzerland AG 2020
S. V. Gupta, *Units of Measurement*, Springer Series in Materials Science 122,
https://doi.org/10.1007/978-3-030-43969-9_1

in-animates) and is also the cause of creation and preservation of everything. It is a continuous entity with no beginning or end. The second one is the time interval, which can be known; this is again of two kinds. One is measurable and the other is immeasurable. It may be immeasurable due to either its largeness like the day of *Brahma* of 4.32 billion years or being very small like *truti* 0.031 μs in Table 1.8.

1.1.1.3   Types of Time Scales

According to Surya Siddhant [2], there are nine types of standard time scales. Their names are (1) *Brahma*, (2) *Divya*, (3) *Prajapati*, (4) *Pitra*, (5) Jupiter, (6) Solar, (7) Terrestrial, (8) Lunar and (9) Sidereal. Each of these depends upon how the day is defined. Out of these nine scales, four, namely, Sidereal, Lunar, Terrestrial and Solar, are mostly used [2].

Terrestrial Day

The time between two consecutive sunrises is the terrestrial day. Its Hindi name is *Savan*.

Sidereal Day

Duration of one complete revolution of starry sphere is the Sidereal day. The sidereal day, in terms of SI units, is 23 h 56 m 4.1 s, slightly shorter than the solar day. The reason is the Earth's orbital motion about the Sun.

Solar Day

The solar day is the duration of time, which the Earth takes to make one complete revolution on its axis relative to the Sun. The solar day is the duration of day plus night at the equinoctial time (when the duration of day and night is equal).

Lunar Day

The lunar day is the time interval which Earth's Moon takes to complete one rotation on its axis with respect to the Sun. Due to tidal locking, it is also the time the Moon takes to complete one orbit around Earth and return to the same phase [3]. Lunar day is also the duration which Moon takes to describe 12° from the Sun.

1.1.2 Time Intervals

Oldest system for time measurement comes from India. Indian scriptures are full of information about the use of different time intervals. Smaller time intervals are in terms of the fractions of the day, while larger time intervals are multiples of a day or year. The span of time intervals is vast. *Vedic* and *Puranic* texts describe units of time intervals from *truti*, which is as small as 0.031 μs, to the age of *Brahma*, which is as large as 311.04 trillion years.

There are quite a few versions of smaller time intervals especially time intervals which are fraction of a day. From a day onward, the time intervals are practically the same.

1.1.2.1 Mention of Permanu, Anu and Treserenu in Shrimad Bhagwad Puran

The verse 1 of the *Srimad Bhagwad* Puran [5] states that the smallest particle of material substance, which has not yet combined with any other similar particles, is called "*permanu*, परमाणु" (a sub-atomic particle of matter). *Permanu* exists in both the dormant and manifest states of material existence. It is the combination of more than one *permanu* (sub-atomic particle) which gives rise to the illusory concept of a (material) unit. A combination of two *permanu* constitutes an "anu, अणु" (atom); and three "anu" (atoms) make one "*tresrenu*, त्रसरेणु" [6]. *Tresrenu* is visible to the naked eye and can be seen wandering in the air while viewed through rays of sunlight entering a dark room through a latticed window. Perhaps, this was the beginning of concept of defining time intervals in terms of *permanu* and *anu*.

1.1.2.2 Time Intervals as Fraction of a Day

Two sets of time intervals in which day has been divided into 182,250,000 parts [6–8], smallest part being named as truti equal to 473 μs approximately, are given in Tables 1.1 and 1.2.

Similar to the above table, there is another set of time intervals in which *permanu* and *anu* have been replaced by celestial atoms [8].

1.1.2.3 Time Intervals in Terms of Nimesh

In some scriptures, it is given that 1 निमेष is the time taken to pronounce a letter with one syllable *maatraa* मात्रा or time taken for twinkling of eye.

Table 1.1 Smaller time intervals as given in Bhagwat

Name in Roman script	In Hindi	Equivalence in SI
permanu	परमाणु	Sub-atomic particle, indivisible and cannot contain life
2 *permanu*	1 *anu* अणु	Combination of *permanu* is the smallest particle, which can freely exist
3 *aṇu*	1 *tresreṇu* त्रसरेणु	A particle of dust; this can be seen coming from a window flying around in sunrays, can contain life and is divisible
3 *tresareṇu*	*truṭi* त्रुटि	Whatever time the Sun takes to cross 3 Tresarenu is Truti, which equals nearly 473 μs
100 *truṭi*	*vedha* वेघ	47.3 ms
3 *vedha*	*lava* लव	0.14 s
3 *lava*	*nimeṣh* निमेष	0.43 s
3 *nimesh*	*kṣaṇa* or *chhun* क्षण	1.28 s
5 *kṣaṇa* or *chhun*	*kaaṣṭhaa* काष्ठा	6.4 s
15 *kāṣṭhā*	*laghu* लघू	1.6 min
15 *laghu*	*dand*, nadika दण्ड, नाडिका	24 min
2 *dand* or nadika	*muhoort* मुहूर्त	48 min
6 or 7 nadika	*prahar* प्रहर	Variable value depends upon time of the year
30 *muhooūrt*	*ahorātram* (Day) अहोरात्रम	24 h
30 *ahorātram*	*maash* (Month) मास	30 days
2 *maash*	*ritu* (Season) रितु	2 months
3 *ritu*	*ayan* अयन	6 months
2 *ayan*	*samvatsara* (year) समवत्सर	360 days

Note *Depending upon the increase or decrease of the day time, there are 6 or 7 *nadika* in a *prahar*, which is also called as *yam*. Prahar is one-fourth of the day or night. The *prahar* is not of a fixed time. It depends upon whether we are talking about it for a day or for a night. In summer daytime, its value will be bigger in comparison to that at night time. The reverse will happen in winter season

**Dividing 86,400 s (the duration of the complete day) by number of partitions made of the day gives the value of the smallest time interval. The value of other time intervals is calculated by multiplying with successive multiplication numbers

Time Interval from Vishnu Puran

There is a set of time intervals given in *Vishnu Puran* [9] and *Harivans Puran* [10]; the day has been divided into 405,000.

Table 1.2 Smaller units of time used in the Vedas

Name in Roman script		In Hindi	Equivalence in SI
Celestial atom अणु		It is the smallest particle, which can freely exist	
6 celestial atoms	*tresrenu* त्रसरेणु	A particle of dust; this can be seen coming from a window flying around in sunrays, can contain life and is divisible	
3 *tresrenu*	1 *truti*	त्रुटि	473 μs
100 *truti*	1 *vedha*	वेध	47.3 ms
3 *vedha*	1 *lava*	लव	0.14 s
3 *lava*	1 *nimesh*	निमेष	0.43 s
3 *nimesh*	1 *kshana*	क्षण	1.28 s
5 *kshana*	1 *kaashthaa*	काष्ठा	6.4 s
15 *kashtha*	1 *laghu*	लघू	1.6 min
15 *laghu*	1 *nadika* or *dand*	नाडिका दण्ड	24 min
2 *dand*	1 *muhoort*	महूरत	48 min
6 or 7 *dand*	1 *yam*	यम	Variable
4 *yam*	1 day or night	दिन य रात	Variable
8 *yam*	1 day and night	दिन और रात	24 h

Table 1.3 Time intervals in Vishnu Puraan

Name in Roman script		In Hindi	Equivalence in SI
nimesh		निमेष	0.2133 s
15 *nimesh*	*kaashthaa*	काष्ठा	3.2 s
30 *kaashthaa*	*kalaa*	कला	1.6 min
30 *kalaa*	*muhoort*	महूरत	48 min
30 *muhoort*	day and night	दिन और रात	24 h
15 days	1 *paksh*	पक्ष	
2 *paksh*	1 *maash*	मास	
2 maash	*ritu*	रितु	
3 *ritu*	1 *ayan*	अयन	
2 *ayan*	1 year	वर्ष	

Two ayans are, respectively, named as *Uttarayan* उत्तरायन, and *Dakshinayan* दक्षिणायन.

Time Intervals from Bhavishya Puran

Verse 231.15 of *Vishnu Puran* [9] states that for humans, Sun divides time into day and night. The day is for work and night is for sleep. A similar set of time intervals as given in Table 1.3 with two added steps from *kalaa* कला to *chhun* क्षन

Table 1.4 Smaller time intervals given in Bhavishya Puraan

Name in Roman script		Hindi	Equivalence in SI
nimesh		निमेष	0.018 s
15 *nimesh*	1 *kaashthaa*	काष्ठा	0.266 s
30 *kaashthaa*	1 *kalaa*	कला	8 s
30 *kalaa*	1 *kshan or chhan*	क्षण	4 min
12 *kshan* or *chhan*	*muhoort*	महूरत	48 min
30 *muhoort*	1 day and night	दिन और रात	24 h
30 day	1 month	मास	
2 months	1 *ritu*	रितु	
3 seasons	1 *ayan*	अयन	
2 ayan	1 *samvatsar*	समवतसर	

Table 1.5 Smaller time interval with an extra step Chhun and muhoort

Name in Roman script		In Hindi	Equivalence in SI
1 *nimesh*		निमेष	0.018 s
15 *nimesh*	1 *kaashthaa*	काष्ठा	2.7 s
30 *kaashthaa*	1 *kalaa*	कला	8 s
30 *kalaa*	1 *chhun*	क्षण	4 min
6 *chhun*	1 *ghadi*	घडिं	24 min
2 *ghadi*	1 *muhoort*	महूरत	48 min
30 *muhoort*	1 day	दिन	24 h
30 days	1 month	मास	
15 days	1 *paksh*	पक्ष	
2 *paksh*	1 month	मास	
2 months	1 season	रितु	
3 seasons	1 *ayan*	अयन	
2 *ayan*	1 year, Samvatsar	समवतसर	

and *chun* to *muhoort* महूरत are given in *Bhavishya Puran* [11]. These are given in Table 1.4 (4,860,000 parts in day).

A similar table with an extra step from *kala* कला to *chhunn* क्षन, *chhun* क्षण to *ghadi* घडिं and *ghadi* to *muhoort* महूरत [10] is given Table 1.5. A day is 4 860 000 parts.

1.1.2.4   Smaller Time Intervals in Steps of 60

Time Intervals Given in Steps of 60

Shushma [12] gave a set of time intervals in steps of 60. These are given in Table 1.6. Here we see that smallest time interval is *tatpar* त्तपर. It is 777 600 000th part of the day i.e. 0.111 ms.

Table 1.6 Smaller time intervals in terms of tatpar

Name in Roman script		In Hindi	Equivalence in SI
tatpar		त्तपर	0.111 ms
60 tatpar	1 paraa	परा	6.667 ms
60 para	1 vilipt	विलिपत	0.4 s
60 vilipit	1 lipt	लिपत	24 s
60 lipt	1 ghatikaa or dand	घटिका	1440 s
60 ghatikaa	1 day and night	दिन और रात	86,400 s

Table 1.7 Smaller time intervals from Surya Siddhant

Name in Roman script		Hindi	Equivalence in SI
pran		प्राण	4 s
6 pran	1 pal	पल	24 s
60 pal	1 ghatika	घटिका	24 min
60 ghatika	1 nakshatra sidereal day	नक्षेत्र आहोराज्म	24 h
30 nakshatra	1 maash	मास	30 days

A set of smaller time intervals is given by Sushma Gupta [12]. In which the complete day has been divided into 291,600,000 parts in six unequal steps, the smallest of the time interval is truti which is approximately 0.0296 ms.

Yet, another set of smaller time intervals is given by the same author [12], in which the day is divided into 725,920,000 parts, smallest time interval named as truti which is equivalent to 0.0033333 s (Table 1.7).

Time Intervals from Surya Siddhant

A set of smaller time intervals is given in *Surya Siddhant* [13] and reproduced in Table 1.7. It may be seen that steps are in terms of 60 or its sub-multiple. Smallest time interval is 4 s, which is suitable for day-to-day use.

Time Intervals with Multiple Names

In the following Table 1.8, it may be seen that different names have been assigned to the same time interval. Source is Hindu units of time from Wikipedia [14].

Time Interval in Steps of 30

A set of time intervals in steps of 30 except the first step for *truti* [14] is given in Table 1.9. Here, a complete day is divided into 2,430,000,000 parts.

Table 1.8 Smaller time intervals with multiple names

Name in Roman script		Hindi	Equivalence in SI
truti		त्रुटि	0.031 μs
60 truti	renu	रेणु	1.86 μs
60 renu	lava	लव	0.11 ms
60 lava	līkṣaka	लिकषक	6.696 ms
60 likshaka	lipta	लिपत	0.401 s
	vipala	विपल	
60 lipta	pal	पल	24.1056 s
	vighaṭi	विघटि	
	vinaadī	विनाडि	
60 vighati	ghaṭi	घटि	24 min
	naadī	नाडि	
	dand	दँड	
2 ghati	muhoort	महूरत	48 min
60 ghati	nakṣatra	नक्षेत्र	24 h
30 muhoort	ahoratram	आहौरात्रम	24 h

Table 1.9 Time intervals in steps of 30

Name in Roman script		In Hindi	Equivalence SI
truti		त्रुटि	35.5 μs
100 truti	tatpara	त्तपर	3.55 ms
30 tatpara	nimesh	निमेष	106.7 ms
30 nimesh	kaaṣṭhaa	काष्ठा	3.2 s
30 kaashthaa	kalaa	कला	1.6 min
30 kala	muhoort	महूरत	48 min
30 muhoort	nakṣatra, ahorātram	नक्षेत्र आहौरात्रम	24 h

Ahoratram आहौरात्रम is the sidereal day

Table 1.10 Smaller range of Time intervals

Name in Roman script		In Hindi	Equivalence in SI
1 vipal		विपल	0.4 s
60 vipal	1 pal	पल	24 s
2 pal	1 kalaa	कला	48 s
30 kalaa	1 ghati	घटि	24 min
2.5 ghati	1 hora	हौरा	1 h

Another set of time intervals given in [15] with fewer steps is cited in Table 1.10. In this set, the day has been divided into 9000 parts, smallest time interval is vital equivalent to 0.4 s.

1.1.3 Sidereal Metrics

Time measurement in ancient India under the heading sidereal metrics [16] is given in Table 1.11. The sidereal day is the duration between two consecutive sunrises. In this case, one complete day has been divided into 21,600 parts.

1.1.4 Time Intervals in Chanakiya Arthsashtra

The time intervals as given by Chanakiya [17] are tabulated in Table 1.12. Here, a day is 1,440,000 parts.

Table 1.11 Sidereal metrics

Name in Roman script		In Hindi	Equivalence in SI
permanu		परमाणू	4 s
6 *permanu*	*vighati*	वघटि	24 s
60 *vighati*	*Gadhuya*	घडि	1440
2 *gadhuya*	*muhoort*	महूरत	2880 s
30 *muhoort*	*nakshatra ahoratram*	नक्षेत्र आहौरात्रम	86,400 s

Table 1.12 Time intervals

Name of the units		SI equivalent	By Patrick
tuta		0.06 s	0.053 s
2 *tuta*	1 *lava*	0.12 s	0.107 s
2 *lava*	1 *nimesa*	0.24 s	0.2133 s
5 *nimesa*	1 *kasta*	1.2 s	3.2 s
30 *kasta*	1 *kala*	36 s	36 s
40 *kala*	1 *nalika*	24 min	24 min
2 *nalika*	1 *muhurta*	48 min	48 min
15 *Muhurta*	1 day or 1 night of the month of *Chaitra* or *Asvayuja*	12 h	12 h
30 *muhurta*	One day and night	24 h 86,400 s	24 h
15 complete days	1 fortnight	15×24 h	360 h
2 fortnights	1 month	30×24 h	720 h
2 months	1 season	60×24 h	1440 h
3 seasons	1 *ayan*	180×24 h	4320 h
2 *ayan*	1 year	360×24 h	8664 h
5 year	1 *yug*		5 years

The durations of day or night are variable. But duration of one day plus ensuing night, i.e. one sunrise to next, is practically constant and is taken as twenty-four hours. There is a particular day in *Chaitra* (March–April) and *Asvayuja* (September–October) when durations of day and night are equal. 15 *Muhroot* in the table refers to that day or night. For example, 23 March and 23 September were such days in 2017. Hence, a step of 30 *muhroot* must be introduced after the row of 15 *Muhroot*. This will help to establish the value of *Muhroot* as 48 min. Rest of the time intervals will be defined in terms of one complete day and night, usually referred to as one day.

The two fortnights are Bright *Paksh* during which Moon waxes and Krishna *Paksh* during which it wanes.

There are two *Ayan*, namely, *Uttarayan* which starts with cooler season, and the other is called *Daksinayana* which begins with rainy season [17] (2.20.61). If Sun is on *Uttar* (North) of equator it is *Uttarayan*, and if it is south of equator it is *Daksinayana*.

1.1.5   Multiplicity in Smaller Time Intervals

We know, as evidenced by the ancient literature, that Astronomy was the favourite subject in ancient India needing knowledge of smaller time intervals. All scientific work was carried out by sages living away from the cities and towns. These sages were respected by one and all because of their devotion to their thoughts. Each sage had its own school, which was isolated from the other schools. Each sage interested in astronomy divided the day into different steps of various magnitudes giving rise to different sets of time intervals.

One may notice that there are fewer sets for time intervals of the multiples of a day. In fact, there is almost uniformity in larger time intervals which are multiples of a year.

It has been seen that though the different sets of time interval given above are in terms of the multiple or fractions of a day, the day is chosen as per the standard time scale adopted. However, a practical way of realizing a time interval equivalent of 1/60th of the day is defined, which is independent of the adopted type of the day.

1.1.6   Realization of Naadika: A Standard of a Time Interval

One *naadika* is one-sixtieth of the day, i.e. 24 min. This term, though with different names, is present in all the sets of time interval.

The method of realizing *naadika* a unit of time interval has been given in *Srimad Bhagwad Puran* [4]. This is the time taken for sinking of the vessel of specified mass, capacity and material with a hole of specified diameter in its bottom when placed on still water.

Specification of the Vessel: A cylindrical vessel of copper of mass 6 pal and capacity 1 *prasth* of water.

Specifications of hole: The hole was to be made by the cylindrical plug of gold of mass 4 *maashaa* and length 4 *angul,* thus specifying the diameter of plug of the hole drilled in the vessel.

The author could not find the authentic conversions of *pal* and *prasth* in metric units. However, one author has taken 6 Pal = 8 Tola and 1 prasth as 14 oz. This roughly gives mass of the vessel as 100 g and I prasth of water as 400 g. The other author has taken 8 *pal* = 1 *prasth* = 400 g, giving 1 *pal* = 50 g and mass of the vessel as 300 g.

However, the diameter of the hole as given by both the authors is the same. This comes out to be approximately 0.980 mm.

1.1.7 Lunar Metrics

Time intervals depending upon the relative motion of Moon with respect to the Sun give Lunar metrics. The system is used by Hindu community for all religious purposes [18].

1.1.7.1 Tithi

In Vedic time keeping, a *tithi* तिथि [18] or lunar day is defined as the time taken for the longitudinal angle between the Moon and the Sun to increase by 12°. *Tithi* begins at varying times of day and varies in duration from 19 to 26 h.

1.1.7.2 Paksh

A *paksh* or lunar fortnight consists of 15 *tithi.*

1.1.7.3 Lunar Month

Two *pakhsa* make a *maash*, i.e. lunar month [19] or lunar month (approximately 29.5 days). The *paksh* is between New Moon and Full Moon. It is called *gaura* (bright) or *shukla paksh*. The other one between Full Moon and New Moon is *krishna* (dark) *paksh.*

1.1.7.4 Lunar Ritu, Ayan

Two lunar months make a *ritu* and 3 ritu makes an ayan. The lunar time intervals are given in Table 1.13 [20, 21].

Table 1.13 *Lunar Tithi. Pakash, month and year*

Units in Roman script		In Hindi
tithi		तिथि
15 *tithi*	1 *paksh*	पक्ष
2 *paksh*	1 lunar month	चन्द्रॅमास
2 lunar month	1 *ritu*	रितु
3 *ritu*	1 *ayan*	अयान
2 *ayan*	1 lunar year	चन्द्रवर्ष

1.1.8 Adjustment in Calendars

1.1.8.1 Gregorian Calendar

Gregorian calendar is a most worldwide used calendar. It is based upon the movement of Earth around the Sun. The Earth takes 365.25 days to complete its revolution about the Sun. Normally, a solar year consists of 365 days, February having 28 days. To compensate for the 0.25 day, for every 4 years, there is a leap year, in which February has 29 days.

1.1.8.2 Lunar Calendar

Out of many Hindu calendars, the most popular Hindu calendar is *Vikrami Samvat*. Its days and months are based on the movement of the Moon, i.e. in terms of *thithi* and *paksh*. One *samvatsar* (Hindu year) has 354 days and the month has 29.5 solar days, and the year of the Moon takes only 354 days to revolve around the Earth. To keep pace with solar calendar, there is a provision of having leap month or *adhik maas* after every say N solar months. N is such that

$$N \times 354 = (N - 1) \times 365.25$$

giving

$$N = 32.4$$

Therefore, 32.4 lunar months would equal to 31.4 Gregorian calendar months. It means that for every 31.4 lunar months, a lunar leap month is to be added in order to catch up with the solar year. This is what Hindu calendar does in the form of leap or अधमास (Extra month).

1.1.9 Middle-Level Time Intervals

To take into account various historical events, the year becomes little small. So time intervals, namely, century or *satabdee* and millennium or *sahasrabdee* consisting of 100 and 1000 years, respectively, are used.

1.1.10 Bigger Time Intervals

Aforesaid time intervals are good enough for reckoning terrestrial events, but to observe astronomical happenings of various celestial bodies, we need much bigger time intervals.

1.1.10.1 Charan

The number 108 is considered very sacred number in many religions. There are four yug. The product of these two numbers is 432. First time interval in the bigger range is 432 times *sahasrabdee,* i.e. 432,000 human years. This is called as *charan.*

1.1.10.2 Yug

There are four yug, namely, *Satyug, Tretayug, Dwapuryug* and *Kaliyug* [22, 23]. Their durations, respectively, are 4, 3, 2, 1 *charan.*

1.1.10.3 Duration of Each Yug in Human Years

According to Srimad Bhagavata Purana 3.11.19, each yug has one *sandhiya* in the beginning and *Sandhiyance* at the end. The duration of each of these *sandhiya* and *sandhiyance* is 10% of the main duration of the yug. The actual break up for each yug in human years is as follows:

kaliyug $36,000 + 360,000 + 36,000 = 432,000$ human years
dwaparyug $72,000 + 720,000 + 72,000 = 864,000$ human years
tretayug $108,000 + 1,080,000 + 108,000 = 1,296,000$ human years
satyug $144,000 + 1,440,000 + 144,000 = 1,728,000$ human years

1.1.10.4 Durations of Each Yug in Divine Years

The *Surya Siddhant* [24, 25] and *Vishnu Puran* [9] describe the durations of four yug in divine years. Devine years have been used quite often, when relating time intervals with other units or physical constant (length or speed of light). So details of duration of various yug are given below. One divine year is equal to 360 human years.

1 kaliyug $100 + 1000 + 100 = 1200$ divine years
1 dwaparyug $200 + 2000 + 200 = 2400$ divine years
1 tretayug $300 + 3000 + 300 = 3600$ divine years
1 satyug $400 + 4000 + 400 = 4800$ divine years

1.1.10.5 Mahayug

Mahayug [24, 25] is the sum of durations of all the four *yug*. Total duration of the sum of durations of *kaliyag, dwaparyug, tretayug* and *satyug* is 10 *charan* or 12,000 divine years or 4,320,000 human years.

1.1.10.6 Manvantar

Seventy-one *mahayug* make a *manvantar* [26]. Its duration, in human years, is 306,720,000 human years. Each *manvantar* is ruled by a *Manu*. At the beginning of each *manvantar* and at the end of 14th *manvantar*, there is a *sandhi kal*. Duration of each *sandhi kal* is of four *charan*, i.e. 1,728,000 years. It is said that during a *sandhi kal*, the entire Earth is submerged in water.

1.1.10.7 *Kalp*

A *kalp* [26–28] is defined in two ways.

In Terms of Manvantar

A *kalp* (lighted day only) of *Brahma* consists of 14 *manvantar* together with 15 *sandhi kal* [27].

In Terms of Mahayug

According to Srimad Bhagwad *Gita* [28], there are 1000 *Mahayug* in one *kalp* (lighted day) of *Brahma*. The Sloka 17 of chapter 8 of *Gita* states as follows:
    "*sahasra-yuga-paryantam ahar yad brahmaṇo viduḥ rātriṁ yuga-sahasrāntāṁ te'ho-rātra-vido janāḥ*". This means that 1 lighted day of *Brahma* is of 1000 *Mahayug*, and the night of *Brahma* is also of 1000 *Mahayug*.

Equivalence of Two Definitions

Let us examine their equivalence.
    According to the first definition,

$$1\,kalp = 14\,Manvantar + 15\,Sandi\,kal$$
$$(14 \times 71\,Mahayug) + (15 \times 4\,Charan)$$
$$= 994\,Mahayug + 60\,charan$$
$$\text{But } 10\,charan = 1\,Mahayug, \text{giving us}$$
$$1\,kalp = 994\,Mahayug + 6\,Mahayug$$
$$= 1000\,Mahayug$$
$$= 4{,}320{,}000{,}000 \text{ human years or } 4.32 \text{ billion human years.}$$

This duration is the same as given by *Srimad Bhagwad Gita* [28].

1.1.10.8 Age of the Sun

If it is assumed that the only source of light in solar system is Sun. So Sun must be able to send light for the duration of 4.32 billion years. Hence, the age of the Sun must be a little more than 4.32 billion years. This fact has been verified by most modern and updated techniques which assign the age of Sun as 4.59 billion human years.

1.1.10.9 Night of Brahma

As enunciated in *Srimad Bhagwad Gita* [28], the night of *Brahma* is also equal to 1 *kalp*. At the time of *Brahma's* night, when he sleeps, all three *Lok* (entire universe) are destroyed. It is obvious as the Sun is the sustainer of every living creature and most of other material things, no Sun means no life.

1.1.11   Names of 14 Manvantar

Names *of Manvantar* as per *Vishnu Puran* and *Shrimad Bhagwad Puran* [29, 30], both in Roman and Hindi scripts, are given in Table 1.14. Some names are different in the two scriptures especially of those *manvantar* yet to come.

1.1.12   Time Intervals in Terms of Kalp

Time intervals in terms of *Brahma's* days [31, 32] are as follows:

1 lighted day of *Brahma* = 1 *kalp* = 4.32 billion human years.

Table 1.14 Names of 14 *Manvantar*

S N	Name in Roman script	Hindi
1	*Swayambho*	स्वायम्भूव
2	*Swarachis*	स्वारोचिष
3	*Uttam*	उतम
4	*Taamas*	तामस
5	*Revat*	रैवत
6	*Chaskhus*	चाक्षुष
7	*Vavashvat*	वैवश्वत
8	*Savnik*	सावणिक
9	*Daksh Sawarni*	दक्ष सावणि
10	*Brahm Sawarni*	ब्रहम सावणि
11	*Dharm Sawarni*	ध्रम सावणि
12	*Rudra Putra Sawarni*	रूद्र सावणि
13	*Ruchi or Jitendra Sawarni*	रूचि जितेन्द्रिय सावणि
14	*Bhaum or Inder Sawarni*	भौम इन्द्र

Further, as per *Srimad Bhagwad Gita* [28], one night of *Brahma* is also of the same duration as that of the *Brahma*'s day; hence,

One night of *Brahma* = 1 *kalp* = 4.32 billion years

2 *kalp* = 1 day and night of *Brahma* = 8.64 billion human years

30 days of *Brahma* = 1 month of *Brahma* = 259.2 billion human years

12 months of *Brahma* = 1 year of *Brahma* = 3.1104 trillion human years

50 years of *Brahma* = 1 Paraardh = 155.52 trillion human years

100 years of *Brahma* = 2 *Paraardh* = 1 *Para*

= 1 *Maha − Kalp* = 311.04 trillion human years

The life span of *Brahma* is 100 years of *Brahma* = 311.04 trillion human years. Moving to higher time intervals, i.e. day and night of *Vishnu*

2 *Paraardh* = *Brahma*'s Age = 1 day of *Vishnu*

2 *Paraardh* = *Brahma*'s Age = 1 night of *Vishnu*

4 *Paraardh* = *Brahma*'s Two Lives = *Vishnu*'s Complete Day (Day and Night).

1.1.13 Summary of Bigger Time Intervals

A list of names of bigger time intervals (bigger than one year) is given in Table 1.15.

Table 1.15 Time intervals bigger than a year

Name in Roman script		In Hindi	Human years
Century	satabdee	शताब्दि	100 years
Millenium	shasrabdee	सहसराबदि	1000 years
charan	432 shasrabdee	चरण	432,000 years
kaliyug	1 charan	कलियुग	432,000 years
dwapuryug	2 charan	दवापुरयुग	864,000 years
tretayug	3 charan	त्रेतायुग	1,296,000 years
satyug	4 charan	सतयुग	1,728,000 years
mahayug	10 charan	महायुग	4,320,000 years
manvantar	71 mahayug	मन्वन्तर	30,672,000 years
sandhi kal	4 charan	सन्धिकाल	1,728,000 years
kalp	1000 mahayug	कल्प	4.32 billion years
kalp	14 manvantar +15 sandhiya	कल्प	4.32 billion years
1 day & night of *Brahma*	2000 mahayug	रात दिन	8.64 billion years
Month of *Brahma*	30 days of *Brahma*		259.2 billion years
Year of *Brahma*	12 months of Brahma		3.1104 trillion years
paraardh	50 years of *Brahma*	प्रार्ध	155.52 trillion years
2 paraardh	Age of *Brahma*		311.04 trillion
Day only of *Vishnu*	Age of *Brahma*		311.04 trillion
Complete day of *Vishnu*	4 paraadh		622.08 trillion years

1.1.14 The Time Elapsed Since Creation of Universe

According to old scripture [33], we are currently in the first day of the 51st year of *Brahma* [33, 34]. This day of *Brahma* or *Kalp* is named as *Shveta-Varaha Kalp*.

So 50 years of *Brahma* have elapsed. The last *Kalp* at the end of 50th year is called *Padma Kalpa*. Within this *kalp*, six *manvantara* have already elapsed [33] and this is the seventh *manvantara*, named as *Vaivasvatha manvantara* (or *Sraddhadeva manvantara*). Within the *Vaivasvatha manvantara*, 27 *mahayug* [34] and the *satyug*, *tretayug* and *dwaparyug* of the 28th *mahayug* have elapsed [35]. This *Kaliyug* is in the 28th *Mahayug*. This means that we are in the *kaliyug* of 28th *Mahayug* of 7th *Manvantar* of the first day of 51st year of Brahma.

The time elapsed since the current *Brahma* has taken over the task of creation is sum of the following durations:

50 years of *Brahma*
6 *Manvantar* and 7 *Sandhiya Kal*
27 *Mahayug*
Satyug, Tretayug and dwapuryug of 28th *Mahayug*

Kaliyug passed till say 2019

Remembering that one complete day of *Brahma* is 8.64 billion years and 1 year of *Brahma* $= 8.64 \times 10^9 \times 30 \times 12 = 3.1104$ trillion years, we get

50 years of *Brahma*

$$= 3.1104 \times 10^{12} \times 50 = 155.52 \text{ Trillion years} = 155{,}520{,}000{,}000{,}000 \text{ years} \quad (1.1)$$

6 *amanvntar* and 7 *sandhiya*

$$= 6 \times 71 \times 4{,}320{,}000 + 7 \times 1.728 \times 10^6 = 1{,}852{,}416{,}000 \text{ years} \quad (1.2)$$

27 *mahayug*

$$= 27 \times 4{,}320{,}000 = 116{,}640{,}000 \quad (1.3)$$

satyug, *tretayug* and *kaliyug*

$$= 1.728 \times 10^6 + 1.296 \times 10^6 + 864{,}000 = 3{,}888{,}000 \quad (1.4)$$

Years elapsed in current *Kaliyug*

$$= 3102 + 2019 = 5121 \quad (1.5)$$

So the total time elapsed since the current *Brahma* has taken over (Creation of present universe) is

$$155{,}520{,}000{,}000{,}000 + 1{,}852{,}416{,}000 + 116{,}640{,}000$$
$$+ 3{,}888{,}000 + 5121 = 155{,}521{,}972{,}949{,}121 \text{ years.}$$

In other words, as on 2019 AD, one hundred fifty-five trillion, five hundred twenty-one billion, nine hundred seventy-two million, nine hundred forty-nine thousand and one hundred twenty-one years have passed since the present *Brahma* took over. This may also mean that age of universe is of the aforesaid duration. However, the age of Earth may not be that big, because Earth must have been born on the first day of 51st year of *Brahma*.

1.1.15 Date of Commencement of the Present Kaliyug

The current *kaliyug* [36] began at midnight of 17 February/18 February in 3102 BC in the proleptic Julian calendar. 5121 years of 28th *kaliyug* have passed; subtracting this number from 532,000—the duration of kaliyug—another 426,883 years are left to complete this 28th *kaliyug* of *Vaivaswatha Manvantar*.

According to the Vedic scriptures, *Srimad Bhagwad Puran* [37] records *kaliyug* as having begun when the constellation of the seven sages (saptarsi) passed through the lunar mansion of *Magha*. Then, Hindu astrologers have calculated this to have been occurred at 2:27 a.m. on 18 February 3102 BC.

1.2 Length Intervals

1.2.1 Introduction

Unlike several sets of smaller time intervals, there are fewer sets of length intervals. In time measurement, one complete day was taken as base, while in case of length measurements the *angul* (width of a figure) is taken as base. So I propose to write sets of length intervals, as sub-multiples of *angul* for smaller length intervals and multiples of *angul* for distances are used in everyday life. In this chapter also, names of length intervals, hereafter called as units of length, originating from Sanskrit, are given in Hindi.

1.2.2 Sets of Smaller Length Intervals

1.2.2.1 Set of Smaller Units of Length as Given in Agni Puran

Agni Puran, a Hindu scripture [38], has given the units of distances with reference to building of an *Agni Kund* (Fire vessel) for *Yagya* (Holistic rituals). These are shown in Table 1.16 as sub-multiples of *angul*.

Basis of calculation

2097152 *permanu* = 1 *angul* and 1 *angul* is taken equal to 16.764 mm [45]. Giving 1 *permanu* = 0.0000079 mm = 0.0079 μm a particle of molecular dimension.

Table 1.16 Sub-multiple of angul

Units in Roman script		In Hindi	Equivalence in SI (mm)
permanu		परमाणु	0.0000079
8 *permanu*	*tresarenu*	त्रसरेणु	0.0000639
8 *tresarenu*	*renu*	रेणु	0.0005115
8 *renu*	*baalaagra*	बालाग्र	0.0040927
8 *baalaagra*	*likhyaa*	लिरवया	0.327421
8 *likhyaa*	*yookaa*	यूका	0.2619375
8 *yookaa*	*yava*	यव	2.0955
8 *yava*	**angul**	अंगुल	**16.764**
21 *angul*	*ratin*	रतिन	352.044
24 *angul*	*haath*	हाथ	402.336

Table 1.17 Length units in sub-multiples of *angul*

Angul	Names of units		Value in SI
1/8⁵	*parmanu*		0.51159 μm
1/8⁴	8 *parmanu*	*rathachakraviprus*	4.0928 μm
1/8³	8 *rathachakraviprus*	1 *liksa*	32.742 μm
1/8²	8 *liksa*	1 *yuka*	261.93 μm
1/8	8 *yuka*	1 *yavamadhya*	2.0955 mm
1	**8 *yavamadhya***	**1 *angul***	**16.764 mm**

1.2.2.2 Set of Smaller Units of Length in Chanakiya Arthsashtra

In *Chanakiya* system of length measurements, the *angul* has been taken as base. All other length intervals are either multiples or sub-multiples of *angul*. It is enunciated by Prof. Verma [39] and Patrick Olivelle [17]. Observing Table 1.16, though in this case also, smallest unit is *permanu*, but due to lesser number of steps between it and *angul*, one *permanu* is 64 times longer than that given in Table 1.16. The names of length intervals and their metric equivalent are given in column 4 of Table 1.17.

Here also the base unit is *angul* of 16,764 mm. This value is based on the work done by Goyal [45]. In column 5, the values of length units are given by Patrick Olivelle [17], taken *angul* as 20 mm.

The number of *parmanu* in one *angul* is 32768, taking *angul* as 16.764 mm; the value of one *parmanu* comes as 512 nm. It is the wavelength of light in green region of solar spectrum. Reversing the language, it means that there are 32678 wavelengths in an *angul*. Each wavelength is of 512 nm. It may be noted that 514.5 nm is the Argon laser wavelength. Can we, this way, suspect that Chanakiya wished to define a unit of length in terms of wavelength of light.

1.2.3   Units of Length in Multiples of Angul

Names of the units of length in multiples of *angul* with their modern equivalents are given in Table 1.18. Patrick [17] took 1 *angul* equal to 20 mm.

1.2.3.1 Length Units with Different Names But of the Same Value

Miscellaneous length units with the same value but with different names as given in Chanakiya Arthsashtra are given in Table 1.19.

Table 1.18 Length units in integral multiples of angul

Angul	Names of the units		Value in SI	Value by Patrick
1	*angul*		16.764 mm	20 mm
4	*4 angul*	1 dhanurgraha	67.056 mm	80 mm
8	*2 dhanurgrah*	1 dhanurmusti	134.112 mm	160 mm
12	1.5 *dhanurmusti*	1 *vitasti* or 1 *chayapaurusa*	201.168 mm	240 mm
24	2 *vitasti*	1 *aratni* or 1 *prajapati Hast*	402.336 mm	480 mm
108	*dhanus* for roads	1 *dhanus* for roads	1.810512 m	1920 mm
192,000	2000 *dhanus*	1 *goruta*	3621.024 m	3840 m
768,000	4 *doruta*	1 *yojan*	12.874752 km	15.36 km

Notes
1. The term *Chayapaurusa* relates to reading of a sundial, according to Shamasastry [40]; it is the shadow of 12 *angul* cast by a gnomon having a height of 12 *angul*
2. The term *Goruta* is also called *Kosh* (कोस) in Hindi [20]

1.2.3.2 Smaller Units of Length in Times of Bhoja

Coming to post-Christian era, one cannot forget the Legendry King *Bhoja Raj*. He belonged to *Paramara* Dynasty ruled major portion of India from 1010 to 1055. His kingdom extended from Chittore in North to Konkan in south and Sabarmati River in west to Vidisha in east. He was an exceptionally skilled, not only in politics but in different aspects of Science and Technology. Several books (84) like *Samarangna Sutradhar*, *Rajamarganika* and *Rajamartanda* are attributed to him. He guided the scholars in the field of Airplane, Transport System, Astronomy, Astrology, *Yogya shastra*, flying machines like gliders, horses their diseases and the remedies, etc. His patronage to scholars was tremendous. For linear measurements, a set [41] of multiples and sub-multiples of *angul* were devised.

Sub-multiples and Multiples of Angul (Raja Bhoja)

Sub-multiples and multiples of *angul* (finger) up to *Kara* (कर) the units quite often used in those times are given in Table 1.20.
  The system is very similar to that given by Chanakiya of 3rd century BC especially regarding the step and base unit of *angula*. It may be seen that basic step is of 8 times except in defining widths of different fingers. Moreover *Kara* (कर) of Table 1.20 is a Hindi word, which means hand (हाथ), same as defined in Table 1.17 as equal to 24 times the *angula*, except as to which *angula* has been taken for defining the hand (हाथ) in Table 1.17 is not defined. In this sense, units of length defined are more precise.

Table 1.19 Length units of the same value with different names

Angul	Names of the unit		Value in SI mm	Values by Patrick (mm)
	angul		16.764	20
12	12 *angul*	1 *chayapaurus*	201.168	240
14	14 *angul*	1 *sama*	234.696	280
14	14 *angul*	1 *pariraya*	234.696	280
14	14 a*ngula*	1 *sala*	234.696	280
14	14 angul	1 *pada*	234.696	280
32	2 *vitsati*+ 1 dhanurmusti	1 *kishuka* or 1 *kamsa*	536.448 mm	640
42	42 *angul*	1 saw *kisuka* of carpenter	704.08 mm	840
54	54 *angul*	1 *Hast* for forest produce	905.256	1080
84	84 a*ngula*	1 *vyama* for ropes	1408.176	1680
84	84 *angul*	1 *paurusa* for digging	1408.176	1680
96	4 *aratni*	1 *danda*	1609.344	1920
96	4 a*ratni*	1 *nalika*	1609 mm	1920
96	4 a*ratni*	1 *paurusa* for householder	1609 mm	1920
108	108 a*ngula*	1 d*hanus* for roads &walls	1810 mm	2160
108	6 *kimsa*	1 d*anda* measure for gifts	1810 mm	1920
108	108 a*ngula*	1 *paurasa* for fire altar	1810 mm	2160
1080	10 d*anda*	1 *rajju*	18,100 mm	19,200
2160	2 *rajju*	*Paridesa*	36210 mm	38,400
3240	3 *rajju*	*nivartna*	area	
3456	3 *rajju*+ 2 d*anda*	1 *bahu*	area	

Notes
1. *Paurus* is the height of the sacrifier, i.e. height of the common man
2. *Nivartna* is a unit of area. Kangle noted that *Nivartana* initially was a distance which bullock walked before turning around during ploughing
3. *Kimsa* is a reference to measuring a land given to the people as outright gift or as dedicated land from whose harvest guest can be entertained
2. *Bahu* is a unit of area of a rectangle having sides of 32 *danda* and 30 *danda*

Going to the table, we see that the *Jyesta angul* (Big finger), *Madhya angul* (middle finger) and *kaniyste angul* (little finger) are, respectively, equal to 8, 7 and 6 times of one *yavamadhya*.

Taking width of *Jyestha angul* as 1.875 cm [41], the widths of other two *angul* will be

Table 1.20 Sub-multiples and multiples of angula

Units in Roman script		Hindi	In Renu
renu		रेणू	1
8 *renu*	1 *Valgra*	वलगरा	8
8 *valgra*	1 *Liksa*	लिक्सा	64
8 *liksa*	1 *Yuka*	यूका	512
8 *yuka*	1 *Yavamadhya*	यवामध्या	4096
8 *yavamadhya*	1 *Jyestha angul*	ज्येष्ठ अंगुल	32,768
7 *yavamadhya*	1 *madhya angul*	मध्या अंगुल	28,672
6 *yavamadhy*	*kaniyste angul*	कनिष्ठ अंगुल	24,576
24 *Jyestha angul*	1 *kara*	कर	786,432

$$Madhya \, angul = 16.41 \, mm$$

$$Kaniyste \, angul = 14.06 \, mm$$

Kara, depending upon which *angul* it is associated with, was given names like *Prasaya* (*kara*), *Sadharan* and *Saya* giving the values in metric system as given below:

Prasaya or *kara* = 24 *Jeystha angul* = 24 × 8 *yavamadhya* = 45 cm
Sadharan = 24 *madhya angul* = 24 × 7 *yavamadhya* = 39.375 cm
Saya = 24 *kaniyste angul* = 24 × 6 *yavamadhya* = 33.75 cm

Each of Kara with aforesaid name was used for specific items and in specified fields.

Specific Fields of Use of Prasaya, Sadharan or Saya

Prasaya

Prasaya was used in measurement of dimensions of villages, town, cities, houses, moats, Lanes, assembly halls, gardens of any size and region demarcation lines. Units like *yojan*, *krosa* or *gavyuti* were also derived from *prasaya*.

Sadharan

Sadharan was used in the measurement of dimensions of dugs, saw, heaps of grain, etc., elevation of surfaces, base roots of the walls, columns, etc., water ponds below the ground level, flags, hilly houses, lanes inside the plantations and internal dimensions of holes.

Saya

Saya was used for dimensions of weapons, sticks of a bow, vehicles, places, boats, wells, ponds, elephants, height and partial dimensions of a human body, uplifting of water from wells, sugarcane-crushing machines, instruments of harvesting and carpentry, boats, instruments of ironsmith, musical instruments like veena and weavers' instruments.

The practice of defining a unit of slightly different values to be used for specific purpose is similar as given in the Chanakiya Arthsashtra.

1.2.3.3   Yojan in Bhoja Time

For larger length intervals, there were units like cap or *dhanu*, *krose* or *kos*, *gavyuti* and *yojan*. They were related to *Jyestha angul* as follows:

24 *Jyestha angul* = I *kara* = 45 cm
4 *kara* = 1 *cap* or *dhanu* = 180 cm
1000 *dahanu* = 1 *krose* or *kos* = 1800 m or 1.8 km
2 *krose* or *kos* = 1 *gavyuti* = 3600 m or 3.6 km
4 *gavyuti* = I *yojan* = 14.4 km

Taking *Jyestha angul* as 1.875 cm, one *yojan* comes out to be 14.4 km. This almost agrees with the *yojan* given by Chanakiya.

1.2.3.4   Units of Length in Multiples of Angul

One set of length units is given in Arthsashtra [42] as shown in Table 1.21.

1.2.3.5   Units Used for Distance Measurements

The units in multiples of *dand* or *dhanush* given in Chanakiya Arthsashtra [42] are tabulated in Table 1.22.

Table 1.21   Multiples of *angul*

Units in Roman script		In Hindi	Imperial units	SI units (mm)
angul		अंगुल	0.75 in.	16.764
4 *angul*	*dhanurgrah*	धर्नुग्रह	3 in.	67.056
8 *angul*	*dhanurmushti*	धर्नुमुष्टि	6 in.	134.112
12 *angul*	1 vitastaa	बालिस्त	9 in.	201.168
2 *vitastaa*	1 *haath*, cubit or *aratni*	हाथ, अरातनि	18 in.	402.336
4 *aratni, haath*	*dand* or *dhanush*	डण्ड, धनुष	6 ft	1609.344

Notes
1. In some literature [43], one vitastaa is given as 9 in. and 4 *vitastaa* equal to 18 in.; to make the two statements agree, I have written 2 *vitastaa* equal to one *haath* in the above table
2. *Vitastaa* is called as *balisht* in parts of Northern India; it is the distance of stretched out palm between the tips of a person's thumb and little finger
3. The values of unit like *angul, vitastaa or hand* (all body parts) are in simple ratios of imperial units. It shows that the unit of length in imperial units is based on one of the body parts. This trend originated from BC era

Table 1.22 Units in multiples of *dand* or *dhanush*

Units in Roman script		In Hindi	Imperial units	SI units
dand or *dhanush*		डण्ड or धनुष	6 ft	1.829 m
10 *dand* or *dhanush*	1 *rajju*	रज्जू	60 ft	18.289 m
2 rajju	1 *paridesh*	परिदेष	120 ft	36.576 m
2000 *dand*	1 *kos, krosh*	कोस	4000 yards, 9/4 miles	3658 m
4 *kos*	1 *yojan*	योजन	9 miles [39]	14.63 km

Basis of calculation from Imperial units to SI: 1 feet = 0.3048 m

Table 1.23 Multiples of *Angul*

Units in Roman script		Translation	*Angul*	SI units	Imperial units
	angul	finger	1	19.042 mm	0.7497 in.
12 *angul*	*vistati, vitastaa balisht*	span	12	0.2285 m	8.9961 in.
2 *vistati*	*hast*	cubit	24	0.457 m	1.499 ft = 0.5 yd
4 *hast*	*dhanush*	"orgyla", fathom	96	1.828 m	1.999 yd = 0.001 mi
2000 *dhanush*	krosa, *kos* or *krosh*	Purely Hindi word	192000	3656 m	2.272 miles
2 *crosa, kos* or *krosh*	*gavyuti*	Purely Hindi word	384,000	7312 m	4.54 miles
2 *gavyuti*	*yodjana yojan*	Purely Hindi word	768,000	14628.1 m	9.0895 miles

Notes To take the value of *angul* up to ten-thousandth of an inch or 0.1 μm is unrealistic. Taking the nominal value of inch equal to 0.75 in. or 19 mm is good enough. However, the values might have been taken to higher unrealistic precision, perhaps, to reduce arithmetical errors while multiplying fairly big numbers to the unit *angul*

By fairly large number of multiplying factors to if the values of units of length are taken in FPS system instead of metres, the values for the smaller units are such, which gives an impression that these are adopted under British colonial rule. The reason for equivalence is perhaps that both the systems (one based on *angul* and the other based on foot) are based on human limbs

1.2.3.6 Units of Length by Cardarelli

The length intervals starting from *angul* as given by Francois Cardarelli [44] are given in Table 1.23.

1.2.4 Two Kinds of Danush

In the time of Chandragupta Maurya (Chanakiya Arthsashtra), it appears that there were two kinds of *Dhanush* for the length measurement [45]. One *danush* was of

96 *angul*, and another was of 108 *angul*, taking *angul* equal to 16.764 mm from Mohenjo-Daro scale [44].

A *dhanush* of 96 *angul* = 96 × 16.764 mm = 1.609344 m

A *dhanush* of 108 *angul* = 108 × 16.764 mm = 1.810512 m

The *yojan*, a unit for longer distances, was taken [42] as equal to 8000 *dhanush* giving

1 *yojan* = 8000 *dhanush* of 108 *Angul* = 8000 × 1.810512 m = 14.484096 km

But 14.484096 km = 9 miles (exactly)

A *yojan* of 96 *angul* = 8000 × 1.609344 = 12.874 km = 8 miles exactly.

Observations

1. If we take *angul* equivalent to 0.75 inch or 19.0417 mm, then the *yojan* of 8000 *dhanush,* taking *dhanush* of 96, is equal to 14.6281 km or 9.0895 miles.

Goswami Tulsidasji (1497–1623) in his *Hanuman Chalisa* has stated that the distance of the Sun from Earth is 1000 times the number representing the *mahayug*. Taking *mahayug* as 12,000 divine years, we get the distance of Sun from Earth equal to 173.80908 billion metres if we take *dhanush* of 108 *angul*. But the distance of Sun from Earth will be equal to 154.4942 billion metres if the *dhanush* is taken of 96 *angul*. The modern value of Sun's distance from Earth is 149.6 billion metres. So the *yojan* of 8000 *Dhanush* each of 96 *angul* appears to be a better choice. The author has his own reservation for taking *mahayug* in divine years instead of in human years.

1.2.5   Scale of Mohenjo-Daro

1.2.5.1   Situation of Mohenjo-Daro

Mohenjo-daro, in Sindhi language, means Mound of the Dead Men, is an archaeological site. It is situated in the province of Sindh, Pakistan. Built around 2500 BCE, it was one of the largest settlements of the ancient Indus Valley Civilization and one of the world's earliest major urban settlements. It is contemporary with the civilizations of ancient Egypt, Mesopotamia, Minoa (Crete) and Norte Chico. Mohenjo-daro was abandoned in the nineteenth century BCE as the Indus Valley Civilization declined, and the site was not rediscovered until the 1920s. Significant excavation has since been conducted at the site of the city, which was designated a UNESCO World Heritage Site in 1980. The site is currently threatened by erosion and improper restoration [46].

1.2.5.2   Scale of Mohenjo-Daro

In 1930–1931 season of excavation at Mohenjo-daro, Archeologist Ernest Mackay [46] discovered a broken piece of shell bearing eight divisions. There was a dot

Fig. 1.1 Scale found in
Mohenjo-Daro

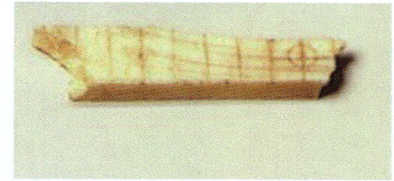

and a circle five graduations apart, see Fig. 1.1. The distance between two graduations when measured accurately was found to be 6.7056 mm. The picture in
Fig. 1.1 is taken from [47].

A dot and circle after five graduations indicated the possibility of use of decimal system in that period. However, attempts by Mackay, to relate such a unit to
the dimensions in Mohenjo-daro with decimal system, were not very successful
and thus were abandoned.

1.2.5.3   Decoding the Mohenjo-Daro Scale

Dr. Goyal [45] took 10 divisions of the Mohenjo-daro scale to be equal to one
dhanurgraha or 4 *angul*. So he obtained precise length of an *angul* as 16.764 mm.
I have quite often used this Fig. 1.1 in calculating the equivalence of units in SI
units.

1.2.6   Supportive Evidences for Taking 1 Angul Equal
to 16.764 mm

1.2.6.1   The Indus Inch

It is said that Indus civilization is at least 8,000 years old. Unit of length widely
known as Indus inch is equal to 1.32 in. of fps system used primarily in UK. In
metric units, it is 33.528 mm, which is just double of *angul*. *Angul* was the base
unit of length in ancient India.

1.2.6.2   Temple Wall Engravings Related to Dhanush

Two engravings on a wall of the temple at Tiruputtkuzhi (twelfth century A.D.) near
Kanchipuram [43] show two scales one measuring 7.24 m in length, with markings
dividing the scale into four equal parts, and the second one measuring 5.69 m in
length and markings dividing the scale into four equal parts. It may be observed
that each division of the first scale is precisely equal to a *dhanush* of 108 *angul* of

16.764 mm each. Interestingly, the second scale is precisely equal to π (3.142) times *dhanush,* i.e. equal to the circumference of a circle with one *dhanush* as its diameter.

It is interesting to note here that Mackay reported the existence of a lane and a doorway each having a width of 1.42 m, which is precisely equal to one division of the second scale at the Tiruputtkuzhi temple. This indicates that both the scales were prevalent in Indus-Saraswati Civilization as well as in South India.

1.2.6.3   Mohenjo-daro's Great Bath

The height of the corbelled drain forming the outlet of Mohenjo-daro's Great Bath is about 1.8 m, which is equal to a *dhanush* of 108 *angul*, each *angul* being 16.764 mm [45].

1.2.7   Various Yojan

"*Yojan*" was a unit of distance in ancient India like the modern mile or kilometre. It has been cited in most of the *Puran*. However, its value does not seem to be a standard even within India. Some consider it as six miles, some as eight miles and some as two and half miles. Hence, it is difficult to have an accurate conversion from *yojan* to miles or to kilometres. Traditionally, a *yojan* (4 *krosh* or *kos*) is said to be as a distance of 10 miles.

1.2.7.1   Yojan in Valmiki Ramayan

According to Verse 29, chapter 2 (Ayodhya Kand) of Valmiki Ramayan [48], Saint Bhardwaj advised Ramchandra ji to stay at a place 30 *krosh* from there. According to the latest measurements, the place mentioned in Valmiki Ramayan is at distance of about 80 miles, this gives

$$krosh \text{ or } kos = 2.67 \text{ miles}$$
$$4\, krosh \text{ or } kos = 1 \text{ yojan}$$

Giving

$$yojan = 10.68 \text{ miles} = 17.088 \text{ km}$$

1.2.7.2   British Yojan

The British revenue has taken a *yojan* equal to 5 mile distance. Consequently, Chambers and Oxford dictionaries indicate one yojan as five miles.

$$yojan = 5 \text{ miles} = 8.047 \text{ km}$$

1.2.7.3   Indian Yojan

In Surya Siddhant [51], the diameter of the Earth has been given as 1600 *yojan*. But the value of the diameter of Earth measured by modern method is 12756.2 km, from which the value of *yojan* comes out to be 7.97 km or 4.95 miles.

1.2.7.4   Units in Terms of Human Limbs

We have seen from Tables 1.16, 1.17, 1.18, 1.19 and 1.20 that in early times, length was defined in terms of the limbs of the human being, for example, by the width of finger (*angul*), palm or the hand. The value of the limb could be average of the limbs of the human beings at that time or could be that of the king. To make the units more lasting and impersonal, efforts were made to translate the distance of a limb into an artefact in the form of a solid rod embedded in a wall where public man could approach and verify his own measures. In Fig. 1.2, unit of length in terms of *hast* (hand) or kar (कर) is shown.

The length from the elbow to the tip of the middle finger (the cubit) was called as *hast, kara* or *hath* (hand). Such standards were both changeable and perishable. The Middle Ages saw many such conflicting and poorly defined standards of weights and measures.

But exact standards of measurement are not solely a modern invention. For example, measurement of distance through latitude was prevalent in ancient India and other places which were in terms of the radius of the Earth which is a constant of nature and is measurable. Measuring distances in terms of *yojan* in terms of latitude indicates at the advanced astronomical knowledge in the ancient Vedic (Hindu) civilization.

1.2.8   Length in Terms of Latitude

Greek astronomer Eratosthenes (276 BC to 194 BC) is usually credited with being the first to measure the size of the Earth by observing latitudes [50]. He is said to

Fig. 1.2 *Hast*

have noted that the Sun, when directly overhead at Syene situated at the Tropic of Cancer, casts a shadow of 7.2° at Alexandria. Knowing the distance between Syene and Alexandria, he computed the length of a degree of latitude and estimated the circumference of the Earth.

But there is reason to believe that the size of the Earth was known long before Eratosthenes. The Italian scholar Livio Stecchini (October 1913 to September 1979) has given extensive evidence that the ancient Egyptians laid out their country using latitude and longitude. He argues that they had accurate knowledge of the dimensions of the Earth and that such knowledge was inherent in the design of the great pyramid at Giza. Since the great pyramid dates to about 2500 BC, this implies that the Earth was measured scientifically at least that long ago.

However, it seems that Indian astronomers discovered much earlier that Earth is spherical; as in Surya Siddhant, Chapter 1, verse 59 [51], the value of diameter of the Earth is given as 1600 *yojan* meaning thereby that Earth is spherical in shape. It may be remembered that Surya Siddhant is a very old scripture (around 2 million years).

1.2.8.1 Change in Distance with Latitude and Longitude

The planes having the same latitude are parallel to the equatorial plane, so distance between each degree change in latitude remains almost constant. Slight change is due to flattening of Earth at the poles. However, longitudinal planes are farthest apart at the equator and converge at the poles; their distance varies greatly from zero to the distance at the equator.

Distance Due to Change in Latitude Only

Distance D_θ along the surface of the Earth between two places on the same meridian but having θ degrees difference between their latitudes is given as

$$D_\theta = R\theta\pi/180$$

So for each degree of latitude $D_\theta = 6378.1 \times 3.1416/180 = 111.32$ km or approximately 69.17 miles apart. Due to the Earth's flattening at the poles, the value of D_θ varies from 110.567 km or (68.703 miles) at the equator to 111.699 km or (69.407 miles) at the poles [50]. Considering the shape of the Earth, the value of R increases from poles to the equator, and distance in km per degree latitude will increase. Reverse will happen if a measured distance is repeated at several latitudes; the number representing the distance would decrease from poles to equator. It may be noted that each minute (1/60th of a degree) will be 1.153 miles approximating to one mile. Here, for a given value of θ, we can define a unit of length in terms of radius of Earth.

For example, 1/600th of the degree of latitude represented an old Greek unit of length known as stadium.

Similarly, one-eighth of the degree of latitude represents an Indian *yojan* of 32,000 *hast*.

Distance Due to Change in Longitude Only

Similarly, the distance D_ϕ between the two places having the same latitude θ but different longitudes ϕ

$$D_\phi = (R\cos\theta)(\pi\phi/180)$$

A degree of longitude will vary from 111.321 km (69.172 miles) at the equator to zero at the poles, as θ is 90° at the poles. At 40° north or south, the distance between degrees of longitude is 53 miles (85 km).

1.2.8.2 Variation of Latitude from Equator to Pole

Here, we must make a technical observation about latitudes. Consider the Earth to be a sphere, rotating on a line through the north and south poles called the polar axis. The latitude of a person facing north at some point in the northern hemisphere is the angle θ from his horizon up to the polar axis. That angle, in degrees, zeroes at the equator and grows to 90° at the North Pole. The length of a degree of latitude is the distance a person would have to travel north for his latitude to increase by 1°. On a perfect sphere, this distance would be the same at all latitudes. But the Earth is slightly flat at the poles and bulges at the equator. This makes for a degree of latitude slightly smaller at the equator than further north.

1.2.8.3 Definition of Metre

It may be mentioned that the metre, the base unit of length in SI (International System of Units), loosely called as metric system, was initially defined as ten-millionth (10^{-7}) part of the quadrant of the Earth's meridian passing through Paris. Earth radius was taken as constant, though now it has been redefined in terms of velocity of light which is a fundamental constant.

1.2.9 Pre-Akbar Length Measures

There are some units of length, which are being used for long time in certain trades [52].

1.2.9.1 Linear Units in Terms of Angul

3 *angul* (width of 3 fingers) = 1 *girah*
8 *girah* = 1 Hath (elbow to the end of the middle finger, approximately 18 in. or
46 cm)
35/6 *hath* = one *kathi*
20 *kathi* = one *pand*
20 *pand* = one *bigah*
2 *hath* = one *gaz*
3 *gaz* = two *karam*
3 *Karam* = one *Kan*

1.2.10 Weights and Measures in Akbar Time

1.2.10.1 System of Weights and Measures by Akbar

Akbar [53] wanted to standardize the weights and measurements taking the barley corn (*Jau*) as base standard. For weights, he wanted to use the weight of *Jau*.
The width of the *Jau* was then used to set the standard for length. But this scheme
did not work out. So different standards were used for different commodities, for
example,

1. **Ilahi Gaz** (33″ to 34″) for length measurements.
2. **Seer** for ordinary commodities like food grains, wood, coal, etc.
3. **Dam** for spices and other costly commodities. *Dam* was a copper coin. It was
   used as a weight as well as currency. One *Dam* was equal to 20 g.
4. **Misqal** for gold, silver and expensive spices. *Misqal* was approximately 6.22 g.

1.2.10.2 Akbar Ilahi Gaz

A proper land revenue system was founded by Akbar [53, 54]. However, the system of Akbar was itself based on what Shershah Suri implemented during his short
tenure. Thus, the land revenue system of Akbar was neither an innovation nor an
invention.

Administration and Standardization of Land Measurement in Akbar's
Period

For political as well as fiscal purposes, Akbar divided his empire into 15 *Subah*
(originally there were 12 *Subah*, but by the time Akbar died, the number stood
at 15), 187 *Sarkar* and 3367 *Mahal*. He ordered standardization of various

Table 1.24 Length units in Akbar period

Unit	Multiple units	SI units
yava	*yava*	3.3 mm
8 *yava*	1 *angul*	2.67 cm
24 *angul*	1 *hast*	64 cm
1.6 *hast*	1 *gaz*	102.4 cm
2.5 gaz	1 *dand*	2.56 m
2.5 *dand*	1 *vans*	6.40 m
2 *vans*	1 bamboo	12.80 m
4 bamboo	1 *tenab*	51.20 m
100 *tenab*	1 *kros* or *kos*	5.12 km
4 *krose* or *kos*	1 *yojan*	20.48 km

measurement units and so-called *Ilahi gaj* was made the definite unit of land measurement. This *Ilahi gaz* was equivalent to some 41 fingers (29–32 in.) and was shorter than the Sikandari *gaz* (approx. 39 in.) used by Shershah. The *gaz* as measurement of land finds its origin during Sikandar Lodi's times. Standardization of land measurement was adopted to brush aside all kinds of vagueness in defining extent of land and to reduce extortion/corruption by officials. For land measurement (*Paimaish*), a rope called *Tenab* was used in those days. Since this rope was subject to variation in its length due to seasonal dryness or humidity, Akbar made reforms in *Tenab* also. Instead of an ordinary rope, Akbar ordered the *Tenab* to be made of pieces of Bamboo joined together with iron rings. This made sure that the length of *Tenab* varies little during different seasons of a year. A further change done by Akbar was to fix definite measurement to *bigha* of land. A *bigha* was made of 3600 Ilahi Gaj, which is roughly half of modern acre. Several *bigha* made a *mahal*. Several *mahal* were grouped into *dastur* [54] (Table 1.24).

1.2.10.3 Smaller Units of Length in Akbar Period (1556–1605)

Unit of length (see Table 1.22).

1.2.11 Length Units Used by Tailors

There are certain units of length which are still used by a certain community for specific purpose for their internal use. Though not for trade or commerce, the tailors still use the following units for their internal use:

Base unit *angul* = 0.75 in.
3 *angul* = 1 *girah* = 2.25 in.

Table 1.25 Units in term of inch

Imperial units		In inches	In SI units
1 inch		1	0.254 m
12 in.	1 foot	12	0.30648
2 feet	1 yard	36	0.91944 m
For bigger length intervals			
198/25 in.	1 link	7.92	0.201168 m
5.5 yards	1 pole	198	5.292 m
4 poles	37 chains	792	201.1168 m
10 chains	1 furlong	7920	201.168 m
8 furlongs	1 mile	63360	1609.344 m
3 miles	1 league	190,080	4828.032 m

8 *girah* = 1 *hath* = 18 in.
2 *hath* = 1 yard = 36 in.

1.2.12 Length Units in Dependent India

The basic unit of length was inch, but for day-to-day working in trade *Gaz* was used as unit of length. However, the value of *gaz* was varying from place to place. For example, in Bengal it was 36″, in Bombay it was 27″, in Madras it was 33″, Government Average: 33″, but standard yard as per British standard was 36 in. Other length units in vogue were as follows [55].

1.2.12.1 Base Unit 1 in.

See Table 1.25.

For smaller length intervals, inch is further divided by 8 and called, in day-to-day parlance, as soot (सूत). Further smaller length intervals are measured as decimal fractions. For example, 1/1000th of an inch was called as *thou*.

1.2.12.2 Imperial Length Units

Base unit of length is 1 in. [55].
12 in. = 1 Foot
3 Feet = 1 Yard
5.5 yard = 1 rod
4 rod = 1 chain = 22 yard = 66 feet

10 chain = 1 Furlong = 660 Feet
8 furlong = 1 mile = 1760 yard = 5280 feet

1.3 Units of Weight and Volume

1.3.1 Introduction

1.3.1.1 Mass and Weight

Mass and weight are two different quantities. Mass is the quantity of matter in a
body, while weight of the body is the force with which it is attracted toward the
centre of Earth. However, the quantity of the matter is felt by the force with which
it is attracted towards the Earth and is measureable by various means. Hence, in
common parlance weight is the synonymous of mass.

1.3.1.2 Grain

To start with it may be noted that the word "grain" has been used in two ways.
Firstly, it is been used as a single piece of the cereals and secondly as a unit of
weight. Since ancient times, weight of a grain of cereals has been used to express
weights of other denominations. That is, weights have been expressed in terms of
the weight of a grain of certain cereals. Most common cereals used for this purpose are wheat, rice and barley. Other cereals/seeds are black mustard, white mustard (*Sarson* सरसों), yellow mustard seed, raktika or *gunja* berry, *Abrus, masaka*
beans, *bakala* common beans and *khaskas*. The basic idea was to go for easily
available but natural standards.

1.3.1.3 Measurement of Weights Per Grain of a Cereals

General Cunningham estimated the weight of each seed of several varie-
ties of Indian cereals, which have been used to define other weights. Details of
Cunningham [56] measurements are given in Table 1.26.
    Constancy in weight of ratti which was defined in terms of seed weighed was
excellent. However, the average weights were higher than anticipated by Edward
Thomas, F R S author of Numismata Orientalia—the Ancient Indian Weights
[57]. The higher value was attributed to the locality of growth, richness of soil and
freshness of the seed.
    From the Bronze Age into the Renaissance, the average masses of wheat and
barley grains were part of the legal definition of units of mass. However, there is

Table 1.26 Weight per grain of cereals in troy grain (symbol gr)

Number and name of seed	Total weight (g)	Weight/seed (g)	N = ratti/seed	ratti in gr
1000 rice seeds	358.5	0.3585	5	1.7925
700 barley corns	418.5	0.5978	3	1.7934
500 *mashaaka* beans	1791	3.5820	1/2	1.7910
60 *bakala* common beans	546	9.1000	1/5	1.820
10 *masaka* black beans	146.0	14.600	1/8	1.8250

no evidence of any country ever having used actual seeds or cereal grains as standard weights.

The grain, a unit of weight, was the legal foundation of traditional imperial weight systems [58] and is the only unit that is equal throughout the troy, avoirdupois and apothecaries systems of weights [59]. The unit was based on the weight of a single grain of barley. Weight of three barley grains is taken equal to that of four grains of wheat [58, 60].

1.3.1.4 Value of Troy Grain

Since the implementation of the international yard and pound agreement of 1 July 1959, the grain or troy grain (Symbol gr) has been defined precisely as 64.79891 mg [60], giving 1 g equal to 15.43236 grain. Milligram and gram are, respectively, equal to 10^{-6} and 10^{-3} kg—the unit of mass in the International System of Units (SI). The unit formerly used by jewelers to measure pearls, diamonds or other precious stones, called the jeweler's grain or pearl grain, is equal to $\frac{1}{4}$ of a carat or 50 mg (~0.7716 g). The grain was also the name of a traditional French unit equal to 53.115 mg.

Conversion factor: 1 troy grain = 64.79891 mg.

1.3.2 Weights Nomenclature from Manusmriti

Manusmriti [61], thereby meaning the Remembered Tradition of *Manu-* (the first man on Earth or supreme king of human beings), is traditionally most authoritative book on Hindu Code of Conduct. In the present form, since 1500 BC, it has twelve chapters on different aspects of life, codes of conducts in various situations, crimes, punishment, etc. The eighth chapter is on the crimes and punishment. The chapter also contains a few verses concerning weights and measures where it is mandated that all weights and measures should be duly marked (meaning thereby verified) periodically and the responsibility of getting them verified was assigned to the owner of the weights and measures. Originally, the Manusmirti was in Sanskrit and was translated presumably the first time in 1794 by Sir William Jones. The author is reproducing the relevant verses from the translated version by Pandya [61].

1.3.2.1 Verses of Manusmriti Pertaining to Weights

132. The very small mote which is seen when the sun shines through a lattice, they declare (to be) the least of (all) quantities and (to be called) a *tresarenu* (a floating particle of dust). The verses 133 to 137 of Manusmriti define a set of weights as follows:

133. Eight *tresarenu* (are equal) in bulk (to) a liksha (the egg of a louse), three of those to one grain of black mustard (*ragasarshapa*), and three of the latter to a white mustard-seed.

134. Six grains of white mustard are one middle-sized barley-corn, and three barley-corns one *krishnala* (*raktika*, or *gunga*-berry); five *krishnala* are one *maasha* (bean), and sixteen of those one *suvarna*.

135. Four suvarna are one *pala*, and ten *pala* are one *dharana*; two krishnala (of silver), weighed together, must be considered one *mahasaka* of silver.

136. Sixteen of those make a silver *dharana*, or *purana*; but know (that) a *karsha* of copper is a *karshapana*, or *pana*.

137. Know (that) ten *dharana* of silver make one *satamana*; four *suvarna* must be taken (equal) in weight to a *nishka*.

Manusmiriti also prohibits adulteration (verse 203) and prescribe for reverification of all weights and measure at regular intervals of time (verse 403). The duty of reverification of weights and measures was assigned to its user. The verses are reproduced below.

203. One commodity mixed with another must not be sold as pure, nor a bad one is sold as good one, nor less than the proper quantity or weight, nor anything that is not at hand or that is concealed. The relationships between weight units enunciated in above verses are illustrated in Table 1.27.

For the purpose of giving values of weight units in terms of grain troy and metric system (SI), the *Krishnala* has been taken equivalent to one ratti of 1.75 g (113.398 mg).

1.3.2.2 Weights in Terms of Grains

Edward Thomas gave the sub-multiples of ratti in his book Numismata Orientalia [57] as follows:

In Tables 1.27 and 1.28, ratti is taken as standard and equal to 1.75 g (113.398 mg).

Table 1.27 Weights as per *Manusmriti*

Name in Roman script		Hindi	Value grain	Value in SI
tresarenu		त्रिसरेणू	0.00135	0.0875 mg
8 *tresarenu*	1 *likhya* or minute poppy seed	लिझा	0.01080	0.6999 mg
3 *likhya*	1 black mustard seed or *raja-sarsharp*	राजसर्षप	0.0324	2.0998 mg
3 *rajasharsharp*	1 white mustard seed or *gaura sarsharp*	गौरसर्षप	0.0972	6.2995 mg
6 white mustard	1 medium barley corn or *yava*	यव	0.5833	37.797 mg
3 medium barley corn or *yava*	1 *krishnala* or *raktika*	कृष्णल	**1.75**	**113.392 mg**
5 *krishnala* or *raktika*	1 gold *maashaa*	माष	8.75	566.961 mg
5 *krishnala* or *raktika*	1 gold *maashaa*	माष	8.75	566.961 mg
16 gold *maasha*	1 *swarn*	सुर्वण	140	9.0714 g
4 *swarn*	1 *pala*	पल	560	36.2854 g
10 *pala*	1 *dharna*	धरण	5600	362.854 g
2 *krishnala*	1 *Maasaka*	माषक	3.5	226.796 mg
16 masaka	1 Silver *dharana* or *purana*	धरण पुराणा	56	3.639 g
10 *dharana*	1 *satamana* of silver	सतमन	560	36.388 g
4 *swarn*	1 *nishaka*	निष्क	560	36.284 g

Table 1.28 Sub- divisions of ratti or krishnala

Name in Roman script		Hindi	Value in grain	Value in SI (mg)
tresarenu		त्रिसरेणू	0.00135	0.0875
8 *tresarenu*	1 *likhya*	लिझा	0.01080	0.69999
3 *likhya*	1 *rajasarshapa*	राजसर्षप	0.0324	2.09996
3 *rajasarshapa*	1 *gaursarshapa*	गौरसर्षप	0.0972	6.2999
6 *gaursashapa*	*yava*	यव	0.5833	37.799
3 *yava*	*krishnala* or *ratti*	कृष्णल रत्ती	1.75	113.398

1.3.2.3 Weights in Multiples of Ratti

Edward Thomas [62] gave the weights in multiples of ratti in two sets. One set of weights was for silver trade, which are given in Table 1.29 and the other was for bullion market and are given Table 1.30.

Silver Trade

See Table 1.29.

Table 1.29 Multiples of ratti in silver trade

Name in Roman script		Hindi	Value in grain	Value in SI
krishnala or *Ratti*		कृष्णल रत्ती	1.75	113.398 mg
2 *ratti*	*masaka* or *maashaa*	माषक माषा	3.5	226.796 mg
16 *maashaa*	*dharana* or *purana*	धरण पुराण	56	3.62874 g
10 *dharna*	*satmana*	सतमान	560	36.287 g

Table 1.30 Multiples of ratti in Gold trade

Name in Roman script		Hindi	Value in gr	Value in SI
ratti		रत्ती	1.75 g	113.398 mg
5 *ratti*	1 *masaka* or *maashaa*	माषक माषा	8.75	566.990 mg
16 *maashaa*	1 *suvarn*	सुर्वण	140	9.07184 g
4 *suvarn*	1 *pala* or *nishk*	पल	560	36.2874 g
10 *suvarn*	1 *dharna*	धरण	1400	90.718 g

Gold Trade

Here, we see that ratti, *maashaa* and *swarn* are common names to Tables 1.29 and 1.30 but *maashaa* is equal to 5 ratti for gold trade and is equal to 2 ratti in silver trade. In copper trade, 80 ratti was called *karshapana* which was equal to 140 grain troy or 9.0718 g.

1.3.3   Weights in Terms of Tresarenu

Tresarenu is the smallest dust particles, which can be seen floating in the rays of light coming from a window in a room. It may be noticed that the term *tresarenu* is used in smaller units of time and length also. A set of weights in terms of *tresarenu* as given by Edward Thomas [62] is as follows (Table 1.31).

For the purpose of calculating the values in grain or in metric units, the value of *tresarenu* has been taken as the starting point. Edward Thomas also used *tresarenu* as the starting point.

1.3.4   Charak System of Weights

Charak system of weight units has been given in Table 1.32 [63] and in Table 1.33 [64].

Table 1.31 Weights in terms of Tresarenu

Name in Roman script		Hindi	Value in grain	Value in SI
tresarenu		त्रिसरेणू	0.00135	0.0875 mg
8 tresarenu	1 nisk	निंसक	0.0108	0.7 mg
3 nisk	1. mustard seed 2. or rajsarshap	राजसर्षप	0.0324	2.1 mg
3 mustard seed	3. yellow mustard seed 4. or gaursarshap	गौरसर्षप	0.0972	6.3 mg
6 yellow mustard seed	1 yava	यव	0.5832	37.8 mg
3 yava	I krishnala	कृष्णल	1.7496	113.4 mg
5 krishnal	1 maashaa	माषा	8.748	567.0 mg
16 maashaa	1 suvarn	सुर्वण	139.968	9.072 g

Table 1.32 Weights given in Charak Samhita

Names of units in Roman script		Hindi	SI equivalent
1 vamsya		वामस्य	0.225 mg
6 vamsya	1 marica	माकैं	1.35 mg
6 marica	1 Sarsapa	सरसप	8.1 mg
6 Sarsapa	1 Yave	यावे	48.6 mg
3 Yave	1 ratika	रतिका	145.8 mg
10 Ratika	1 maasaa	माषा	1.458 g
4 maasaa	1 Sana	सन	5.832 g
2 Sana (nisk)	**1 kola**		**11.664 g**
2 kola	1 karse	करसे	23.328 g
2 karse	1 sukti	सुकति	46.656 g
2 sukti	1 pala	पल	93.312 g
2 pala	1 prasrti	प्रासति	186.624 g
2 prasrti	1 anjali or kudva	अंजलि	373.248 g
2 anjali or kudva	1 prastha	प्रस्थ	746.496 g
2 prastha	1 aadhaka	आढक	1.4923 kg
4 aadhaka	1 drona	द्रोण	5.972 kg
2 drona	1 surpa	सुरपा	11.944 kg
2 surpa	1 droni or vah	द्रोणी वाह	23.888 kg
4 droni or vah	1 khaari = 4096 pala	खारि	95.551 kg
2000 pala	1 bhaar	भार	166.624 kg

Kola has been taken as base unit with metric equivalent of 11.664 g

The scientists in *Bhoja* period (eleventh century AD) use to follow *Charak*, a renowned *Ayurvedic* medicine wizard, thus assuming that term kola in the above table is the same as *tolaa* used in the common man's language. Further taking the internationally agreed value of *tolaa* as 11.664 g, the values of other units depicted in the above table are calculated and given in column 4 of the table.

Table 1.33 Weights used in Ayurved

Name of units in Roman script			Hindi	Value in SI
Tolaa			तोला	11.664 g
8	*pal*		पल	93.312 g
32	4 *pal*	*kudav*	कुडव	373.248 g
80	2.5 *kudev*	*ser*	सेर	933.12 g
320	4 *ser*	*aadhak*	आधक	3.732 kg

Use of binary system may be appreciated from units *sana* to *Adhak*. Range of the units of weights say from tenth of an mg to hundreds of kg is another highlight of the Charak system of units of weights described above.

1.3.4.1 *Weights Used in Ayurveda*

Matil in *Padma Puran* [65], while giving the composition of the human body with quantity of various materials inside the human body like, *kaph, vassa,* etc. used various weight units, defined in terms of Tolaa as follows:

For providing metric equivalents, "*ser*" has been taken as base and equal to 933.12 g.

1.3.4.2 **Pal Tolaa Relationship**

In Ayurveda only, "Pal" is taken equal to 8 *tolaa*; otherwise, it is taken equal to four *tolaa* as given in [66].

1.3.5 *Weight Measurement in Ancient India*

Weight units for dry granular materials in terms of volume were found to be used not only in ancient times but this tradition continued till the metric system was introduced in India. Measurement system for dry materials in terms of volume measure like handful was easy to practice with no extra contrivance required. Otherwise, also in practical life we judge the quantity by the space it occupies.

1.3.5.1 *Weight Units in* **Narad Puran**

In *Narad Puran* [67], capacity of volume measures for dry granular materials has been described in weight units, i.e. no separate unit for volume. The contrivances

Table 1.34 Measures in terms of handful

Name in Roman script			Hindi
Handful			मुट्ठी
8 handful	1 *kinchit*		किन्चित
64 handful	8 *kinchit*	1 *pushkal*	पुष्कल
256 handful	4 *pushkal*	*aadhak*	आधक
1024 handful	4 *aadhak*	1 *drona*	द्रोण
4096 handful	4 *drona*	1 *khaaree*	खारी
16,384 handful	4 *khaaree*	1 *prasth*	प्रस्थ

Table 1.35 Measures for dry materials

Units in Roman script			Hindi
pal			पल
6 double handfuls	2 *pal*	1 *prasit*	प्रसृत
12 double handfuls	2 *prasit*	1 *kudav*	कुडव
48 double handfuls	4 *kudav*	1 *prasth*	प्रस्थ
192 double handfuls	4 *prasth*	1 *aadhak*	आधक
368 double handfuls	4 aadhak	1 drona	द्रोण

used for such purpose are called dry measures. Basis of conversion is that the density of water is taken as unity; hence, units of weight and volume are the same. The descriptions of these units of weight are given in Tables 1.34 and 1.35.

Another system of weights for dry materials described in Narad Puran [67] is given in Table 1.35. Here, it may be noted that the *prasth* and handful have appeared in both the tables but are not equal in value.

I think the weights mentioned in Narad Puran are much older than many other systems of weights. Therefore, no equivalent in modern system of weights or measures could be given.

1.3.5.2 Weights Used for Food Grains

Another weight system for weighing food grains [68] is given in Table 1.36.

It may be noted that each successive weight unit is four times the previous one.

For the purpose of calculating rough values of other weight units in metric units, the value of *maashaa* has been taken equal to 1.1016 g.

1.3.5.3 Volume of Granular Materials

To improve upon the measurement system for food grains based on handful, use of hourglass measures came into existence. These essentially were volume measures [69]. The smallest unit was nilve with the following multiples in Table 1.37.

Table 1.36 System of weights used for food grains

Names in Roman script		Hindi	Equivalent in SI
maashaa		माषा	1.1016 g
16 maashaa	1 karsa	करसा	17.626 g
4 karsa	pala	पल	70.502 g
4 pala	kudava	कुडव	282.010 g
4 kudava	1 prastha	प्रष्थ	1.12804 kg
4 prastha	1 aadhak	आढक	4.5122 kg
4 aadhak	1 drona	द्रोण	18.0486 kg

Table 1.37 Volume measures for dry granular materials

Name of unit in Roman scripts		Hindi	Mass of water contained in g
nilve		निलव	29.159510
4 nilve	1 klove	कलव	116.638038
2 klove	1 chipte	चिंपठे	233.276076
2 chipte	1 mapte	मापठे	466.552152
2 mapte	1 ser	सेर	933.104304

The "*ser*" is a unit of weight (mass); it simply means that such a measure will contain one *ser* of water. Density of water has been taken as unity. Therefore, for comparison purposes, "*ser*" is taken equivalent 80 *tolaa* or 0.933104304 kg, and the values of other units are calculated as sub-multiples of *ser* (सेर).

1.3.6   Weights in Terms of Grain of Rice (chawal)

Basic reason for using a grain of a cereal about which system of weights is woven is its ever-ready availability to the farmers. According to Capt. T. B. Jervis [70], the *chow* or *chawal* (rice) is of very constant weight. Hence, to express weight units in number of *chawal* (rice) is quite natural.

1.3.6.1   Weights in Terms of Rice (Chawal)

Edward Thomas [62] gave the weight units as depicted in Table 1.38.

Starting point may be *chawal* (rice) in this case also, or it may be *khandi* whose value in pounds is known. Values of weights in metric units are given taking *chawal* and *khandi* as base units. The values are, respectively, given in columns 4 and 5, respectively. However, it may be noticed that the values do not match; the ratio of corresponding values is about 4.5. I personally feel that values of different weight units are more reliable when weight of rice is taken as the base unit.

Table 1.38 Weights in terms of rice (*Chawal*)

Name of units in Roman script	Hindi	Value in SI	
		Rice as base	Khandi as base
chawal (husked rice)		चावल	15.1872 mg	68.905 mg
2 *chawal*	1 *dhaan* (rice with husk)	धान	30.3744 mg	137.81 mg
8 *chawal* = 4 *Dhaan*	1 ratti	रत्ती	121.498 mg	551.24 mg
16 *chawal* = 2 *ratti*	1 *maashaa*	माषा	242.995 mg	1.1025 g
64 *chawal* = 4 *maashaa*	1 *tank*	तंक	971.981 mg	4.4099 g
576 *chawal* = 9 *tank*	One-eighth of *ser*	सेर	8.7478 g	39.689 g
1152 *chawal* = 18 *tank*	One-fourth of *ser*	सेर	17.4957 g	79.378 g
2304 *chawal* = 36 *tank*	½ *ser*	सेर	34.9913 g	158.758 g
4608 *chawal* = 72 *tank*	1 *ser*	सेर	69.9826 g	317.15 g
40 ser of 26 *tolaa*	1 *man*	मन	2.7994 kg	12.7006 kg
20 man	1 *khandi*	खान्डि	55.986 kg	254.012 kg
1 khandi	560 lbs (Av.)	पाऊड		254.012 kg

Table 1.39 Weights as multiples of *dhaan* (rice with husk)

Names of units in Roman script		Hindi	Value in SI
dhaan rice with husk or vreehi		धान	30.3774 mg
4 *dhaan*	1 *gunja*	गुन्जा	121.5096 mg
5 *gunja*	1 *pan*	पन	607.548 mg
8 *pan*	1 *dharan*	धरण	4.86038 g
8 *dharan*	1 *karsh*	कश कर्ष	38.8831 g
4 *karsh*	1 *pal*	पल	155.532 g
100 *pal*	1 *tulaa*	तुला	15.553 kg
20 *tulaa*	1 *bhaar*	भार	31.106 kg

1.3.6.2 Weights in Multiples of Rice with Husk (Dhaan)

Sushmajee [71] gave weight units taking dhaan (rice with husk) as base unit. These are given in Table 1.39.

For the purpose of calculating values of weight units, weight of *dhaan* is taken as standard and is equal to 30.3774 mg. *Bhaar* means weight, and it is a type of measure to weigh dry materials.

1.3.6.3 Bullion Weights in Terms of Chawal (Rice)

The following was the standard scale for precious metals (gold and silver) (Table 1.40).

Table 1.40   Weights in Bullion Trade

Units in Roman script		Hindi	Value in SI
1 *chawal*		चावल	15.1872 mg
8 *chawal*	1 *ratti*	रत्ती	121.498 mg
8 *ratti*	1 *maashaa*	माषा	971.981 mg
12 *maashaa*	1 *tolaa*	तोला	11.664 g
5 *tolaa*	1 *chattank*	छटांक	58.319 g
16 *chattank*	1 *ser*	सेर	933.10 g

Table 1.41   Tolaa, maashaa vala system of south India

2 *chawal*	1 *dhaan*				
8 *chawal*	4 d*haan*	1 *ratti*			
16 *chawal*	8 *dhaan*	2 *ratti*	1 *vala*		
64 *chawal*	32 d*haan*	8 *ratti*	4 *vala*	1 *maashaa*	
768 *chawal*	384 *dhaan*	96 *ratti*	48 *vala*	12 *maashaa*	1 *tolaa*

Table 1.42   Weights in terms of *Chawal*

Names in Roman script		Hindi	Value in g
chawal		चावल	0.01518
2 *chawal*	1 *dhaan*	धान	0.03037
4 *dhaan*	1 *ratti*	रत्ती	0.12150
2 *ratti*	1 *vala*	वाल	0.24300
4 *vala*	1 *maashaa*	माषा	0.97198
12 *maashaa*	1 *tolaa*	तोला	11.664

In this case, *tolaa* is taken of 11.664 g to express values for other weights in metric units. Incidentally, the value of weight of one grain of rice matches with values given to it at other places

Though the weights appear to be defined in terms of weight of rice, however, the practical way of realization was the weight of the coin prevalent in the province or the princely state. For example, *tolaa* was the weight of one rupee coin in Colonial rule from nineteenth century till 1947.

1.3.6.4   Weights System Used in Southern Part of India

The weights *tolaa*, *maashaa* and *vala* used principally in Southern India are given in Tables 1.41 and 1.42.

System of weights given in Table 1.42 may be written in a simpler form as follows:

Table 1.43 Weights in terms of *chawal, ratti, maashaa* etc

Names in Roman script		Hindi	Value in SI
4 *chawal*	1 *dhaan* or 1 wheat berry	धान	30.375 mg
4 *dhaan*	1 *ratti*	रत्ती	121.5 mg
8 *ratti*	1 *maashaa*	माषा	0.972 g
12 *maashaa* (96 *ratti*)	1 *bhaari* or Tolaa	भारी	11.664 g
24 *ratti* (96 *dhaan*)	1 *taak*	ताक	2.916 g

1.3.7 Weights Used in Pre-Akbar Period

The system of weights used, even before the period of Akbar, continued to be used till the metric system came into the existence is expressed in Table 1.43. The weights with the same name were having different quantities. There were different systems in Bengal, the Presidency of Madras and Bombay. The following nomenclature was prevalent in Northern India till the metric system was adopted in India.

1.3.7.1 Weights in Terms of chawal, ratti, maashaa, Etc

In Wikipedia, Indian weights [71] has another set of weight units; it is reproduced in Table 1.43.

In my view, the first row of the table above should be 2 *chawal* = 1 *dhaan* instead of 4 *chawal* = 1 *Dhaan*. Prima facie my contention appears to be right as husk is lighter but slightly bigger in volume, so husk or rice should have equal weights. This will keep consistency with values taken for rice and husk by other authors. To calculate the metric equivalents, *bhaari* or Tolaa has been taken as base and assigned the value of 11.664 g.

1.3.7.2 Weights in Terms of Siki

In Table 1.44, *Bhaari* is taken as one *tolaa* and equal to 11.66375 g, and other equivalents in metric units have been calculated.

The terms like s*avaser* for (1¼ *ser or* Seer), *dhai-ser* for (2½) *ser, Paseri* or *adisari* for 5 *ser* and *daseri* for 10 ser were quite often used by general public before the introduction of metric system in 1956.

1.3.8 Weights in Colonial (Pre-Independence) Years

1.3.8.1 Weights in Terms of Khaskas

Sushmajee [71] indicated the system of weights given in Table 1.45, which was used in north India till the introduction of metric system. But the terms involving

Table 1.44 Weights in terms of siki

Names in Roman script		Hindi	Value in SI
siki		सिकि	2.91594 g
4 *siki*	1 *bhaari*	भारी	11.66375 g
5 *siki*	1 *kancha*	क्नचा	14.57969 g
4 *kancha*	1 *chhataank*	छटांक	58.3188 g
5 *bhaari*	1 *chhataank*	छटांक	58.3188 g
4 *chhataank*	1 *pav*	पाव	233.275 g
16 *chhataabk*	1 *ser* (80 Tolaa)	सेर	933.10 g
40 *ser*	1 *maund* or *man*	मन	37.324 kg

Table 1.45 Weights in terms of *khashkas*

Name of units in Roman script		Hindi	SI Equivalent
khaskhas		खसखस	0.00189 g
8 *khaskhas*	1 *chawal*	चावल	0.0152 g
8 *chawal*	1 *ratti*	रत्ती	0.1217 g
8 ratti	1 *maashaa*	माषा	0.972 g
12 *maashaa*	1 *tolaa*	तोला	11.664 g
5 Tolaa	1 *chhatank*	छटांक	58.319 g
4 *chhataank*	1 *paav*	पाव	233.276 g
4 *paav*	1 *ser*	सेर	933.104 g
40 *ser*	I *man*	मन	37.324 kg

smaller weights from *ratti* to *tolaa* were used especially in day-to-day parlance for gold jewelry by the rural public.

I have taken ser of 80 *tolaa* as a starting point and is taken equal to 933.104304 g to compute the values of other units.

Bhaar means weight, and it is a type of measure to weigh dry materials.

1.3.8.2 Variety of Weights Before Independence

Every princely state was having its own system of weights with similar names but of different values. At the advent of 1956 standard of weights and measures act, weights were collected from various parts of the country. The weights bearing the name ser were having different values, starting from 20 *tolaa* to 240 *tolaa*. Weights were by and large of circular flat disc. But weights having rectangular, square or heart shape were also existed.

1.3.8.3 Weights in Terms of Gunja

Sushmajee [71] indicated that weights purported to be written in *Agni Puran*. The author could not find any such weights in *Agni Puran* (Table 1.46).

Table 1.46 Weights given in Gunja Agnipuran

Names in Roman script		Hindi	Value in SI
gunja or *ratti*		गुन्जा रत्ती	0.1217 g
5 *gunja*	1 *maashaa*	माषा	0.6085 g
16 *maashaa*	1 suvarn	सुर्वण	9.736 g
4 suvarn	1 *pal*	पल	38.944 g
100 *Pal*	1 *tulaa*	तुला	3.8944 kg
20 *tulaa*	1 *bhaar*	भार	77.888 kg
4 *Adhak* (60 *Pal*)	1 *Drona*	द्रोण	2.3366 kg

Ratti or gunja is taken as base unit with metric value of 0.1217 g and is used to calculate value of other units in metric system

1.3.9   Conventions Followed by Public for Weights

Although the various acts on weights and measures by different provinces of the country were enacted to bring uniformity in the system of weights and measures, nothing succeeded in achieving the desired objective.

1.3.9.1   Urban Area

In urban areas, for weighing common commodities, the *seer* or *ser* was the unit of weight. In addition, there were weights of 2 seer, 5 seer, 10 seer, 20 seer and 40 seer. The weight of 40 *seer* was called as *maund* or *man* (मन) as written in Hindi. The *maund* was equal to 82.27 lb. For precious metals like gold and silver, *tolaa*, *maashaa and ratti* systems were used.

1.3.9.2   Rural Area

In rural areas, the word *Kutcha* was suffixed for each unit, making it two-fifths of the urban unit. Say they will call one *Maund* of urban area as 2½ *Maund* (kutcha).

1 *maund* as 2½ *maund* (kutcha) मन कच्चा
20 *seer* as 1¼ *maund* (*kutcha*) मन कच्चा
16 *seer* as 1 *maund* (*kutcha*) मन कच्चा
4 *seer* as 1 *dhari* धडि or 10 (*seer kutcha*) सेर कच्चा
2 *seer* as 1 *panjseri* पंजसेरि or 5 (*seer kutcha*) सेर कच्चा
1 *seer* as 2½ (*seer kutcha*) सेर कच्चा

The local *seer* was two-fifths of the standard seer.

1.3.9.3 Present Situation

However, these conventions died down though slowly after the Government of India enacted the Standards of Weights and Measures Act, 1956 (No. 89 of 1956, amended 1960, 1964). The 1956 Act was replaced by more comprehensive Standards of Weights and Measures Act in 1976. This 1976 Act has recently been replaced by another Legal Metrology Act 2009, which became effective from 1 April 2011. However, the units of weights and measure are the same in two Acts; the two Acts differ only in administrative manners.

1.3.10 Weights and Volume Measures by Chanakiya

We have got references in Hindu inscriptions about various units of measurement, for example, Srimad Bhagwad [70] gives units of time intervals, and Agni Puran [72] gives units of length for purpose of making *Haven Kunds* (fire altars), while *Manusmiriti* [61] gives about the units essentially for smaller weights. Subject of weights and measures has been dealt with totality by *Chanakiya* in his *Arthsashtra* [73]. The real name of *Chanakiya* was *Vishnugupt*, also known by western world as *Kautilya*. He assisted the famous king *Chandragupta Maurya* in fourth century B.C. and authored the most ancient interdisciplinary book known as Chanakiya Arthsashtra. This has 15 books dealing with different subjects. The subjects are "Concerning Discipline & Training", "The Duties of Government Superintendents", "Concerning Law & justice", "The Removal of Thorns", "Conduct of Courtiers", The Source of Sovereign States, "On The Six-Fold Policy", Concerning Vices and Calamities, "The Work of an Invader Activity of the king preparing to go into Battle", "Relating to War", "The Conduct of Confederacies", "Concerning a Powerful Enemy", "Strategic Means to Capture a Fortress", "Secret Means or Esoteric Practices" and "The Plan & Organization of a Scientific Treatise".

The Book 2 Chapter 19 deals with the subject of weights and measures. It deals with various units of weights, volume and time, denominations of weights and volumetric measures, material to be used for weights and balances. Four types of weights or measures used for different purposes have been defined. Period of verification along with fee chargeable is also prescribed.

1.3.10.1 Weights

Smaller Units of Weights

Gold Trade

See Table 1.47.

Silver Trade

See Table 1.48.

Here, we see that ratio of weights of silver *maashaa* and *suvaran* (gold) *mashaa* माषा is 40. If gold is 40 times costlier than silver, then one *suvarn maashaa* of gold will cost as much as one mashaa of silver. The values of various weight units have been taken as given by Patrick Olivelle [17]. One *dharana* [17] is 377.6 g approximately.

Diamond Trade

Smaller weights for diamond trade

20 grains of rice = 1, यज्ञ धरण *dharana* of a diamond, approximately equal to 303.74 mg (Taking 1 rice grain as 15.187 mg).

Bigger Units of Weights

Table 1.49 has been constructed taking into the weight values of *Dharnika*, *Pala*, *Dharana*, *Tula* and *Bhar* given by Patrick Olivelle [17]. This means a small

Table 1.47 Smaller weights in Gold Trade

1 *masa* beans ऊडद के दाने (उर्द)		0.06 g
2 *masa* beans	*gunja* berries रत्ती	0.12 g
5 *gunja* berries seed phraseolus radiatus	1 *suvaran maashaa* माषा	0.59 g
10 seed phraseolus radiatus	1 *suvaran maashaa* माषा	0.59 g
16 *Suvaran Maashaa* माषा	1 *Suvaran or Karsa* कर्ष	9.44 g
4 *suvaran*	1 *pal* पल	37.76 g

Table 1.48 Smaller weights for silver trade

white mustered, सफेद सरसौं seeds		0.268 g
88 white mustered seeds	1 silver *maashaa*	23.6 g
16 silver *maashaa*	1 *dharana*	377.6 g
20 *saibya* seed	1 *dharana*	377.6 g

Table 1.49 Sub-multiples of bhar

Name of the units		Value in SI
dharnika		3.776 g
10 *dharnika*	1 *pala*	37.76 g
10 *pala*	1 *dharana*	377.6 g
100 *dharana*	1 *tula*	37.76 kg
20 *tula*	1 *bhar*	755.2 kg

Table 1.50 Assorted weights

Unit	Value in g	Unit/*Maashaa*
maashaa	0.59 g	1
suvarn	9.44 g	16
karsa	151 g	$256 = 16^2$
ghatika	3.15 kg	534
drona	9.6 kg	1627
vrake	9.6 kg	1627
khari = 16 Drona	153.6 kg	26,034
bhar	755.2 kg	1,280,000
vaha	1920 kg	3,254,237

All values to different unit names have been taken from Patrick Olivelle [17]

correction in Table A 2.4 of Patrick Olivelle [17]. The correction is 1000 *Pala* in place of 100 *Pala*.

Miscellaneous Weight Units

See Table 1.50.

Denominations of Weights

Denominations of weights for each category were prescribed in *Chanakiya Arthsashtra*.

Gold Trade

Ardha-maashaa (half a *maasshaa* or 0.295 g), one *maashaa* (0.590 g), two *maashaa* (1.18 g), four *maashaa* (2.36 g), eight *maashaa* (4.72 g), one *suvarna* 9.44 g, two *suvarna* (18.88 g), four *suvarna* 37.76 g, eight *suvarna* 75.52, ten *suvarna* 94.4 g, twenty suvarna 188.8 g, thirty *suvarna* 283.2 g, forty *suvarna* 377.6 g and one hundred *suvarna* (944 g) were prescribed denominations of weights with different units of weights. All these should be 14 weights.

Silver Trade

A similar series comprising weights of half a maashaa (11.8 g), one maashaa (23.6 g), two maashaa (47.2 g), four maashaa (94.4 g) and eight maashaa (188.8 g) was prescribed for silver trade.

General Trade

Similar series of weights was also made in *dharana*, from ½ *dharana* (188.8 g) to 100 *dharana* = 37.76 kg.

Material of Weights

Weights (*pratimánáni*) shall be made of iron. In states of *Magadha* and *Mekala*, these may be made of stones available in there. However, the material should be such that these will neither gain weight when wetted, nor lose weight under the influence of environmental conditions.

1.3.10.2   Balances

Balances in Gold Trade

Equi-arm balances with varying length and mass of the beam were prescribed in Chanakiya Arthsashtra. Beam length in *angul* (16.764 mm) and weight in pala (37.76 g) of each beam are tabulated below.

Length	6	14	22	30	38	46	54	62	70	78
Weight	1	2	3	4	5	6	7	8	9	10

All balances were equi-arm and having pan on each end of the beam.

Note by the author:

Generally, capacity of the balance is roughly equal to the weight of the beam. Hence, capacity of the biggest balance is likely to be around 10 pala (377.6 g). Such a range of balances is sufficient for bullion trade. But a balance having a beam length of 78 *angul* (1.3 m) appears to be a little impractical especially for a balance whose capacity is only around a kilogram.

Balances for Other Commodities

Weighing systems for other commodities were of steelyard type. The beam is divided into two unequal parts. The load to be weighed is placed on the shorter side. The weight is measured by moving poise along the graduated beam. Every fifth marking was called as *aksesu*, and these special marks, each being multiple 5, were highlighted. Nandi mark is an auspicious mark; Nandi containing Swastika at its centre was marked at multiples of 5.

Samavritta Balance

A balance called *samavrittá*, with its lever 72 angul long and weighing 35 *pala* in its metallic mass, was made. The term *samavritta* indicates that the beam was circular. A scale pan of 5 *palas* in weight was attached to its edge; the horizontal position of the lever (*samakarana*) when weighing a *karsha* was marked on that part of the lever when it became horizontal. To the left of that mark, 1 to 4 *pala* were marked. Pala marks greater than 5 would be on the right of the mark. After that, every 10th mark place was marked with special picture. In the place of *Aksesu*, the sign of *Nándi* was marked. Adjustment devices like screwed plug were in use.

Parimani Balance

From the word *Parimani* in the title, it appears that these types of balances were used to verify other balances. *Parimani* comes from a Hindi word *pariman,* which means standard.

Mass of the beam of this balance was twice as that of *samavrittá*, i.e. *70 pal* and the beam was of 96 *angul* in length. The beam should be marked the same way as samarvritta's beam. On its lever, marks such as 20, 50 and 100 above its initial weight of 100 shall be carved.

Commercial Balances

In addition, there were three other types of balances, namely, *Vyavaharika* for ordinary trade and commerce, *Bhajni* used in distribution of wages and *antahpurbajini* used inside the palace. Weight of beam of each balance would be decreasing by 5 pala, i.e. 95 pala of *Vyavaharika*, 90 *pala* of *bhajni*i and 85 of *antahpurbhajini*. Similarly, their lengths will be successively decreasing by 6 *angul*. A levi (to be given to the king) was paid for weighing in the first two balances if the commodity weighed was more than 5 *pala* and it was not flesh, metals, salt and precious stones, when they are weighed in the two first-named balances. In all, there were 16 types of balances and 14 types of weights.

1.3.10.3   Volume Measurements

The basic unit of volume was *drona*; other units were integral multiples and sub-multiples of *drona*.

Types of Drona

There were four types of *Drona*:

1. *Ayamani* (Standard) *Drona* = 200 *pala* used for the revenue of the Government.
2. *Vyavaharika Drona* = 187.5 *pala* used for normal sale and purchase.
3. *Bhajini drona* = 175 *pala* used with the balance of same name for distribution of servants wages.
4. *Antahpur drona* = 162.5 *pala* used with *antahpur Bhajini*.

Each of *drona* had its own aa*dhaka*, *prastha* and *kudumba*, each of which was one-fourth of the previous one.

Other Units of Volume

Various units of volume starting from 150 g to 1920 kg and special units used for liquid oils and ghee [17] are given in Table 1.51. These units have been taken from the book "King, Governance and Law in Ancient India" [17]. Volume units are given in mass units on the basis that 1 kg of water occupies the space of one litre. Unit of volume given as 0.15 kg means a space of 0.15 l.

It is worth noting that units are increasing in steps of 4.

Table 1.51   Volume units

Name of units		Weight of water contained (kg)
kuduba		0.15
4 *kuduba*	1 *prastha*	0.6
4 *prastha*	1 *aadhaka*	2.4
4 *aadhaka*	1 *drona*	9.6
16 *drona*	1 *khari*	153.6
20 *drona*	1 *kumbha*	192
10 *kumbha*	1 *vaha*	1920
21 *kuduba*	1 *ghatika* of ghee	3.15
84 *kuduba*	1 *varaka* of Ghee	12.6
16 *kuduba*	1 *ghatika* of oil	2.4
64 *kuduba*	1 *varaka* of oil	9.6

Construction of Volumetric Measures

Volumetric Measures for Granular Material

Volumetric measures for granular material were of two types.

Type 1

Volumetric measures were made of dry and strong wood with vertical walls, mostly in cylindrical form. In type I, the mouth of the main body was such that when filled with grains, the conically heaped-up portion of the grains standing on the mouth of the measure is equal to one-fourth of the capacity of the volumetric measure. That is, for a measure of 20 *drona*, 15 drona is contained in the main body and 5 *drona* in the form of heap.

Type II

The measures were also made to contain the total quantity of the commodity up to the brim of the volumetric measure.

Volumetric Measures for Liquids

For liquids, the measure shall be filled up to level of the mouth of the volumetric measure. The quantity contained should be equal to its declared capacity.

For six items, namely, wine, flowers, fruits, bran, charcoal and slaked lime, the upper part of the volumetric measures should be twice the quantity of the heaped-up portion (i.e. one-fourth of the measure), and neck should be made separately from the main body of the volumetric measures.

1.3.10.4   Administrative Measures

Price Control on Weight and Measure

It appears that even in those days (fourth century BC), provisions used to be made to control the prices of various weights and measures. For example, the following data has been given in *Chanakiya Arthsashtra* (Table 1.52).

Table 1.52 Price of various weights and measures

Volumetric measures and weights	Price
drona measure	5/4 *Pana*
aadhaka measure	3/4 *Pana*
prastha measure	6 *Masaka*
kuduba measure	1 *Masaka*
The price of measures for juice is two times of those given above	
One complete set of 14 types of counterweights	20 Pana
One complete set of 14 types of balances	20/3 Pana

Verification Period and Fee Chargeable

Every weight and measure was to be verified and stamped at every 4 months. The penalty for the use of unstamped weight or measure was 27 and one-fourth *Pana*. Traders were required to pay, every day, one *kákaní* to the Superintendent of weights and measures towards the charge of stamping the weights and measures. (*Kakani* was a copper coin equal to one-fourth of *Masaka* or 1/64th of a *Pana*.)

Taptavyaji

To compensate for the volume of adhesive liquids like ghee and oils remained sticking in the measure, there was a provision to give some extra amount of such materials to the purchaser. This was called *taptavyaji*. *Taptavyaji* were as follows:

- For ghee, it was 1/32th of the volume;
- For oils, it was 1/64th of volume;
- For other liquids, it was 1/50th of the volume.

Smaller Standard Measures

The superintendent of weights and measures was required to have volumetric measures of one, half, one-fourth and one-eighth parts of the *Kuduba*. Perhaps, these were used to find out errors in commercial volumetric measures.

1.3.11 Conversion Factors

Metric conversion, as the Government of India defined in the Standards of Weights and Measures Act 1976 [74], is as follows:

Indian system	British system	Metric system
1 *tolaa*	0.375 oz approximately	11.66375 g
1 *ser* (80 tolaa)	2.5 troy lb, 2.2 lb	933.10 g
1 *man* (40 ser)	100 troy lb	37.324 kg

1 lb avoirdupois 453.592 g
1 *bhari* or *tolaa* = 11.66375 g = 0.375 troy oz
Weight of 64 *dhaan* (Wheat berries) = Weight of 45 *Jau* (b14/5/17 *barley* corns)
Weight of 1 *barley* corn = 64.79891 mg.

References

1. Surya Siddhant, Translation by Pundit Bapu Dev Shastri (Chap. 1, Verse 2, 3) (Bapist Mission Press, Calcutta, 1861)
2. Surya Siddhant, Translation by Pundit Bapu Dev Shastri (Chap. 1, verse 10 Surya) (Bapist Mission Press, Calcutta, 1861)
3. Surya Siddhant, Translation by Pundit Bapu Dev Shastri (Chap. 14, verses 1 to 3) (Bapist Mission Press, Calcutta, 1861)
4. Srimad Bhagwat Puraan (Part 3, Chap. 11, verse 1, p. 216) (Geeta Press Gorakhpur, India)
5. https://en.wikipedia.org/wiki/Lunar_day
6. Srimad Bhagwat Puran (Part 3, Chap. 11, verse 8, p. 216) (Geeta Press Gorakhpur, India)
7. Bharat Main Vigyan Ki Oejwal Permpara, Suresh Soni, Archana Prakashan, Mahavir Nagar, Bhopal, India, p. 82
8. S.V. Gupta, *Units of Measurement- Past, Present and Future, International System of Units* (Springer, Germany), p. 5
9. Shri Vishnu Puraan, Ram ji Sharma, Shri Durga Pustak Bhandar, Allahabad, India (Part 1, Chap. 3), pp. 18, 163
10. Shri Harivansh Maha Puran,Vivek Kaushik & Vishvak Mitra, Puja Prakashan, Delhi, p. 84
11. Bhavishya Puraan 1/2
12. http://www.sushmajee.com/reldictionary/dictionary/page-M/measure-time-1.htm
13. Surya Siddhant, Translation by Pundit Bapu Dev Shastri (Chap. 1, verse 11&12) (Bapist Mission Press, Calcutta, 1861)
14. https://en.wikipedia.org/wiki/Hindu_units_of_time
15. http://sushmajee.com/reldictionary/dictionary/page-M/measure-time-2.htm
16. http://creative.sulekha.com/time-measurement-in-ancient-india_217765_blog#
17. King, *Governance and Law in Ancient India- Annotated Translation of Kautilya Arthasastra by Patrick Olivelle* (Oxford University Press, India, 2014)
18. Surya Siddhant, Translation by Pundit Bapu Dev Shastri (Chap. 14, verse 12) (Bapist Mission Press, Calcutta, 1861)
19. Surya Siddhant, Translation by Pundit Bapu Dev Shastri (Chap. 14, verse 9) (Bapist Mission Press, Calcutta, 1861)
20. H. Defouw, R. Svoboda, *Light on Life: An Introduction to the Astrology of India* (Lotus Press, 2003), p. 186. ISBN 0-940985-69-1
21. http://veda.wikidot.com/vedic-time-system
22. Surya Siddhant, Translation by Pundit Bapu Dev Shastri (Chap. 1, verse 7) (Bapist Mission Press, Calcutta, 1861)
23. Introduction to Rigveda, Dayanand Sarswati, Ajmernagar Vedic yantralye (1970), p. 23
24. Surya Siddhant, Translation by Pundit Bapu Dev Shastri (verse Chap. 1, verse 15, 16) (Bapist Mission Press, Calcutta, 1861)
25. Surya Siddhant, Translation by Pundit Bapu Dev Shastri (Chap. 1, verse 17) (Bapist Mission Press, Calcutta, 1861)
26. Surya Siddhant, Translation by Pundit Bapu Dev Shastri (Chap. 1, verse 18, 22) (Bapist Mission Press, Calcutta, 1861)
27. Surya Siddhant, Translation by Pundit Bapu Dev Shastri (Chap. 1, verse 19, 20) (Bapist Mission Press, Calcutta, 1861)
28. Srimad Bhagwat Geeta (Chap. 8, verse 17) (Geeta Press Gorakh pur India)
29. Shri Vishnu paran, Ramji Sharma, Shri Durga Pustak Bhandar, Allahabad (3rd part, Chap. 1), p. 199
30. Srimad Bhagwat Puran (8th Part, Chaps. 1 and 13) (Geeta Press Gorakhpur, India), pp. 757, 815

31. http://veda.wikidot.com/vedic-time-system#
32. Shri Naraad Puran, p. 19
33. Surya Siddhant, Translation by Pundit Bapu Dev Shastri (Chap. 1, verse 21) (Bapist Mission Press, Calcutta, 1861)
34. SrimadBhagwat Puran (Part 3, Chap. 11, verse 5) (Geeta Press Gorakhpur, India), pp. 218, 219
35. Surya Siddhant, Translation by Pundit Bapu Dev Shastri (Bapist Mission Press, Calcutta, 1861), chapter 1, verse 22, 23
36. Surya Siddhant, Translation by Pundit Bapu Dev Shastri (Bapist Mission Press, Calcutta, 1861), chapter 1, verse 23
37. Srimad Bhagwad Puran (12th Part, Chap. 2 sloke 31 (Geeta Press Gorakhpur, India), p. 776
38. Agni Puran (Chap. 24) (Geeta Press Gorakhpur, India), p. 40
39. A.R. Verma, National Measurements and Standards, National Physical Laboratory, New Delhi, p. 4
40. Kautil ya's Arthasahastra English Translation by R. ShamasastryLink, https://archive.org/details/Arthasastra_English_Translation
41. S.A. Paramhans, Units of Measurements in Medieval India and their modern equivalents. Indian J. Hist. Sci. 19(1), 27–36 (1984)
42. King, Governance and Law in ancient India Kautalya's Arthasastra Patrick Olivelle (Oxford University Press, 2013). ISBN 978-0-19-809626-9
43. http://www.sushmajee.com/reldictionary/dictionary/page-M/measure-distance-2.htm
44. F. Cardarelli, *Scientific Unit Conversion* (Springer, Berlin, 1998). ISBN 3-540-76022-9
45. Dr M.R. Goyal, *Units of Length Measurement and Speed of Light in Ancient India*, mrgoyal@gmail.com, 8 July 2014
46. https://en.wikipedia.org/wiki/Mohenjo-daro
47. http://www.mitchellteachers.org/WorldHistory/IndiaUnit/images/mohenjodaro/SoneWeightsPic_large.jpg
48. Valmiki Ramayan (Chap. 2 (Ayodhiya Kand) verse 29) (Geeta Press Gorakhpur, India)
49. Valmiki Ramayan (Chap. 5 (Sunder Kand) verse 76) (Geeta Press Gorakhpur, India)
50. Exact Science in the Srimad-Bhagavatam, Sadaputa Dasa, www.krishna.com
51. Surya Siddhant, Translation, Pandit Bapu Deve Shastri and C.B. Lancelot Wilkinson (Chap. 1, verse 59) (Bapist Mission Press, Calcutta, 1861)
52. https://en.wikipedia.org/wiki/Indian_units_of_measurement
53. https://en.wikipedia.org/wiki/Indian_weights_and_measures
54. http://www.gktoday.in/blog/land-revenue-system-of-akbar/
55. www.indiacurry.com/Miscel/indiahistoricweightsmeasure.htm
56. General Cunningham (-Numismatic Chronicle, 1873), p. 197
57. E. Thomas (F.R.S), *"Numismata Orientalia" Part I, Ancient Indian Weights*
58. Trubner & Co., 57 and 59 (Ludgate Hill London, 1874)
59. R. Rowlett, *A Dictionary of Units of Measurement* (University of North Carolina at Chapel Hill, Chapel Hill, 2001). Grain (gr) [1–3]. Accessed 4 July 2012; W. Ridgeway, Metrological Notes: III. - Had the People of Pre-historic Mycenae a Weight Standard? J. Hell. Stud. (1889). London:
60. Manusmiriti English Translation, P.H. Pandya (Chap. 8, verses 132 to 137) (1913), https://docs.google.com/file/d/0Bz1OumJznV7ucmwyelNvQy1CcUU/edit
61. E. Thomas (F.R.S.), Ancient Indian Weights Trubner & Co., 57 and 59 (Ludgate Hill London, 1874), pp. 13, 14
62. Charak samhita (vol 2, part 7 kalapasthan, Chap. 12)
63. S.A. Paramhans,Units of Measurements in medieval India and their modern equivalents. Indian J. Sci. 19 (1), 27–36 (1984)
64. Padma Puraan, translated by Acharya Rishikesh, Development of body of a child inside the womb and amount of different body materials (2nd part "Bhoomi Khand", Chap. 11)
65. Agni Puraan (Chap. 281) (Geeta Press, Gorakhpur, India)

66. Naarad Puraan (Part 1, Chap. 3), p. 452, https://archive.org/stream/puran_narad/Narad
67. S.V. Gupta, *Units of Measurement*. (Springer Germany), p. 10
68. http://www.indiacurry.com/Miscel/indiahistoricweightsmeasure.htm,   https://en.wikipedia.org/wiki/Indian_units_of_measurement
69. Srimad Bhagwat Puran (Part 3, Chap. 11, verse 5, p. 216) (Geeta Press, Gorakhpur, India)
70. http://www.sushmajee.com/reldictionary/dictionary/page-M/measure-weight.htm
71. Agni Puraan (Chap. 24) (Geeta Press, Gorakhpur), p. 40
72. Kautilya's Arthasahastra, English Translation by R Shamasastry
73. https://archive.org/details/Arthasastra_English_Translation
74. S.V. Gupta, *A Treatise on Standards of Weights and Measures* (Commercial Law Publishers Pvt. Ltd., India)

Chapter 2
System of Quantities and Units

2.1 Quantities

There are a large number of quantities like length, volume, acceleration, force, momentum, electric charge, current, potential, inductance, etc., which requires measurement. It must be clear from the very beginning that there is no fundamental difference in the basic principles of measurement, whether the measurements are made in physics, chemistry, laboratory medicine, biology or engineering. An attempt, therefore, has been made to meet conceptual needs of measurements in fields such as biochemistry, food science, forensic science and molecular biology.

However, most of the quantities are either connected with each other by definition or through a physical phenomenon. A system of quantities, therefore, is a set of quantities together with a set of non-contradictory equations relating those quantities.

For example:

1. Velocity and acceleration are connected with length and time by definition.
2. In fact, all mechanical quantities can be expressed in terms of mass, length and time.
3. Similarly gravitational force and interaction between the charges are connected through a physical phenomenon.

So we need not have to define every quantity. We take a system containing only a fewer quantities such that all other quantities are expressed in terms of those quantities.

A subset of quantities, in terms of which every other quantity may be expressed, is known as system of base quantities. In the following paragraphs, we will discuss about quantity, base and derived quantities and their algebra.

© Springer Nature Switzerland AG 2020
S. V. Gupta, *Units of Measurement*, Springer Series in Materials Science 122,
https://doi.org/10.1007/978-3-030-43969-9_2

2.2   System of Quantities

2.2.1   Quantity

Quantity may be a property of a phenomenon, body or substance, to which a number can be assigned with respect to a reference.

The reference can be a measurement unit, a measurement procedure or a reference material.

All quantities together with their defined relations form a set, known as a system of quantities.

2.2.2   Base Quantity

Base quantity is a conventionally chosen quantity. No base quantity can be expressed as a product of powers of the other base quantities. Hence, base quantities are referred to as being mutually independent.

Note: A fairly good amount of material has been taken from the draft document "The International System of Units", 2019, 9th Edition being prepared by International Bureau of Weights and Measures (BIPM).

2.2.3   System of Base Quantities

A subset of base quantities is known as system of base quantities. The system of base quantities should be such that every other quantity can be conveniently expressed in terms of base quantities. Theoretically speaking, a minimum number of four base quantities is needed to express any other quantity. However, it may not be convenient from the point of understanding and realization of every quantity. For example, the International System of Quantities (ISQ) consists of seven base quantities, namely, mass, length, time, temperature, electric current, luminous intensity and mole. Base quantities, the symbols used for the base quantity and symbols used to denote their dimension, as adopted in SI, are given in Table 2.1. Normally the symbol of a quantity is written in italics and that of its dimension in capital letters in upright form.

2.2.4   Derived Quantity

A quantity, in a system of quantities, which is defined in terms of its base quantities, is known as a derived quantity.

Table 2.1 Base quantity symbols and their units with respective symbols

Quantity	Symbol	Name of unit	Symbol of unit	Symbol of dimension
Length	L, x, r, etc.	metre	m	L
Mass	m	kilogram	kg	M
Time	T	second	s	T
Electric current	I, i	ampere	A	I
Intensity of illumination	I_v	candela	cd	J
Temperature	T	kelvin	K	Θ
Mole	n	mole	mol	N

For example, in a system of quantities having length and mass as base quantities, mass density is a derived quantity defined as the quotient of mass and volume. Volume is length raised to the power three.

2.2.5   Quantity Equation

Quantity equation is a mathematical relationship between quantities in a given system of quantities, independent of measurement units.

If a quantity $Q1$ is a product of two quantities $Q2$ and $Q3$ and a number n, then its quantity equation is

$$Q1 = n\,Q2 \cdot Q3. \tag{2.1}$$

For example, kinetic energy E of a moving particle of mass m and velocity v is given as

$$E = (1/2)\,mv^2. \tag{2.2}$$

Then $E = Q1$, $1/2 = n$, $m = Q2$ and finally $v = Q3$.

Another example is the expression for m *which is* the mass of amount of substance of a univalent component deposited on an electrode, when a constant current I is passing in a voltameter for time t, then

$$m = I \cdot t/F. \tag{2.3}$$

Here F is Faraday constant.

2.2.6   Quantity Value Equation

Every quantity is a measureable entity. Its value is the product of number and a unit or product of powers of many units. It can be expressed as

$$Q = n\{Q\}. \tag{2.4}$$

Similarly, the dimension of quantity is represented as $[Q]$ and dimensional equation as

$$\mathrm{Dim}(Q) = [Q]. \tag{2.5}$$

2.2.7 Dimension of Derived Unit

There is a subset of quantities known as base quantities, all other quantities are derived quantities and can be written as product of powers of base quantities.

The dimensions of the derived quantities are written as products of the dimensions of the base quantities each raised to an integral power using the equations that relate the derived quantities to the base quantities. In general, the dimension of any quantity Q is written in the form of a dimensional product as

$$\dim Q = L^{\alpha} M^{\beta} T^{\gamma} I^{\delta} \Theta^{\varepsilon} N^{\zeta} J^{\eta}, \tag{2.6}$$

where the exponents α, β, γ, δ, ε, ζ and η, which are generally small integers which can be positive, negative or zero, are called the dimensional exponents.

The dimension of a derived quantity provides the same information about the relation of that quantity to the base quantities as is provided by the SI unit of the derived quantity as a product of powers of the SI base units.

There are some derived quantities Q for which the defining equation is such that all of the dimensional exponents in the equation for the dimension of Q are zero. This is true, in particular, for any quantity that is defined as the ratio of two quantities of the same kind. Such quantities are described as being *dimensionless*, and are simply numbers. However, the coherent derived unit for such dimensionless quantities is always the number one, 1, since it is the ratio of two identical units for two quantities of the same kind. For that reason dimensionless quantities are sometimes described as being of dimension one.

2.3 Measurement Unit

A unit is a scalar quantity defined and adopted by convention, with which any other quantity of the same kind can be compared. The ratio of the two quantities of same kind is a pure number.

2.3.1 System of Measurement Units

A set of measurement units corresponding to every quantity in system of quantities is a system of measurements. The set consists of base units, derived units and dimensionless or quantities of dimension 1.

2.3.2 System of Base Units

Corresponding to a system of base quantities, there is the system of units. For every base quantity, there exists a unit. Every other unit can be expressed in terms of base units. Such a subset of units, in terms of which all other units are expressed, is called system of base units. In this way, we can express the magnitude of any given quantity by a number equal to the ratio of that quantity to its unit.

2.3.2.1 Properties of Base Units

1. In every system of units there is only one base unit for each base quantity. For example, in the SI, the metre is the base unit of length. The centimetre and the kilometre are also units of length, but they are not base units in the SI. However, in the CGS systems, the centimetre is the base unit of length.
2. A base unit may also serve for a derived quantity of the same dimension.

For example:

Rainfall, when defined as volume per unit area, has the metre as a coherent derived unit in the SI.

3. For number of entities, the number one, symbol 1, can be regarded as a base unit in any system of units.

2.3.2.2 Minimum Number of Base Units

A system of three base units, consisting units of mass, length and time, is good enough to express the units of all other mechanical quantities. As volume is length cube, speed is length divided by time taken to travel that length, magnitude of linear acceleration is rate of change in speed with respect to time. Force is mass multiplied by acceleration, energy is force multiplied by length and so on. In the initial stages of measurement, the length, mass and time were taken to form a system of base quantities.

You will see in the next chapter that a minimum of four base quantities is required to express each and every other quantity. However, for the sake of convenience and easy understanding, seven base units, corresponding to seven base quantities enumerated in Table 2.1, have been adopted to make the International System of Units.

2.3.3 Derived Unit

A measurement unit for a derived quantity is the derived unit. It is expressible as a product of base units with integral exponents.

For example, the metre per second, with symbol m/s, or the centimetre per second, with symbol cm/s, is a derived unit of speed in the SI. The kilometre per hour, symbol km/h, is a unit of speed outside the SI but accepted for use with the SI. The knot, equal to one nautical mile per hour, is a unit of speed outside the SI.

Derived unit of force in SI is kg m s^{-2}. In expressing the derived units in terms of base unit, the sign of multiplication is optional, instead a space may be left between the symbols of base unit.

2.3.4 Unit Equation

Unit equation is a mathematical relationship of base units, coherent derived units or other measurement units. Symbol of unit of a quantity Q is $\{Q\}$.

Considering the example of quantity equation in Sect. 2.2.5, the unit equation is given as

$$\{Q1\} = \{Q2\}\{Q3\}, \tag{2.7}$$

where $\{Q1\}$, $\{Q2\}$ and $\{Q3\}$ are the measurement units of $Q1$, $Q2$ and $Q3$, respectively, provided that these measurement units are in a coherent system of units.

Quantity equation of energy with force and displacement is

$$\text{Energy} = \text{Force} \cdot \text{displacement.}$$

Giving unit equation for energy as

$$\text{Joule} = \text{newton} \cdot \text{metre.} \tag{2.8}$$

But

$$\text{Newton} = \text{kilogram} \cdot \text{metre}/(\text{second})^2. \tag{2.9}$$

Hence, taking J as the symbol of joule, we get

$$\text{J} = \text{kg m}^2/\text{s}^2, \text{or kg m}^2 \text{ s}^{-2}, \tag{2.10}$$

where kg, m and s are the symbols for the kilogram, metre and second, respectively, in SI.

Above is example of coherent system of units. Unit of speed in kilometre per hour is not a coherent unit as

$$1\,\text{km/h} = 1000\,\text{m}/3600\,\text{s} = (1/3.6)\,\text{m/s.} \tag{2.11}$$

2.3.5 Properties of Units of Measurement

Unit of measurement is a scalar quantity that is defined and adopted by convention. Any quantity can be compared to its corresponding unit and their ratio is always a pure number. It has following properties:

1. These are designated by conventionally assigned names and symbols.
2. Measurement units of quantities of the same dimension may be designated by the same name and symbol even when the quantities are not of the same kind. For example, joule per kelvin (J/K) is a measurement unit of heat capacity and a unit of entropy. But heat capacity and entropy are generally not considered to be the quantities of the same kind. However, in some special cases of measurements, unit names are restricted to be used with quantities of specific kind only. For example, the unit 1/s is called hertz when used for frequencies and becquerel when used for activities of radionuclide.
3. Measurement units of quantities of dimension one are numbers. In some cases, these units are given special names, e.g. radian, steradian and decibel, or are expressed by quotients such as millimole per mole equal to 10^{-3} and microgram per kilogram equal to 10^{-9}.
4. For a given quantity, the short term "unit" is often combined with the quantity name, such as "mass unit" or "unit of mass" [2].

2.3.6 Coherent Derived Unit

The derived unit, for a given system of quantities and for a chosen set of base units, is a product of integral exponents of base units with no other proportionality factor than one.

1. Coherence can be determined only with respect to a particular system of quantities and a given set of base units. For example, if the metre, the second and the mole are base units, the metre per second is the coherent derived unit of velocity when velocity is defined by the quantity equation $v = dr/dt$ and the mole per cubic metre is the coherent derived unit of the amount-of-substance concentration when amount-of-substance concentration is defined by the quantity equation $c = n/V$. But the kilometre per hour and the knot, as given in examples of derived units, are not coherent derived units in this system.
2. A derived unit can be coherent with respect to one system of quantities, but not to another.
   For example, as said earlier the centimetre per second is the coherent derived unit of speed in the CGS system of units but is not in the SI.
3. The coherent derived unit for every derived quantity of dimension one, in a given system of units, is the number one, with symbol 1. Name and symbol of the measurement unit one are generally not indicated.

Ionizing radiation deposits energy in irradiated matter. The ratio of deposited energy to mass is termed absorbed dose. High doses of ionizing radiation kill cells, and this is used in radiation therapy. Appropriate biological weighting functions are used to compare therapeutic effects of different radiation treatments. Low sub-lethal doses can cause damage to living organisms, for instance, by inducing cancer. Appropriate risk-weighted functions are used at low doses as the basis of radiation protection regulations.

There is a class of units for quantifying the biological activity of certain substances used in medical diagnosis and therapy that cannot yet be defined in terms of the units of the SI. This is because the mechanism of the specific biological effect that gives these substances their medical use is not yet sufficiently well understood for it to be quantifiable in terms of physico-chemical parameters. In view of their importance for human health and safety, the World Health Organization (WHO) has taken responsibility for defining WHO International Units (IU) for the biological activity of such substances.

2.4   Quantity of Dimension 1 or Dimensionless Quantity

Before we discuss these quantities, we may like to know a little more about the dimensions.

2.4.1   Dimension of a Quantity

If a quantity Q is expressed as a product of several base quantities with symbols as given in column five of Table 2.1 as

$$Q = L^{\alpha} M^{\beta} T^{\gamma} I^{\delta} \Theta^{\varepsilon} N^{\zeta} J^{\eta}, \tag{2.12}$$

where α, β, γ, δ, ε, ζ and η are exponents of the base quantities, which may be any integer or zero. These are called the dimensional exponents.

There are two versions of the definition of dimension, each is equally prevalent. According to one version, dimensions of a quantity are the powers to which base quantities must be raised to represent that quantity. That is powers (exponents) of base quantities like α, β, γ, δ, etc. are the dimensions of the quantity Q. So a quantity having each exponent as zero is called dimensionless.

According to second version as given in [1], dimension of a quantity is the expression representing the quantity in terms of base quantities raised to the integral powers. That is, dimension Q is expressed as

$$\mathrm{Dim}\, Q = L^{\alpha} M^{\beta} T^{\gamma} I^{\delta} \Theta^{\varepsilon} N^{\xi} J^{\eta}. \tag{2.13}$$

If each of exponents α, β, γ, δ, etc. is zero then the dimension of the quantity will be as

$$\mathrm{Dim}\, Q = L^{0} M^{0} T^{0} \big|^{0} H^{0} N^{0} J^{0} = 1. \tag{2.14}$$

Thus, a quantity having each of the exponents of base quantity as zero has the dimension 1.

We see here, a quantity having each of the exponents as zero will be called dimensionless or of dimension 1, respectively, if the dimensions of the quantity are defined as exponents or as an expression consisting of the products of base units raised to an integral power. In literature, therefore, we may come across both words, namely, "dimensionless" as well as "of dimension 1" for one and the same quantity.

2.4.2 Quantities of Dimension 1 or Dimensionless Quantities

Thus, there are certain quantities, which may be called dimensionless or have a dimension 1. Roughly, the aforesaid quantities fall into three categories.

1. Many quantities are the ratios of two quantities of the same kind. Examples of such quantities are angle, solid angle, refractive index, relative permeability, friction factor, Neper and decibel.
2. There are some quantities that are defined as a complex product of simpler quantities in such a way that when each simpler quantity is expressed in terms of the base units, then algebraic sum of exponents of each base unit becomes zero, and hence the quantity is dimensionless or of dimension 1 depending upon the convention followed. For example, Reynolds number (R_e) is defined as

$$R_e = \rho \upsilon I / \eta$$

$$[Re] = ML^{-3} \cdot LT^{-1}L/M \cdot L^{-1}T^{-1} = M^0L^0T^0 = 1. \tag{2.15}$$

3. Yet there is another class of quantities, which represent a count, such as a number of molecules, degeneracy (number of energy levels) and partition function in statistical thermodynamics, etc., these are also called quantities of dimension 1 or dimensionless quantities.

All of these quantities are described of dimension one or as dimensionless, and have the coherent SI unit 1. Their values are simply expressed as numbers and, in general, the unit 1 is not explicitly shown. In a few cases, however, special names are given to such units, mainly to avoid confusion between some compound derived units involving such quantities, for example, the radian, steradian and refractive index.

To summarize we may state that

1. The term "dimensionless quantity" is commonly used for historical reasons. It stems from the fact that exponents are zero in the symbolic representation of the dimension for such quantities.

   The term "quantity of dimension one" reflects the convention in which the symbolic representation of the dimension is as indicated in (2.13) above. Symbol for such quantities is 1 [5, 7].

2. The measurement units and values of quantities of dimension one are numbers, but such quantities convey more information than a number.
3. Some quantities of dimension one are defined as the ratios of two quantities of the same kind.
   Examples are plane angle, solid angle, refractive index, relative permeability, mass fraction, friction factor and Mach number.
4. Quantities of dimension one can also be numbers of entities.
   Examples are number of turns in a coil, number of molecules in a given sample and degeneracy (number of energy levels) in quantum mechanics.

2.4.3   Ordinal Quantity

A quantity defined by a conventional measurement procedure, for which a total ordering relation, according to magnitude, with other quantities of the same kind is defined, but for which no algebraic operations among those quantities are defined, is called ordinal quantity. Examples are given below:

(a) Rockwell C hardness.
(b) Octane number for petroleum fuel.
(c) Earthquake strength on the Richter scale.

Notes

1. Ordinal quantities can enter into empirical relations only and have neither measurement units nor quantity dimension.
2. Ordinal quantities are arranged according to ordinal quantity scales.

2.4.4   Quantity Scale, Measurement Scale

An ordered set of values of quantities of a given kind used in ranking, according to their magnitude, is a quantity scale.

Examples are as follows:

1. Celsius temperature scale,
2. Time scale and
3. Rockwell C hardness scale.

2.4.5   *Ordinal Quantity Scale, Ordinal Scale*

A conventional reference scale or a quantity scale, defined by formal agreement, on which only comparison of magnitude applies is known as ordinal quantity scale.

Examples are as follows:

(a)   Rockwell C hardness scale and
(b)   Scale of octane numbers for petroleum fuel.

It is to note that

1. An ordinal quantity scale may be established by measurements according to a given measurement procedure.
2. Ordinal quantities are ordered on ordinal quantity scales.

2.4.6   *Nominal Property*

A property of a phenomenon, body or substance, that can be identical but not a comparable property and cannot be ordered with it according to magnitude, is a nominal property.

Examples are as follows:

1. Sex of a human being,
2. Colour of a paint sample,
3. Colour of a spot test in chemistry,
4. ISO two-letter country code and
5. Sequence of amino acids in a polypeptide.

2.5   Conversion Factor Between Units

The ratio of two measurement units of quantities of the same kind is known as conversion factor.

For example,
km/m = 1000 and thus 1 km = 1000 m.

Note—The measurement units may belong to different systems of units but for the same quantity.

Examples are given below:

1   1 pound (avoirdupois) = 0.45359237 kg;
2   h/s = 3600 and thus 1 h = 3600 s;
3   (km/h)/(m/s) = (1/3.6) and thus 1 km/h = (1/3.6) m/s.

2.6   Quantity Relations

2.6.1   Quantity Value

Quantity value is a number multiplied by its unit or its reference. We may say in detail as follows:
   A quantity value either is

- A product of a number and a measurement unit (the unit one is generally not indicated for a quantity of dimension one) or
- A number and a reference to a measurement procedure or
- A number and a reference material.

   1. The number can be real or complex.
   2. A quantity value can be presented in more than one way.
   3. In the case of vector or tensor quantities, each component has a value as defined above.

Examples are as follows:

(a)   Length of a given rod is 5.34 m or 534 cm.
(b)   Mass of a given body is 0.152 kg or 152 g.
(c)   Curvature of a given arc 112 m^{-1}.
(d)   Celsius temperature of a given sample -5 °C.
(e)   Electric impedance of a given circuit element at a given frequency, $(7 + 3j) \text{ }\Omega$, here j is the imaginary unit.
(f)   Refractive index of a given sample of glass 1.32.
(g)   Rockwell C hardness of a given sample (150 kg load) HRC (150 kg) is 43.5.
(h)   Mass fraction of cadmium in a given sample of copper is 3 μg/kg or 3×10^{-9}.
(i)   Molality of Pb_2^+ in a given sample of water is 1.76 mmol/kg.
(j)   Force acting on a given particle $(-31.5; 43.2; 17.0) \text{ N}$.

2.6.2   Numerical Quantity Value

A number in the expression of a quantity value, other than any number serving as the reference, is a numerical value of the quantity.

Notes

1. For quantities of dimension one, the reference is a measurement unit which is a number and this is not considered as a part of the numerical quantity value.

For example,

In an amount-of-substance fraction equal to 3 mmol/mol, the numerical value is 3 and the unit is mmol/mol. The unit mmol/mol is numerically equal to 0.001, but this number 0.001 is not part of the numerical quantity value that remains 3.

2. For quantities that have a measurement unit (i.e. those other than ordinal quantities), the numerical value Q_n of a quantity Q is frequently denoted $Q_n = Q/[Q]$, where $[Q]$ denotes the measurement unit of Q.

For example, a mass value of 5 kg, the numerical value in kilograms is $\{m\} = (5\,kg)/kg = 5$. Numerical value of the same quantity depends upon the unit chosen for expressing the quantity. For example, for body of 5.123 kg, the numerical value is 5.123 if unit is kg, and it will become 5123 if unit is g.

2.6.3   Quantity Calculus

A set of mathematical rules and operations applied to quantities other than ordinal quantities is a quantity calculus. In quantity calculus, quantity equations are rather preferred to numerical value equations because quantity equations are independent of the choice of measurement units.

2.7   Units Used in Biology, Biochemistry, Molecular Biology, Forensic Science Biological Effects

Units for quantities that describe biological effects are often difficult to relate to units of the SI because they typically involve weighting factors that may not be precisely known or defined, and which may be both energy and frequency dependent. These units, which are not SI units, are described briefly in this section.

There is a class of units for quantifying the biological activity of certain substances used in medical diagnosis and therapy that cannot yet be defined in terms of the units of the SI. The mechanism of the specific biological effect that gives these substances their medical use is not yet sufficiently well understood. Hence, it is difficult to quantify such units in terms of physico-chemical parameters. In view of their importance for human health and safety, the World Health Organization (WHO) has taken the responsibility for defining WHO International Units (IU) for the biological activity of such substances.

2.7.1 Photochemical or Photo-Biological Quantities and Their Units

The photometric quantities and photometric units, which are used at present for vision, are well established and have been widely used for a long time. They are not affected by the following paragraphs. For all other photochemical and photo-biological quantities, the following rules shall be applied for defining the units to be used.

A photochemical or photo-biological quantity is defined in purely physical terms as the quantity derived from the corresponding radiant quantity by evaluating the radiation according to its action upon a selective receptor, the spectral sensitivity of which is defined by the actinic action spectrum of the photochemical or photo-biological effect considered. The quantity is given by the integral over wavelength of the spectral distribution of the radiant quantity weighted by the appropriate actinic action spectrum. The use of integrals implicitly assumes a law of arithmetic addition for actinic quantities, although such a law is not perfectly obeyed by actual actinic effects. The action spectrum is a relative quantity; it is a quantity of dimension one, with the SI unit one. The radiant quantity has the radiometric unit corresponding to that quantity. Thus, following the rule for obtaining the SI unit for a derived quantity, the unit of the photochemical or photo-biological quantity is the radiometric unit of the corresponding radiant quantity. When giving a quantitative value, it is essential to specify whether a radiometric or actinic quantity is intended as the unit is the same. If an actinic effect exists in several action spectra, the action spectrum used for measurement has to be clearly specified.

This method of defining the unit should be used for photochemical or photo-biological quantities. The Consultative Committee for Photometry and Radiometry at its ninth meeting in 1977 has recommended this method.

As an example, the erythemal effective irradiance E_{er} from a source of ultraviolet radiation is obtained by weighting the spectral irradiance of the radiation at wavelength λ by the effectiveness of radiation at this wavelength to cause an erythema, and summing over all wavelengths present in the source spectrum. This can be expressed mathematically as follows:

$$E_\sigma = \int E_\lambda s_{er}(\lambda) d\lambda, \tag{2.16}$$

where

E_λ is the spectral irradiance at wavelength λ (usually reported in the SI unit $Wm^{-2}\,nm^{-1}$) and $s_{er}(\lambda)$ is the actinic spectrum normalized to 1 at its maximum spectral value. The erythemal irradiance E_{er} determined in this way is usually quoted in the SI unit Wm^{-2}.

2.7.2   Conversion of Radiometric to Photometric Quantities

Radiometric quantity is spread over a very large range of frequency, but photometry covers only the visible region. So it requires a factor V_x which depends on acuity of vision. By mutual agreement with International Commission of Illumination CIE and International Committee of Weights and measures CIPM in 2007, it was decided that

- the CIPM is responsible for the definition of the photometric units in the SI and
- the CIE is responsible for the standardization of the spectral luminous efficiency functions of the human eye.

Though better definitive way to locate a monochromatic radiation within the spectrum is to state its frequency (f); however, traditional practice in photometry is to state the wavelengths in air, (λ). The frequency is independent of the optical medium. The values of f and λ are related by

$$f\lambda = c/na(\lambda).$$ (2.17)

Here c is the speed of light in vacuum and equals 2.99792458×108 m s^{-1}, and $na(\lambda)$ is the refractive index of air. It should be noted that the value of $na(\lambda)$ depends upon the partial pressure of each constituent of the air and is also wavelength dependent. In the case of standard air, the refractive index in air, $na(\lambda)$, is approximately equal to 1.00028 throughout the visible spectrum.

For a practical light source, i.e. any source emitting radiation not only at the frequency 540×10^{12} Hz, the corresponding photometric quantities are defined in purely physical terms as physical quantities proportional to the integral of the spectral power distribution of the light source (determined for the appropriate geometric configuration), weighted according to the specified spectral luminous efficiency function and converted to absolute photometric values using the luminous efficacy as defined for the candela.

Thus, the photometric quantities (human observer-based) relate to the radiometric quantities through simple relations. Each quantity like V_x or $X_{e\lambda}$ is λ dependent.

The general form of the equation relating a given spectral radiometric quantity $X_{e\lambda}$ to its corresponding photometric quantity $X_{v, x}$ is given below:

$$X_{vx} = \frac{K_{cd}}{V_x} \int_\lambda V_x X_{e\lambda} d\lambda.$$ (2.18)

The photopic luminous efficiency functions for light adopted eye $V(\lambda)$ are most important, which CIE defined over the wavelength range 360–830 nm at 1 nm intervals. If there is a need for wavelengths in between the two values, linear interpolation is carried out. This function V_x is maximum at a wavelength λ of exactly 555 nm in standard air.

For dark-adapted conditions, the CIE standardized the scotopic luminous efficiency function, $V'(\lambda)$, which is similar in shape to $V(\lambda)$ but its peak is shifted to shorter wavelength than the photopic curve.

2.7.3 Photometry and Photon-Number-Based Quantities

Photon-number-based quantities are quantities of optical radiation which are expressed in terms of a known number of photons or photon flux. Because of the dual aspect of electromagnetic radiation, photometric and/or spectral radiant quantities can also be expressed in terms of photon-number-based quantities. For wavelengths in air, the relationship between the spectral radiant quantity at a given wavelength, $X_{e,\lambda}$, and the corresponding photon-number-based quantity, $X_{p,\lambda}$, is

$$X_{e,\lambda} = \frac{h \cdot c}{\lambda} \cdot n_a \cdot X_{p,\lambda}, \qquad (2.19)$$

where h is the Planck constant, c is the speed of light in vacuum and n_a is the refractive index in air at the given wavelength, λ.

Therefore, combining (2.18) and (2.19), the general form of the equation relating a given photometric quantity to its corresponding photon-number-based quantity is given by $X_{v,x}\, X_{p,x}$

$$K_{v,x} = K_{p,x} \int_{\lambda} X_{p,\lambda} \frac{K_{p,\lambda} n_a}{\lambda} V_{x,} d\lambda.$$

Here $K_{p,x} = \frac{h \cdot c \cdot K_{cd}}{V_x}$,
where $K_{p,x}$ is the conversion factor from photometric to photon-number-based quantities for the spectral luminous efficiency function Vx.

2.7.4 Units Used in Photometry

Optical radiation may cause chemical changes in living or non-living materials: this property is called activism, and radiation capable of causing such changes is referred to as actinic radiation. In some cases, the results of measurements of photochemical and photo-biological quantities of this kind can be expressed in terms of SI units. This is discussed briefly here.

Optical radiation is able to cause chemical changes in certain living or non-living materials: this property is called activism, and radiation capable of causing such changes is referred to as actinic radiation. Actinic radiation has the fundamental characteristic that, at the molecular level, one photon interacts with one molecule to alter or break the molecule into a new molecular species. It is, therefore, possible to define specific photochemical or photo-biological quantities in terms of the result of optical radiation on the associated chemical or biological receptors.

In the field of metrology, the only photo-biological quantity, which has been formally defined for measurement in the SI, is for the interaction of light with the human eye in vision. An SI base unit, the candela, has been defined for this important photo-biological quantity. Several other photometric quantities with units derived from the candela have also been defined (such as the lumen and the lux defined and described in following chapter).

2.7.5 Actinic Action Spectrum

Optical radiation can be characterized by its spectral power distribution. The mechanisms by which optical radiation is absorbed by chemical or biological systems are usually complicated and are always wavelength (or frequency) dependent. For metrological purposes, however, the complexities of the absorption mechanisms can be ignored, and the actinic effect is characterized simply by an actinic action spectrum linking the photochemical or the photo-biological response to the incident radiation. This actinic action spectrum describes the relative effectiveness of monochromatic optical radiation at wavelength λ to elicit a given actinic response. It is given in relative values, normalized to 1 for the maximum of efficacy. Usually actinic action spectra are defined and recommended by international scientific or standardizing organizations.

2.7.6 Types of Visions

For vision, two action spectra have been defined by the International Commission on Illumination (CIE) and endorsed by the CIPM: $V(\lambda)$ for photopic vision and $V'(\lambda)$ for scotopic vision. These are used in the measurement of photometric quantities and are an implicit part of the definition of the SI unit for photometry, the candela. Photopic vision is detected by the cones on the retina of the eye, which are sensitive to a high level of luminance L for $L > $ca·$10$ cd m^{-2} and are used in daytime vision. Scotopic vision is detected by the rods of the retina, which are sensitive to low-level luminance for $L < ($ca·10^{-3} cd m$^{-2})$, used in night vision. In the domain between these levels of luminance, both cones and rods are used, and this is described as mesopic vision.

Other action spectra for other actinic effects have also been defined by the CIE, such as the erythemal (skin reddening) action spectrum for ultraviolet radiation, but these have not been given any special status within the SI.

For further details and definition of photometric quantities and units, one may refer to CIE publication [8], the IEC publication [9] or BIPM monograph [10].

2.7.7   Unit in the Field of Sound

Sound causes small pressure fluctuations in the air, superimposed on the normal atmospheric pressure, that are sensed by the human ear. The sensitivity of the ear depends on the frequency of the sound, but is not a simple function of either the pressure changes or the frequency. Therefore, frequency-weighted quantities are used in acoustics to approximate the way in which sound is perceived. Such quantities with frequency as weight factors are employed, for example, in work to protect against hearing damage. The effects of ultrasonic acoustic waves pose similar concerns in medical diagnosis and therapy.

2.7.8   Units in the Field of Ionizing Radiations

Ionizing radiation deposits energy in irradiated matter. The ratio of deposited energy to mass is termed absorbed dose. High doses of ionizing radiation kill cells, and this is used in radiation therapy. Appropriate biological weighting functions are used to compare therapeutic effects of different radiation treatments. Low sub-lethal doses can cause damage to living organisms, for instance, by inducing cancer. Appropriate risk-weighted functions are used at low doses as the basis of radiation protection regulations.

2.8   SI Units in the Framework of General Relativity

The question of proper units is addressed in Resolution A4 adopted by the 21st General Assembly of the International Astronomical Union (IAU) in 1991 and by the report of the CCDS Working Group on the Application of General Relativity to Metrology [4, 6].

   The definitions of the base units of the SI were adopted in a context that takes no account of relativistic effects. When such account is taken, it is clear that the definitions apply only in a small spatial domain sharing the motion of the standards that realize them. These units are known as proper units; they are realized from local experiments in which the relativistic effects that need to be taken into account are those of special relativity. The constants of physics are local quantities with their values expressed in proper units.

   Physical realizations of the definition of a unit are usually compared locally. For frequency standards, however, it is possible to make such comparisons at a distance by means of electromagnetic signals. To interpret the results, the theory of general relativity is required since it predicts, among other things, a relative frequency shift between standards of about 1 part in 10^{16} per metre of altitude difference at the surface of the Earth [3]. Effects of this magnitude cannot be neglected when comparing the best frequency standards.

References

1. BIPM, Le Systeme Internatinal d'Unites, 8th edn. (BIPM, Sevres, 2006)
2. BIPM, International Vocabulary of Metrological Terms, VIM, 3rd edn. (2006)
3. BIPM, *The International System of Units*, 9th edn. (BIPM, Sevres, 2019)
4. B. Guinot, International report: application of general relativity to metrology. Metrologia **34**, 261–290 (1997)
5. International Standards ISO 31-0:1992, sub-clause 2.2.6
6. International Standard ISO 31, Quantities and units, subsequently replaced by ISO/IEC 80000
7. International Standards ISO 704, ISO 1087-1, and ISO 10241
8. International Lighting Vocabulary, CIE publication 17.4 (1987)
9. International Electro-technical Vocabulary, IEC publication 50. Lighting (Chap. 845)
10. Principles governing photometry, Monographie, BIPM (1983), 32 pp.

Chapter 3
Various Systems of Units

Notations used in the chapter are

Dimension of base quantities by upper case letters.
Dimension of any other quantity symbol Q by $[Q]$.
Unit of any other quantity Q by $\{Q\}$.
SI means International System of Units.

For symbols SI base units, symbols as prescribed in BIPM brochure on SI (International System of units) [1].

3.1 Introduction

We have seen in the previous chapter that a proper system of base quantities and their respective units, agreed by convention with a set of proper algebraic relations, can be used to represent other quantities and their respective units. In the following paragraphs, I first intend to give relations connecting other quantities with base quantities and then various systems of base quantities. A few examples will also be given to make use of relations to arrive at expressions of units of other quantities in terms of units of base quantities. After going through this chapter, you will notice that a set of only four base quantities and their respective base units are essentially required to express all other units of measurement.

3.2 Relations Between the Quantities

Taking length, mass, time and electric current as the base quantities of the system, some relations expressing the quantities in terms of the base quantities are given below. There are two types of quantities in any measuring system, some

© Springer Nature Switzerland AG 2020
S. V. Gupta, *Units of Measurement*, Springer Series in Materials Science 122,
https://doi.org/10.1007/978-3-030-43969-9_3

are defined in terms of the base quantities directly and others through some phenomena.

3.2.1 Derived Quantities by Definition

Normally a quantity and its unit are expressed in terms of base quantities and their respective units without giving any consideration to the directional properties. Vector quantities and their units simply represent the scalar product of base quantities and their respective units.

1. Area is length square.
2. Volume is length cube.
3. Density is mass divided by volume.
4. Concentration is amount of substance in unit volume of solution.
5. Velocity is rate of change of displacement with respect to time.
6. Acceleration is rate of change in velocity with respect to time.
7. Force is the product of mass and acceleration and is in the direction of acceleration.
8. Surface tension is force per unit length.
9. Pressure is force per unit area.
10. Work or energy of any kind is force multiplied by displacement in the direction of force.
11. Moment of the force is the force multiplied by the shortest distance from the point about which moment is taken to the line of action of force.
    Note: Both energy and moment of force are essentially the product of force and distance. Hence, unit of each is the product of units of distance and force. However, we can consider energy as the dot product of two vector quantities and moment of the force as a cross product of force and displacement.
12. Power is rate of change of energy with respect to time.
13. Wave number is number of waves per unit length.
14. Vergency or power of an optical system or lens is the reciprocal of its focal length.
15. Frequency is number of vibration per unit time.
16. Temperature is the average kinetic energy of a molecule of a gas.
    However, for convenience, we may choose a separate unit for temperature. For example, kelvin is chosen as unit of temperature in SI.
17. Heat capacity is energy required to change its temperature through one kelvin. (Earlier this term used to be called thermal capacity.)
18. Specific heat capacity is the energy exchanged by unit mass of homogenous substance to change its temperature through one kelvin. (Earlier it was used to be called as specific heat.)
19. Latent heat is the heat contained in unit mass of a homogenous substance.
20. Specific energy is the heat exchanged by unit mass of the substance for transition from one phase to another at the temperature of its changing phase. No

change in temperature occurs during the phase transition. (Earlier it was used to be called as latent heat.)

21. Entropy of a system is the ratio of quantity of heat contained and thermodynamic temperature.
22. Specific entropy is the ratio of entropy of a system of a homogeneous mass and mass of the system.
23. Radiant intensity of a point source is the power radiated per unit solid angle.
24. Irradiance is the ratio of power irradiated per unit area.
25. Radiance of a source is the power radiated in a unit solid angle per unit area.
26. Luminance is the intensity of illumination per unit area.
27. Luminous flux of a point source is the product of luminous intensity and the area of illumination.
28. Illuminance is the luminous flux per unit area.

    Note: Definitions from 23 to 28 are concerned with radiometry and photometry. However, all radiometric units are in terms of base units of length, mass, time and solid angle. But photometric units involve the process of vision, so depend upon the sensitivity of eye to radiations of different frequencies in the visible region. But radiometry is for the entire electromagnetic radiations except the visible region.

    For photometry, the base quantity is the luminous intensity with SI unit candela, which is a certain fraction of power of a monochromatic source of certain frequency in a unit solid angle. The candela is defined at the frequency at which eye has the maximum response. While for radiometry the starting quantity is power with unit watt. Radiant intensity is the power emitted in a unit solid angle. Its counterpart in photometry is intensity of illumination with unit candela. Other units are shown in Table 3.1.

29. Activity in relation to radioactive substances is the number of transformations or transitions per second.
30. Absorbed dose is the energy received per unit mass of the absorber.

Table 3.1 Units in photometry and radiometry

Quantity	Radiometry		Photometry	
			Point source	
Power	Radiant power	Watts W	Luminous power	Lumenslm = cd · sr
Directionality power per unit solid angle	Radiant intensity	W/sr	Intensity of illumination	cd
	Extended source			
Power per unit area	Radiance	W/m^2	Luminance	lm/m^2
Directionality	Power per unit area and solid angle	W/m^2sr	Power per unit area and solid angle	cd/m^2
	Looking at the illuminated object			
Power/area	Irradiance	W/m^2	Illuminance	$lm/m^2 = lux$

31. Molar energy is the energy per mole of substance.
32. Molar entropy is the ratio of molar energy and temperature of the substance.
33. Molar heat capacity is the energy required to change one kelvin of temperature of one mole of substance.

3.2.2 Derived Quantities by a Phenomenon

1. Moment of inertia of a body is the product of its mass and square of its radius of gyration, i.e. mass multiplied by square of length (phenomenon of rotation).
2. Electric charge is the product of electric steady current and time during which current has passed.
3. Electric potential or potential difference or electromotive force is the ratio of power and electric current. Electric potential at a point is the work done on a unit positive charge to bring it from infinity to the point. This definition was used in defining unit of electric field.
4. For other electrical units, Ohm's law $V = I \cdot R$ is used.
5. Capacitance of a condenser is the ratio of charge and the potential difference across it.
6. Rate of change of magnetic of flux Φ with time is induced electromotive force (emf), so total magnetic flux is the product of emf produced and time of duration for the change, giving

$$\Delta\Phi/\mathrm{d}t = \text{Voltage}.$$

Units of $\Delta\Phi$ and Δt are the same as that of Φ and time respectively, hence

$$\Phi = \text{voltage} \cdot \text{time}.$$

7. Magnetic moment is the product of current flowing in circular loop of wire and its area. Or pole strength multiplied by distance between the two poles.
8. Magnetic pole strength is magnetic moment divided by distance between the poles. Pole strength can also be derived from the formula corresponding to Coulomb's law, namely

$$F = \mu_0 P_1 P_2 / 4\pi r^2.$$

Here F is force, μ_0 is permeability of free space, P_1, P_2 are pole strengths and r is the distance between the two poles.

9. Magnetic field strength $= K \cdot I/r$, magnetic field strength from a thin wire of uniform cross-section and of infinite length carrying current I along the surface of a cylinder of radius r and having wire as its axis is $K \cdot I/r$. Here K is constant of proportionality used to be $\mu_0/4\pi$ before redefinition of SI base.
10. Permeability of free space before redefinition was calculated from the formula for force between the two parallel conductors of infinite length and negligible cross-section and from the given definition of electric current.
11. Electrical field strength $= \mathrm{d}V/\mathrm{d}r$ vector r is in the direction of electric field.

12. Inductance · current = flux (Φ). giving
13. Inductance = Φ/Current.
14. Permittivity is derived by using the relation for capacity of a parallel plate condenser giving
    permittivity = capacitance multiplied by the distance between the two plates and divided by the common area between the plate, i.e.

$$\text{Permittivity} = \text{Capacity/length.}$$

15. Permeability is related to permittivity and velocity of light as

$$\text{permeability} \cdot \text{permittivity} = 1/(\text{velocity of light})^2$$

$$(\text{permeability}) = 1/(\text{permittivity}) \cdot (\text{velocity of light})^2.$$

16. Thermodynamic temperature: As per kinetic theory of gases, temperature is the average kinetic energy of a molecule. That is, unit of temperature is same as that of energy.
17. Thermal conductivity k is given by
    Energy/Time = k · difference in temperature · Area of cross-section/length of the conducting rod, giving dimension of k in SI as

$$[k] = ML^2T^3 \cdot L/\left(ML^2T^{-2} \cdot L^2\right) = T^{-1}L^{-1} \text{ or}$$
$$k = \text{power/(temperature} \cdot \text{Length).}$$

However, in SI units, temperature is a base unit named as kelvin with symbol (K). Replacing ML^2T^{-2} by k, we get SI unit of thermal conductivity as watt per metre kelvin and in terms of base units as

$$\text{m kg s}^{-3}\,\text{K}^{-1}.$$

18. Inductance L is defined from the formula:

$$V = L\mathrm{d}I/\mathrm{d}t \text{ i.e.} \{L\} = V/(A/s) = VA^{-1} \cdot s^1$$

19. yGravitational constant G is obtained from the formula:

$$F = Gm_1m_2/r^2.$$

20. Dynamic viscosity is the force divided by the product of area of cross-section of the flowing fluid and the velocity gradient normal to the direction of flow. The force is in the direction of fluid flow and tangential to the layers having a relative motion. Poiseuille's formula may also be used to drive the units of dynamic viscosity. $Q = \pi pa^4/8\eta l$, where Q is volume flow rate, p is pressure, "a" is the radius of the capillary tube of length l and η is the dynamic viscosity of the liquid flowing. Giving us $\{\eta\} = Pa \cdot m^4/m \cdot m^3 \cdot s^{-1} = Pa \cdot s$.
21. Kinematic viscosity v is the ratio of dynamic viscosity and density of the fluid, giving us

$$\{v\} = \{\eta\}/\{\text{density}\} = Pa \cdot s = \text{kg m}^{-1}\text{s}^{-2}\text{s/kg m}^{-3} = \text{m}^2\text{s}^{-1}.$$

3.3   Three-Dimensional System of Units

In general, there are two types of systems of units, namely, three-dimensional system of units and four-dimensional system of units. Using three-dimensional system of units, one can express all the mechanical quantities in unique way but there are some ambiguity in case of electrical, magnetic and electromagnetic quantities One example is that of CGS system described in Sect. 3.3.2.

3.3.1   Gauss System

The need for a coherent system of units, which could be accepted internationally was realized sometimes before French revolution. The creation of decimal and metric system at the time of French revolution and subsequent deposition of two platinum standards representing "metre" and "kilogram" on 22 June 1799 in Paris can be seen as the first step in the development of the present international system of units. Carl Friedrich Gauss, in 1832, proposed an absolute system of quantities of mass, length and time with their respective units of kilogram, metre and second. Units of the system were based upon the metric standards established at that time. Gauss advocated for unit of time as defined in astronomy and strongly promoted the application of "metric system". The three base quantities of mass, length and time can represent all mechanical quantities but gives rise to ambiguous systems of units in the field of electrostatics, electromagnetic and practical units.

3.3.2   CGS System

W. E. Weber, in 1851, proposed a three-dimensional coherent system of units in which units of length, mass and time, respectively, were centimetre, gram and second. By applying separately the inverse square law of force between electric charges and magnetic poles, he arrived at with two sets of electrostatic and electromagnetic units. Prefixes ranging from micro to mega were part of the system. For the purpose of electrical measurements, British Association for Advancement of Science (BAAS), in 1863, defined ohm, ampere and volt being, respectively, 10^9, 10^{-1} and 10^8 times of the CGS electromagnetic units.

   In 1881, the BASS along with International Electrical Congress (IEC) approved mutually coherent set of practical units. The system besides centimetre, gram and second as units also included ohm for electrical resistance, the volt for electromotive force and ampere for electric current. The unit of ohm was taken as the resistance offered by a column of mercury of uniform cross-section having the length of 106.300 cm and mass 14.521 g. The ampere was defined as the steady electric current, which when passed through a silver nitrate solution deposits silver at the rate of 0.00111800 g s^{-1}. The volt was taken as the pressure to produce a current of one ampere through a resistance of one ohm.

3.3.3 FPS System

FPS system is one of the oldest systems of measurement of modern times, which is still being used in countries like Great Britain and United States of America. Like CGS system it is also based on three quantities, namely, length, mass and time. Only the units of length and mass are different from the units in CGS system. Units of length and mass, respectively, are Imperial yard and pound avoirdupois. The standard of length in the British System of Measurement is the yard, a length, which has been preserved almost unchanged from the time of the king Edward I. The Ulna was the predecessor of the yard, which gave its name to the yard of Edward I.

The actual standard bar created by Edward I was lost and earliest authentic standard of yard in brass, which could be available is of 1496. This yard differs from the Imperial yard by 0.037 in. The yard constructed by the parliamentary committee in 1758 was given the name Imperial yard and legalized by the Act of 1824. It was also made in brass and was within 0.01 in. of the present Imperial yard. The present legal standards were constructed after the destruction by fire in 1834. To avoid the problem of destruction of the standards due to any reason, the copies of this yard have been deposited at several places like House of Parliament, Greenwich Royal Observatory, Royal Society of London, Royal Mint and Board of Trade.

The present Imperial yard is a solid square bar, 38 inches long and one square inch in transverse section. The bar is made from gunmetal (bronze). Near each end a cylindrical hole is sunk to the depth of half an inch. The distance between the centres of two holes is 36 inches. At the bottom of each hole, a smaller gold plug of 0.1 in. diameter is inserted. Upon the polished surface of this gold plug there are three transverse lines separated by 0.01 in. and two lines with almost same separation but parallel to the axis of the bar, Fig. 3.1. The measure of the length of the yard is the distance between the two central transverse lines on each end. The

Fig. 3.1 Imperial yard

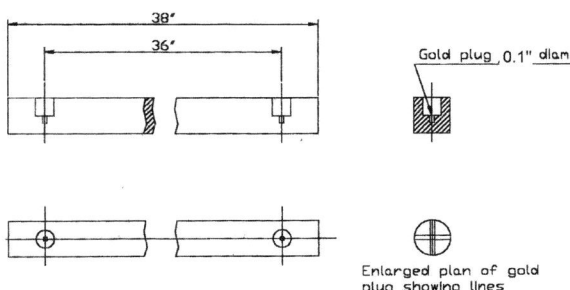

midpoints of the transverse central lines lying in between the two axial lines are always to be used to define the yard.

For further information on old length measures, one may consult [13].

The history of the standard of mass is similar to that of yard. At different times, "pounds" of various kinds have been used for different purposes. Royal Mint of U. K. also used mass standards for minting the coins. The term "sterling" is the earlier name of penny and pennyweight of 24 grains. One grain is taken as 1/7000th part of the present Avoirdupois pound. It took very much longer for the standard of mass to be coordinated and regulated than that of length. At one time, five different pounds were in use, which were reduced to two, namely, Troy pound and Avoirdupois pound. An act of 1855 legalized these standards and at the same time reversed the relative positions of Avoirdupois and Troy weight. Avoirdupois pound was made the legal standard for general purpose and Troy pound for weighing gold, silver and precious stones and retail sale of drugs. The Act of 1866 transferred custody of the imperial standards from the Comptroller-General of the Exchequer to the Board of Trade. The weights and measures Act of 1878 retained the part pertaining to standards of 1855 Act but abolished the Troy pound, though the Troy ounce of 480 grains remained the legal unit for bullion trade.

The imperial pound Avoirdupois is the mass of certain cylinder of pure platinum. The cylinder is about 1.35 in. high and 1.15 in. in diameter. A groove around the cylinder has been cut about 0.34 in. from the top (Fig. 3.2) so that the prongs of an ivory fork fit into it, while lifting. This standard was prepared, not from the previously existing Avoirdupois standard but from the certain authenticated copies of old brass Troy pound of 1758, which, up to the fire in 1834, occupied the position of principle standard [10].

3.4 Four-Dimensional Systems of Units

Minimum number of base quantities in a measuring system so that it can take care of all the measurable quantities, which is four. This type of system is capable of expressing all quantities in all fields of measurements in terms of four base units. The units of all quantities defined in such a system are unique.

Fig. 3.2 Imperial pound

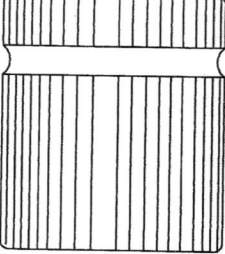

3.4.1 Giorgi System of Units

Now onwards we will discuss the systems of units having four base quantities. First to suggest such a system was G. L. T. Giorgi [3]. He, in 1902, some 30 years after the Metric Treaty was signed, suggested that in addition to metre, kilogram and second, the ampere—the unit of current—may be taken as fourth unit and named it as fourth dimension. The system started to be called as MKSA system.

3.4.2 Maxwell System

Maxwell [8] proposed a system of units in which permeability of free space was taken as unity and other units of length, mass and time were as follows:

Length = Earth Quadrant = 10^7 m,
Mass = 10^{-11} g and
Time = 1 s.

3.4.3 Hartree System

Hartree [4], in 1927, proposed a system of units based upon physical constants. The charge and rest mass of an electron were taken as units for electric charge and mass, respectively. The units of length and time were taken, respectively, as the Bohr radius and reciprocal of angular velocity of the electron. Aforesaid units in terms of SI units are equivalent to

Unit of charge = e (Charge on an electron) = $160 \cdot 10^{-21}$ C,
Unit of mass = rest mass of electron = $900 \cdot 10^{-33}$ kg,
Unit of length = a (Bohr radius) = $53 \cdot 10^{-12}$ m and
Unit of time = Reciprocal of angular velocity of electron = $1/4\pi Rc = 24 \cdot 10^{-8}$ s.

Basic problem with this system is that units are too small to express quantities coming across in daily life.

3.4.4 Units for Atomic and Molecular Measurements

Around 1950s, it was felt that comparison of results in quantum mechanical calculations was difficult because of multiplicity of units and symbols used. For example, energy used to be measured in kcal/mol (kilocalories per mol) or in eV (electron volts). Shull and Hall [11] suggested three base units from which other units could be derived. Base units were mass of electron (symbol m), charge of electron (symbol e) and rationalized Planck's constant (symbol $\hbar$). Other units like those of length and energy were taken as derived units. The unit of length (symbol b) was taken as Bohr radius which is expressed as

$$b = \hbar^2/m \cdot e^2.$$

Unit of energy was given the name Hartree symbol H given as

$$H = m \cdot e^4/\hbar^2.$$

Another most commonly used unit in atomic physics was electric moment, which was the product of Bohr's radius b and charge of the electron e given by

$$e \cdot b = \hbar^2/m \cdot e.$$

3.4.5　McWeeny System of Units

In 1973, McWeeny [9], in addition of e, m, $\hbar$ as base units, introduced permittivity as another base quantity with symbol κ_o related to permittivity of free space ε_o by the following relation:

$$\kappa_o = 4\pi\varepsilon_o.$$

The values of each base unit and other important derived units in terms of SI units are given in Table 3.2. The numerical values given in column 3 of Table 3.2 are based on the values of constants as were available in 1973.

3.4.6　Ohm, Ampere, Second and Metre System

Tarbouriech [12], in 1945, suggested a system of units comprising ohm, ampere, second and metre. The units of ohm and ampere chosen were the same as defined by BASS in 1881. The second unit of time was taken as 1/86,400 of the mean solar day.

3.4.7　Force, Length and Time System

Bullock [2] discussed the possibility of replacing the concept of mass to that of weight. Instead of taking unit of mass, he suggested that gravitational pull on one unit mass may be taken as one unit of force, and other units of length and time remained unchanged in his system. The unit of force was defined as the force experienced by a body of mass equal to one kilogram at a specific location where the value of g—the acceleration due to gravity—was 9.80665 ms^{-2}. Any location at sea level and having the latitude very close to 45° north will have the required

Table 3.2 Units in terms of mass, charge, action and permittivity

Base units		
Quantity	Natural unit	Value in SI units
Mass M	$m =$ mass of one electron	$9.1091 \cdot 10^{-31}$ kg
Charge Q	$e =$ charge on the electron	$1.60210 \cdot 10^{-19}$ C
Action	$\hbar$ Rationalized Planck's constant $h/2\pi$	$1.05450 \cdot 10^{-34}$ J s
Permittivity	$\kappa_o = 4\pi\varepsilon_o$	$4\pi \cdot 8.8542 \cdot 10^{-12}$ Fm^{-1}
Derived units (mechanical)		
Quantity	In terms of base units	Value in SI units
Length	1 Bohr $= \kappa_o \hbar^2/me^2$	$5.29167 \cdot 10^{-11}$ m
Time	$\kappa_o^2\hbar^3/me^4 = \hbar/E_o$	$2.41889 \cdot 10^{-17}$ s
Velocity	$e^2/\kappa_o\hbar$	$2.18764 \cdot 10^6$ m s^{-1}
Force	$m^2e^6/\kappa_o^3\hbar^4$	$8.23831 \cdot 10^{-8}$ N
Energy	$me^4/\kappa_o^2\hbar^2$	$4.35944 \cdot 10^{18}$ J
Power	$m^2e^8/\kappa_o^4\hbar^5$	$1.80225 \cdot 10^{-1}$ W
Derived units (electrical)		
Current	$me^5/\kappa_o^2\hbar^3$	$6.62329 \cdot 10^{-3}$ A
Potential	$me^3/\kappa_o^2\hbar^2$	27.2108 V
Capacitance	$\kappa_o^2\hbar^2/me^2$	$5.88774 \cdot 10^{-21}$ F
Field strength	$m^2e^5/\kappa_o^3\hbar^4$	$5.14220 \cdot 10^{11}$ V m^{-1}
Dipole moment	$\kappa_o\hbar^2/me$	$8.47778 \cdot 10^{-30}$ C m
Displacement	$m^2e^5/\kappa_o^2\hbar^4$	57.2142 C m^{-2}

value of g. The system became quite prevalent in engineering industry and gave birth to units like kilogram force, gram force abbreviated, respectively, as kgf and gf. In Britain, the unit of force was pound force as the unit of mass in the country was pound.

3.4.8   System in Terms of Universal Constants (G, H, E and Q)

Ludovici [7] proposed a system in which four quantities were G, gravitational constant; E, the permittivity of free space; H, the permeability of free space and the Q electric charge on one electron formed a system of units. The great advantage, according to him, was that defined unit values for each of four standards were absolutely constant and can be regarded as true standards representing infinite accuracy (zero uncertainty) at all times. The unit values of G, E, H and Q in terms of SI units will approximately be given as follows:

$$1\{G\} = 6.670 \times 10^{-11} \text{m}^3\text{kg}^{-1}\text{s}^{-2}$$

$$1\{E\} = 8.855 \times 10^{-12}\text{m}^{-3}\text{kg}^{-1}\text{s}^2\text{C}^2$$

$$1\{H\} = 1.256 \times 10^{-6}\text{m kg C}^{-2}$$

$$1\{Q\} = 1.601 \times 10^{-19}\text{C}.$$

One may see that from above equation that dimension of

$$\text{Length is } [G]^{1/2}[E]^{1/2}[H][Q]$$

$$\text{Mass is } [G]^{-1/2}[E]^{-1/2}[Q]$$

$$\text{Time is } [G]^{1/2}[E][H]^{3/2}[Q].$$

To distinguish his units of length, mass, time and charge from the SI system he used the prefix basic for each unit. For example, units of length, mass, time and charge in the proposed system of measurements were called basic metre, basic kilogram, basic second and basic coulomb. From these equations, one can express the SI units in terms of proposed units of length, mass, time and charge.

1 m $= 2.05 \times 10^{35}$ basic metres,
1 kg $= 1.515 \times 10^8$ basic kilograms,
1 s $= 6.15 \times 10^{43}$ basic seconds and
1 C $= 6.25 \times 10^{18}$ basic coulombs.

Inversion of the above equation will express proposed units of length, mass, time and charge in terms of SI units as

1 basic metre $= 4.88 \times 10^{-36}$ m,
1 basic kilogram $= 6.60 \times 10^{-9}$ kg,
1 basic second $= 1.628 \times 10^{-44}$ s and
1 basic coulomb $= 1.60 \times 110^{-19}$ C.

3.4.9 System in Terms of Electric Charge, Flux, Length and Time

Kalantaroff [5], in 1929, proposed a system of quantities comprising length, time, charge and flux. However, the proposal being in German language could not get worldwide publicity. Kinitsky [6] again described his work. One thing was good that they adopted the then existing units for proposed base quantities. That is, metre was taken for length, second for time, coulomb for charge and weber for flux. Taking L, T, Q and Φ as respective symbols of length, time, charge and flux, the other quantities may be expressed as given in column 3 of Table 3.3.

Table 3.3 Units in terms of length, time, flux and charge

Quantity	Relation used	In terms of $\{L\}$, $\{T\}$, $\{\Phi\}$, $\{Q\}$	In terms of $\{M\}$, $\{L\}$, $\{T\}$, $\{R\}$
Length	Base quantity	$\{L\}$	$\{L\}$
Time	Base quantity	$\{T\}$	$\{T\}$
Electric charge	Base quantity	$\{Q\}$	$\{M\}^{1/2}\{L\}\{T\}^{-1/2}\{R\}^{-1/2}$
Magnetic flux	Base quantity (column 3)	$\{\Phi\}$	$\{M\}^{1/2}\{L\}\{T\}^{-1/2}\{R\}^{1/2}$
Resistance	Base quantity (column 4)	–	$\{R\}$
Displacement	Charge/area	$\{Q\}\{L\}^{-2}$	$\{M\}^{1/2}\{L\}^{-1}\{T\}^{-1/2}\{R\}^{-1/2}$
Current	Charge/time	$\{Q\}\{T\}^{-1}$	$\{M\}^{1/2}\{L\}\{T\}^{-3/2}\{R\}^{-1/2}$
Magnetic field intensity	$B = \mu_0 I/4r$	$\{Q\}\{L\}^{-1}\{T\}^{-1}$	$\{M\}^{1/2}\{R\}^{-1/2}\{T\}^{-3/2}$
Induction	Magnetic flux/area	$\{\Phi\}\{L\}^{-2}$	$\{M\}^{1/2}\{L\}^{-1}\{T\}^{-1/2}\{R\}^{1/2}$
Electric voltage	$d\Phi/dt$	$\{\Phi\}\{T\}^{-1}$	$\{M\}^{1/2}\{L\}\{T\}^{-3/2}\{R\}^{1/2}$
Electric field intensity	dV/dr	$\{\Phi\}\{L\}^{-1}\{T\}^{-1}$	$\{M\}^{1/2}\{T\}^{-3/2}\{R\}^{1/2}$
Conductance	1/resistance	$\{Q\}\{\Phi\}^{-1}$	$\{R\}^{-1}$
Resistance	Voltage/current	$\{\Phi\}\{Q\}^{-1}$	–
Inductance	Magnetic flux/current	$\{Q\}^{-1}\{\Phi\}\{T\}$	$\{R\}\{T\}$
Capacitance	Charge/voltage	$\{Q\}\{\Phi\}^{-1}\mathrm{T}^{-1}\}$	$\{T\}\{R\}^{-1}$
Permittivity or dielectric constant	Capacity of a parallel plate condenser	$\{Q\}\{\Phi\}^{-1} \cdot \{L\}^{-1}\{T\}$	$\{R\}^{-1}\{L\}^{-1}\{T\}$
Permeability	$\mu_o \varepsilon_o = 1/c^2$	$\{Q\}^{-1}\{\Phi\{L\}^{-1}\{T\}$	$\{R\}\{L\}^{-1}\{T\}$
Planck's constant	Action = energy · time	$\{Q\}\{\Phi\}$	$\{M\}\{L\}^2\{T\}^{-1}$
Energy	Energy = $h\nu$	$\{Q\}\{\Phi\}\{T\}^{-1}$	$\{M\}\{L\}^2\{T\}^{-2}$
Power	Energy/time	$\{Q\{\Phi\}\{T\}^{-2}$	$\{M\}\{L\}^2\{T\}^{-3}$
Force	Energy/distance	$\{Q\}\{\Phi\{\mathrm{T}^{-1}\{L\}^{-1}$	$\{M\}\{L\}\{T\}^{-2}$
Mass	Force/acceleration	$\{Q\}\{\Phi\}\{T\}\{L\}^{-2}$	$\{M\}$
Momentum	Mass · velocity	$\{Q\}\{\Phi\}\{L\}^{-1}$	$\{M\}\{L\}\{T\}^{-1}$
Moment of inertia	Mass · length^2	$\{Q\}\{\Phi\}\{T\}$	$\{M\}\{L\}^2$
Angular momentum	Moment of inertia · angular velocity	$\{Q\}\{\Phi\} = h$	$\{M\}\{L\}^2\{T\}^{-1}$
Pressure	Force/area	$\{Q\}\{\Phi\}\{T\}^{-1}\{L\}^{-3}$	$\{M\}\{L\}^{-1}\{T\}^{-2}$
Torque	Moment of Inertia · angular acceleration	$\{Q\}\{\Phi\}\{T\}^{-1}$	$\{M\}\{L\}^2\{T\}^{-2}$

(continued)

Table 3.3 (continued)

Quantity	Relation used	In terms of $\{L\}$, $\{T\}$, $\{\Phi\}$, $\{Q\}$	In terms of $\{M\}$, $\{L\}$, $\{T\}$, $\{R\}$
Mass density	Mass/volume	$\{Q\}\{\Phi\}\{T\}\{L\}^{-5}$	$\{M\}\{L\}^{-3}$
Gravitational constant	$G = \text{Force} \cdot \text{distance}^2$ mass^2	$\{Q\}^{-1}\{\Phi\}^{-1}\{T\}^{-3}$ $\{L\}^5$	$\{M\}^{-1}\{L\}^3\{T\}^{-2}$
Specific weight		$\{Q\}\{\Phi\}\{L\}^{-4}\{T\}^{-1}$	$\{M\}\{L\}^{-2}\{T\}^{-2}$
Magnetic moment	Magnetic flux distance	$\{\Phi\}\{L\}$	$\{M\}^{1/2}\{L^2\{T\}^{-1/2}$ $\{R\}^{1/2}$
Electric dipole moment	Charge $\cdot$ distance	$\{Q\}\{L\}$	$\{M\}^{1/2}\{L\}^2\{T\}^{-1/2}$ $\{R\}^{-1/2}$
Quadrupole moment	Charge $\cdot$ distance^2	$\{Q\}\{L\}^2$	$\{M\}^{1/2}\{L\}^3\{T\}^{-1/2}$ $\{R\}^{-1/2}$
Temperature	Energy per molecule	$\{Q\}\{\Phi\}\{T\}^{-1}$	$\{M\}\{L\}^2\{T\}^{-2}$
Specific heat	Heat per unit mass and temperature	$\{Q\}^{-1}\{\Phi\}^{-1}$ $\cdot\{L\}^2\cdot\{T^{-1}\}$	$\{M\}^{-1}$
Thermal conductivity		$\{L\}^{-1}\{T^{-1}\}$	$\{L\}^{-1}\{T\}^{-1}$

3.4.10 System in Terms of L, M, T and R

A system of units, similar to that of Giorgi given in subsection 3.4.1, may be based on four base quantities of length symbol L, mass symbol M, time symbol T and resistance symbol R. Here the quantity of electric current has been replaced by resistance.

3.5 Derived Quantities in Terms of *L, M, T* and *R*—An Example

If a system of units comprises units of quantities of length L, mass M, time T and the electrical resistance R, then other quantities may be expressed dimensionally in terms of M, L, T and R as follows:

1. Velocity = length/time; $\{\text{Velocity}\} = \{L\}\{T\}^{-1}$.
2. Acceleration = change in velocity/time; $\{\text{Acceleration}\} = \{L\}\{T\}^{-2}$.
3. Force = mass $\cdot$ Acceleration; $\{\text{Force}\} = \{M\}\{L\}\{T\}^{-2}$.
4. Moment of inertia = mass of a body $\cdot$ square of radius of gyration;

$$\{\text{Moment of inertia}\} = \{M\}\{L\}^2.$$

5. Work done = Force $\cdot$ Distance; $\{\text{Work done}\} = \{M\}\{L\}^2\{T\}^{-2}$.
6. Power = Rate of doing work; $\{\text{Power}\} = \{M\}\{L\}^2\{T\}^{-3}$.
7. Gravitational Constant $G = $ Force $\cdot$ (Distance)^2/(Mass)^2
   Giving us

$$\{G\} = \{M\}\{L\}\{T\}^{-2}\{L\}^2/\{M\}^2 = \{M\}^{-1}\{L\}^3\{T\}^{-2}.$$

8. Voltage: Power = Voltage · Current = (Voltage)^2/Resistance.
   Representing voltage by *V* and electrical resistance by *R*, we get

$$\text{Power} = \left(V^2/R\right);$$
$$\{\text{Power}\} = \{M\}\{L\}^2\{T\}^{-3}, \text{ giving}$$
$$\{V\} = \{M\}^{1/2}\{L\}\{T\}^{-3/2}\{R\}^{1/2}.$$

9. Once we know voltage, we can determine the units of the current by

$$I = V/R, \text{giving}$$
$$\{I\} = \{M\}^{1/2}\{L\}\{T\}^{-3/2}\{R\}^{-1/2}.$$

10. Charge *Q* = Current · Time, so

$$\{\text{Charge } Q\} = \{M\}^{1/2}\{L\}\{T\}^{-3/2}\{R\}^{-1/2}\{T\}$$
$$= \{M\}^{1/2}\{L\}\{T\}^{-1/2}\{R\}^{-1/2}.$$

11. Rate of change of flux Φ is voltage *V*, so we get

$$\Phi/T = V \text{ or}$$
$$\Phi = V \cdot T.$$

Giving

$$\{\Phi\} = \{M\}^{1/2}\{L\}\{T\}^{-1/2}\{R\}^{1/2}.$$

12. Magnetic induction is flux per unit area so

$$\{\text{Induction}\} = \{M\}^{1/2}\{L\}^{-1}\{T\}^{-3/2}\{R\}^{1/2}.$$

13. Electric field strength = d*V*/d*r*, giving us

$$\{\text{Electric field strength}\} = \{M\}^{1/2}\{T\}^{-3/2}\{R\}^{1/2}.$$

14. Capacitance = charge/voltage, giving us

$$\{\text{Capacitance }\} = \{M\}^{1/2}\{L\}\{T\}^{-1/2}\{R\}^{-1/2}/\left[\{M\}^{1/2}\{L\}\{T\}^{-3/2}\{R\}^{1/2}\right]$$
$$= \{T\}\{R\}^{-1}.$$

15. Inductance = Magnetic flux/current

$$\{\text{ Inductance }\} = \{M\}^{1/2}\{L\}\{T\}^{-1/2}\{R\}^{1/2}/\{M\}^{1/2}\{L\}\{T\}^{-3/2}\{R\}^{-1/2}$$
$$= \{T\}\{R\}.$$

16. Permittivity in free space ε_o = square of charge/Force · Length^2 (Coulomb's Law)

$$\{\text{permittivity}\} = \left(\{M\}^{1/2}\{L\}\{T\}^{-1/2}\{R\}^{-1/2}\right)^2/\{M\}\{L\}\{T\}^{-2} \cdot \{L\}^2$$
$$= \left(\{M\}\{L\}^2\{T\}^{-1}\{R\}^{-1}\right)/\{M\}\{L\}^3\{T\}^{-2}$$
$$= \{L\}^{-1}\{T\}\{R\}^{-1}.$$

17. Permeability = 1/{Permitivity · (Velocity)^2}, giving

$$\{\text{permeability}\} = 1/\{L\}^{-1}\{T\}\{R\}^{-1}\{L\}^2\{T\}^{-2}$$
$$= 1/\{L\}\{T\}^{-1}\{R\}^{-1}$$
$$= \{L\}^{-1}\{T\}\{R\}.$$

We have seen that any quantity in any field of measurement can be expressed in terms of any four arbitrarily chosen units. For mechanical measurements, people have been using length, mass and time as base units for very long time. Quite often these units are called as fundamental units. However, to express the quantities in simpler forms in all the fields of measurements, two more units, one each in thermal and optical fields, are taken.

3.6 Measurement System in Terms of Length Time Flux and Charge

The examples of expressing other units in terms of a set of units of length, time, flux and charge are given in Table 3.3. Column 1 of the table gives the quantity for which units are expressed in columns 3 and 4. Column 2 gives the expression of the quantity in column 1, in terms of units of base quantities.

References

1. BIPM, *Le Systeme Internatinal d'Unites*, 8th edn. (BIPM, Sevres, 2006)
2. M.L. Bullock, Am. J. Phys. **22**, 293 (1954)
3. G. Giorgi, Unita razionali di elettromagnetismo. Atti Assoc. Elettroteen **5**, 402–418 (1901)
4. D.R. Hartree, Proc. Camb. Philos. Soc. **24**, 89 (1926)
5. P. Kalantaroff, Rev`. Gen`. Elect. **16**, 235–236 (1929)
6. V.A.Q. Kinitsky, Am. J. Phys. **30**, 89 (1962)
7. B.F. Ludovici, Am. J. Phys. **24**, 400 (1956)
8. C.J. Maxwell, *A Treatise on Electricity and Magnetism*, vol. II (Oxford Press, Oxford, 1873)
9. R. McWeeny, Nature(GB) **243**, 196 (1973)
10. H.W. Miller, Philos. Trans. cxivi (1856)
11. H. Shull, G.G. Hall, Atomic units. Nature (GB) **184**, 1559 (1959)
12. M. Tarbouriech, C. R. Acad. Sci. (France) **221**, 745 (1945)
13. A.J. Wallard, Evolution of old length and other standards -"There or thereabout". Proc. R. Inst. **69**, 107–122 (1998)

Chapter 4
Metre Convention and Evolution of Base Units

4.1 BIPM and Metre Convention

On 20 May 1875 "Metre Convention", a diplomatic treaty between 17 nations was signed in Paris. The Metre Convention gave authority to General Conference on Weights and Measures (Conference Generale des Poids et Mesure-CGPM) and International Committee for Weights and Measures (Comite International des Poids et Mesure—CIPM) to set up International Bureau of Weights and Measures (Bureau International des Poids et Mesure-BIPM) and to act in the matters related to units of measurement. Apart from 17 countries, Italy in 1876, Norway in 1882, Sweden in 1889 and Denmark in 1912 were among the first few countries that joined the treaty later. This convention was amended in 1921. Presently there are 59 member states, 42 associate states and 4 international organizations. These are

1. International Atomic Energy Agency (IAEA), Vienna, Austria (1999).
2. Institute for Reference Materials and Measurements (IRMM), Geel, Belgium (1999).
3. World Meteorological Organization (WMO), Geneva, Switzerland (2010).
4. European Space Agency (ESA), Paris, France (2012).

India signed "the Metre Convention Treaty" in 1957 after the Standards of Weights and Measures Act 1956 was enacted by the Parliament.

It may be noted that foundation of metric system in relation to mass and length was established by the deposition of two platinum standards representing "metre" and "kilogram" on 22 June 1799 with French Archives in Paris. Following this some European countries like the Netherlands in 1820, France in 1837 and Spain in 1860 started using metre and kilogram even before the "Metre Convention".

© Springer Nature Switzerland AG 2020
S. V. Gupta, *Units of Measurement*, Springer Series in Materials Science 122,
https://doi.org/10.1007/978-3-030-43969-9_4

4.1.1   General Conference on Weights and Measures (CGPM)

CGPM is composed of representatives of all the member countries and it meets every 4 years. The main objectives of CGPM are as follows:

1. Discussing and instigating the arrangements required for to ensure the propagation and improvement of the International System of Units (SI), which is the modern form of the metric system,
2. Confirming the results of new fundamental metrological determinations and the various scientific resolutions of international scope and
3. Adopting the important decisions concerning the organization and development of the BIPM.

CGPM adopts all resolutions/decisions through voting with no dissent vote. All proposals for final decision are mooted through CIPM.

4.1.2   International Committee for Weights and Measures (CIPM)

CIPM, a committee of select representatives of member countries, has 18 members each from a different country, who are elected by the CGPM on the basis of their contribution to metrology. The CIPM officially governs the BIPM.

4.1.3   Consultative Committees

With the extension of work in diverse areas of measurements entrusted to BIPM, the CIPM set up, since 1927, various consultative committees in specific areas of measurement. At present, there are 10 consultative committees whose function is to study, advice and provide for the information on matters that are referred to them. These consultative committees are responsible for coordinating the international work carried out in their respective fields and for proposing recommendations to the CIPM concerning units. The committees may form temporary or permanent working groups to study special topics.

The consultative committees have common regulations [1]. They meet at irregular intervals. The president of each consultative committee is designated by the CIPM and is normally a member of the CIPM. The members of the consultative committees are metrology laboratories and specialized institutes, agreed by the CIPM, which send delegates of their choice.

In addition, there are individual members appointed by the CIPM, and a representative of the BIPM. The criteria for membership of consultative committees are according to [4]. At present, there are ten such committees, namely, those given in the following.

4.1.3.1 Consultative Committee for Electricity and Magnetism (CCEM)

Initially, a Consultative Committee for Electricity was set up in 1927 to look after the units in the area of electricity. On the inclusion of work in the area of magnetism in 1997, the present name Consultative Committee for Electricity and Magnetism (CCEM) was assigned.

4.1.3.2 Consultative Committee for Photometry and Radiometry (CCPR)

To look after the units of photometry, the Consultative Committee for Photometry was established in 1930. After the inclusion of work pertaining to radiometry, the present name Consultative Committee for Photometry and Radiometry (CCPR) was assigned to that in 1971.

4.1.3.3 Consultative Committee for Thermometry (CCT)

The committee was set up in 1937.

4.1.3.4 Consultative Committee for Length (CCL)

Initially, the name of this committee was Consultative Committee for the Definition of Metre and it was set up in 1952. To include wider perspective of length measurement, it was given this new name in 1997.

4.1.3.5 Consultative Committee for Time and Frequency (CCTF)

This name was given to the old Consultative Committee for Definition of the Second (CCDS), which was set up in 1956.

4.1.3.6 Consultative Committee for Ionizing Radiation (CCRI)

A new name was given in 1997 to the old Consultative Committee for Standards of Ionizing Radiation (CCEMRI). The CCEMRI was set up in 1958. In 1969, the committee established four sections, which are given below:

Section 4.1, X-rays and γ rays, electrons; Sect. 4.2, Measurement of radionu-clides; Sect. 4.3, Neutron measurements and Sect. 4, α-energy standards. In 1975, this last section was dissolved and Sect. 4.2 was made responsible for its field of activity [5].

4.1.3.7   Consultative Committee for Units (CCU)

This committee was set up in 1964 and replaced the Commission for the System of Units set up by CIPM in 1954.

4.1.3.8   Consultative Committee for Mass and Related Quantities (CCM)

The committee was set up in 1980.

4.1.3.9   Consultative Committee for Amount of Substance: Metrology in Chemistry (CCQM)

The committee was set up in 1993.

4.1.3.10   Consultative Committee for Acoustics, Ultrasound and Vibration (CCAUV)

This is the youngest committee as it was set up in 1999.

Each of these committees may meet as many times in a year as it wishes to do so. The committees give their recommendations to CIPM for approval, which in turn submits to CGPM for ratification.

4.1.4   International Bureau of Weights and Measures (BIPM)

The headquarters of BIPM are in Sevres near Paris, on the Pavillon de Breteuil (Parc de Saint-Cloud) having ground area of 43,520 m^2. The French Government placed the whole area at the disposal of BIPM. Its upkeep is financed jointly by the Member States of the Metre Convention.

4.1.4.1 Scientific Activities

The activities of the BIPM, which in the beginning were limited to measurements of length and mass, and to metrological studies in relation to these quantities, have been extended to standards of measurement of electricity (1927), photometry and radiometry (1937), ionizing radiation (1960), time scales (1988) and chemistry (2000). The original laboratories were built in 1876–1878 and were enlarged in 1929. Further new buildings were constructed in 1963–1964 for the ionizing radiation laboratories, for the laser work in 1984 and in 1988 for a library and offices. In 2001, a new building for the workshop, offices and meeting rooms was inaugurated.

4.1.4.2 Objects of BIPM

BIPM is the custodian of all International Standards of Units and is involved in the following activities:

1. Establishing the fundamental standards and scales of measurement of the principal physical quantities and maintaining the international prototypes.
2. Carrying out comparisons of national standards and international standards.
3. Ensuring the coordination of corresponding measuring techniques.
4. Carrying out and coordinating determinations relating to the fundamental physical constants that are involved in the abovementioned activities.
5. Mutual Recognition Arrangement with National Measurements Institutes.

4.1.4.3 Staff at BIPM

Some 45 physicists and technicians work in the BIPM laboratories. They mainly conduct metrological research, carry out international comparisons for realizations of units and do calibrations of standards. An annual report and the Director's Report on the activity and management of the International Bureau of Weights and Measures gives details of the work in progress.

4.1.4.4 Publications

The proceedings of the General Conference and the CIPM are published by the BIPM in the following series:

- Report of the meeting of the General Conference on Weights and Measures;
- Report of the meeting of the International Committee for Weights and Measures.

One can get all the reports of meetings of the Consultative Committees held 2003 and onwards in their original language on BIPM website.

The BIPM also publishes monographs on special metrological subjects, and the brochure "The International System of Units (SI)" is periodically updated. All decisions and recommendations concerning units are also given in this brochure.

The scientific work of the BIPM is published in the open scientific literature and an annual list of publications appears in the Director's Report on the activity and management of the International Bureau of Weights and Measures.

4.1.4.5 Metrologia

Since 1965 Metrologia, an international journal published under the auspices of the CIPM, has printed articles dealing with scientific metrology, improvements in methods of measurement, work on standards and units, as well as reports concerning the activities, decisions and recommendations of the various bodies created under the Metre Convention.

4.1.5 Linkages of Various Organs of Metre Convention

Linkages of various organs of the metre convention, functions of BIPM and various consultative Committees are shown in Fig. 4.1.

Linkages of Organs of Metre Convention and CGPM 1875
Normally any scientific suggestion is sent to BIPM, which, in turn, sends it to concerned consultant committee, who after due discussions send it to CIPM, which after elaborate discussions and considering all pros and cons recommend to CGPM for approval.

4.2 International System of Units SI

Starting with metre and kilogram in 1875 as base units, CGPM with the help of CIPM and consultative committees kept on adding units of measurement in various other areas, like photometric, temperature and electric units were added in 1948. The practical international system having four units, namely, metre, kilogram, second and ampere (MKSA) was amalgamated with other units by 11th CGPM in 1960, and named as International System of Units abbreviated as SI. The system is in use since then not only in the signatory countries of Metre Convention but also in many other countries. To start with International System of Units was having only six base units. The seventh base unit mole for amount of

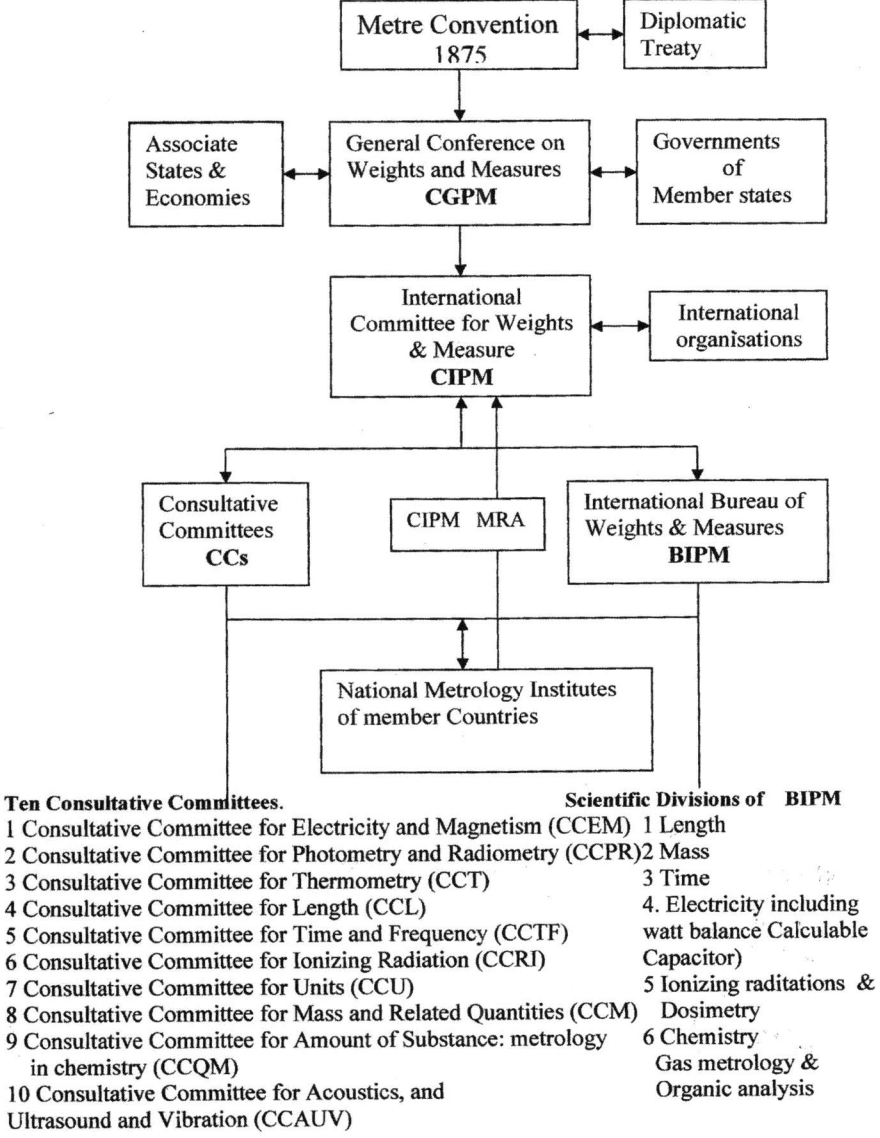

Ten Consultative Committees.   Scientific Divisions of   BIPM
1 Consultative Committee for Electricity and Magnetism (CCEM) 1 Length
2 Consultative Committee for Photometry and Radiometry (CCPR)2 Mass
3 Consultative Committee for Thermometry (CCT)   3 Time
4 Consultative Committee for Length (CCL)   4. Electricity including
5 Consultative Committee for Time and Frequency (CCTF)   watt balance Calculable
6 Consultative Committee for Ionizing Radiation (CCRI)   Capacitor)
7 Consultative Committee for Units (CCU)   5 Ionizing raditations &
8 Consultative Committee for Mass and Related Quantities (CCM) Dosimetry
9 Consultative Committee for Amount of Substance: metrology 6 Chemistry
   in chemistry (CCQM)   Gas metrology &
10 Consultative Committee for Acoustics, and   Organic analysis
Ultrasound and Vibration (CCAUV)

Fig. 4.1 Linkages of organs of metre convention and CGPM

substance was added in 1971. Hence, the present International System of Units is built on seven base quantities, namely, length, mass, time, electric current, temperature, luminous intensity and amount of substance. The system includes units of base quantities, their respective symbols and host of units of other quantities. The well-defined relations connect all quantities with base quantities. The units form a coherent system of units. It also covers some units, which are not within SI but permitted for the use with SI units. The units cover practically all fields of measurements including human health and safety.

4.2.1 Base Units

We have seen in previous chapter that only four base units are sufficient for describing any system of units. The unit of luminous intensity, temperature and amount of substance, though not necessary, have been included for the matter of convenience, ease in expressing and understanding the units of measurement in specific areas. The base units of the present-day International System of Units are as follows:

(1) second for time, with symbol s;
(2) metre for length, with symbol m;
(3) kilogram for mass, with symbol kg;
(4) ampere for electric current, with symbol A;
(5) kelvin for temperature, with symbol K;
(6) mole for amount of substance with symbol mol and
(7) candela for intensity of illumination, with symbol cd.

Inter-relationships between the units of length, mass, time and ampere and several derived units are shown in Fig. 4.2. Solid lines show the multiplication while dotted lines indicate division by that unit.

Base quantities and base units with their respective names and symbols, years of inclusion, modification and year of final definition are given in Table 4.1 [5].

4.2.2 Latest Definitions of SI Base Units

All SI base units have been redefined by 26th CGPM held on 13–16 November 2018. These definitions have been given at end of paragraphs for each unit. However, the definitions with their defining constants have been detailed in Chap. 5. All new definitions of SI base units will be effective from 20 May 2019.

4.3 Evolution of Base Units

The foundation stone of the metric system was laid on 20 May 1875, when 17 countries signed the famous Metre Convention Treaty (French name Convention du metre). The present-day International System of Units, French name, System

Units of length, mass time and electric current

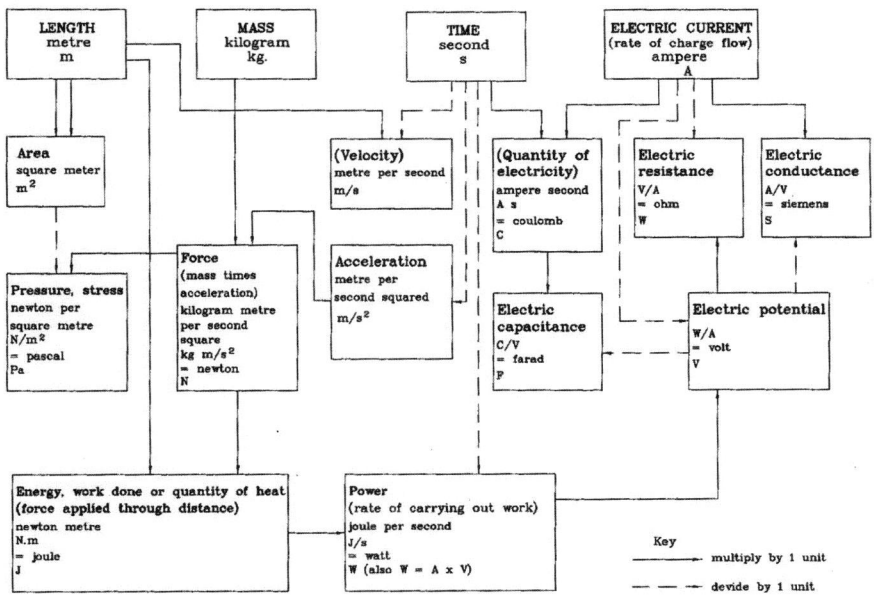

Fig. 4.2 Inter-relation of units of mass, length, time and ampere

Table 4.1 Base quantities and base units

Quantity	Symbol	Name of unit	Symbol of unit	Introduced year/CGPM	Modified year/CGPM		
					1st	2nd	Final
Length	$L, x, r,$ etc.	metre	m	1889 1st	1960 11th	1983 17th	2018 26th
Mass	m	kilogram	kg	1889 1st	–	1889 1st	2018 26th
Time	T	second	s	1960 11th	1968 13th	1968 13th	2018 26th
Electric current	I, i	ampere	A	1948 9th	1948 11th	1948 9th	2018 26th
Intensity of illumination	I_v	candela	cd	1948 9th	1968 13th	1979 16th	2018 26th
Temperature	T	kelvin	K	1948 9th	1954 10th	1954 10th	2018 20th
Mole	n	mole	mol	1971 14th	–	–	2018 26th

International d' unites, with universally adopted abbreviation SI was formally announced in 1960. It took some 85 years to evolve, a convenient and worldwide acceptable system of units. Worldwide national metrological laboratories spent lot of time to come to a consensus for a system of units based on the sound scientific principles and supported by experimental results.

It is important to distinguish between the definition of a unit and its realization. The definition of each base unit of the SI is carefully drawn up so that it is unique and provides a sound theoretical basis upon which the most accurate and reproducible measurements can be made. The realization of the definition of a unit is the procedure by which the definition may be used to establish the value and associated uncertainty of a quantity of the same kind as the unit. A description of how the definitions of some important units are realized in practice is given on the BIPM website, www.bipm.org/en/si/si_brochure/appendix2/. However, any method consistent with the laws of physics could be used to realize any SI unit. For example, the unit ohm can be realized with high accuracy using the quantum Hall effect and the value of the von Klitzing constant recommended by the CIPM [5, appendix 1].

A coherent SI derived unit is defined uniquely only in terms of SI base units. For example, the coherent SI derived unit of resistance: the ohm, symbol Ω, is uniquely defined by the relation $\Omega = m^2\,kg\,s^{-3}\,A^{-2}$, which follows from the definition of the quantity of electrical resistance.

Finally, it should be recognized that although the seven base quantities—length, mass, time, electric current, thermodynamic temperature, amount of substance and luminous intensity—are by convention regarded as independent, their respective base units—the metre, kilogram, second, ampere, kelvin, mole and candela—are in a number of instances interdependent. For example, the definition of the metre incorporates the second; the definition of the ampere incorporates the metre, kilogram and second; the definition of the mole incorporates the kilogram and the definition of the candela incorporates the metre, kilogram and second [5]. This situation further exaggerates when base units are expressed in terms of seven defining constants approved by 25th CGPM, November 2018. Its recommendations will come in force on 20 May 2019.

4.3.1   Unit of Time

The unit of time, the second, was at one time considered to be the fraction 1/86,400 of the mean solar day, which came from the assumption that 24 h is a day, 60 min is one hour and 60 s make a minute. The exact definition of "mean solar day" was based on astronomical theories. However, measurement showed that irregularities in the rotation of the Earth could not be taken into account by the theory, and hence this definition does not allow the required accuracy to be achieved.

In order to define the unit of time more precisely, the 11th CGPM (1960) adopted a definition given by the International Astronomical Union, defining second with symbol "s" as 1/31,556,925,9747 of the tropical year for 1900, January 0 at 12 h ephemeris time. However, experimental work showed that for time interval, an atomic clock, based on a transition between two energy levels of an atom or a molecule, could be realized and reproduced much more precisely.

Considering that a very precise definition of the unit of time is indispensable for the SI units, the 13th CGPM (1967–68) [11] replaced the above definition of the second by the following:

The second is the duration of 9,192,631,770 periods of the radiation corresponding to the transition between the two hyperfine levels of the ground state of the caesium-133 atom.

At its 1997 meeting, the CIPM affirmed that this definition refers to a caesium atom in its ground state at a temperature of 0 K and that the splitting in ground state of the caesium-133 atom is exactly 9,192,631,770 Hz.

Formal definition as approved by 26th CGPM (November 2018) effective from 20 May 2019 is as follows:

The second, symbol s, is the SI unit of time. Its magnitude is set by fixing the numerical value of the caesium frequency $\Delta \nu$Cs, the unperturbed ground-state hyperfine transition frequency of the caesium-133 atom, as 9,192,631,770 when expressed in the unit hertz, which is equal to s^{-1}.

4.3.2 Unit of Length

Initially, one metre was defined as (1/40,000,000)th part of Earth's meridian passing through Paris. The length of the meridian was measured in terms of old French unit of length named as toise. From the best measurements of the meridian, it was found that theoretical length of metre should be 0.513074 toise. Sintered platinum flat bar was adjusted to this length and was deposited with Archives de France. The section of the bar was 25 mm wide and 4 mm thick. This standard was in the form of an end standard, i.e. the distance between the centres of the end faces of the bar was one metre. This metre was officially declared as the "final standard of the metre" on 10 December 1799.

After the metre convention was signed, several platinum–iridium bars were fabricated and two transverse marks were provided on each bar so that the distance between the two marks is close to 1 m. The bar on which distance between the two transverse marks was as close as possible to the distance between the end faces of the metre des Archives of 1799 was taken as International Prototype of Metre. The cross-section of the prototype bar is shown in Fig. 4.3.

Engineer G Tresca worked out the design of the cross-section of the bar. The design has two distinct advantages.

- It has a uniform surface in the neutral plane where sub-divisions of metre can be graduated.
- It has greater rigidity for the given mass of metal used.

Latter point is important from the cost point of view of the bar, as platinum–iridium alloy is an expensive material.

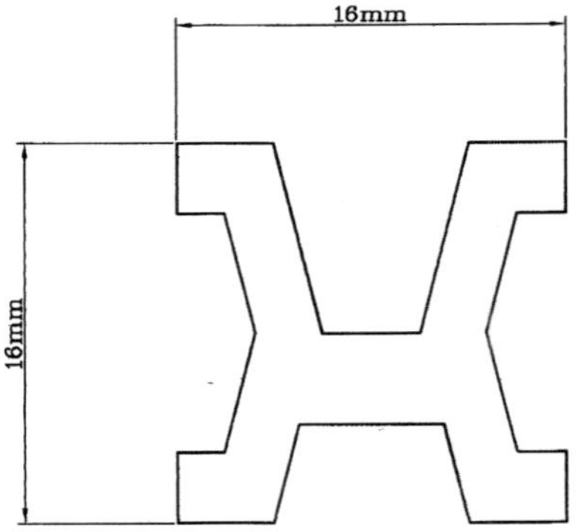

Fig. 4.3 End section of the
international prototype metre
bar

Fig. 4.4 Description of
international prototype metre
bar. *Note* This description is
based upon the information
from Dr. R. S. Davis, Head
Mass Standards, BIPM, from
the book by H. Moreau, who
was also the member of staff
of the BIPM

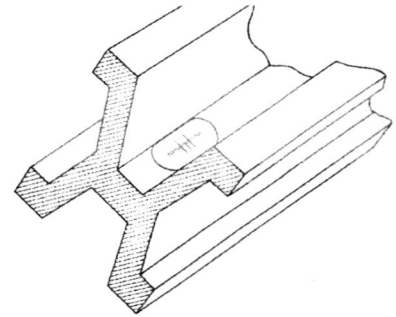

CIPM selected a bar in which the distance between the transverse lines was
closest to the distance between the centres of the end faces of the metre des
Archives, France. The first CGPM, in 1889, adopted that bar as International
Prototype of Metre. On each end of the bar, there is a spot having three transverse
lines each 0.5 mm apart and two fiducial longitudinal lines, the two fiducial lines
are separated by 0.2 mm. The end part of the bar having different lines is shown in
Fig. 4.4.

Metre was then defined as the distance between two centres of transverse lines
on each end of the bar at the temperature of melting ice. Temperature was measured on the hydrogen thermometer on centigrade scale. The two longitudinal fiducial lines bound the portion of the transverse lines on each side, to be used.

In fact, 7th CGPM in 1927 formally defined the metre as follows:

"The unit of length is the metre, defined by the distance at 0 °C, between the
axes of the two central lines marked on the bar of platinum-iridium selected by the
1st CGPM, this bar being subject to standard atmospheric pressure and supported
on two cylinders of at least one centimetre diameter, symmetrically placed in the
same horizontal plane at a distance of 571 mm from each other".

Later it was felt that International Prototype of Metre did not define the metre with the accuracy adequate for the needs of metrology. Moreover, it was desirable to adopt a natural and indestructible standard. So 11th CGPM, in 1960, defined metre in terms of wavelength of visible radiation and declared that the metre was the length equal to 1,650,763.73 wavelengths, in vacuum, of the radiation, due to the transition between the levels $2p_{10}$ and $5d_5$ of the krypton 86 atom. The metre was realized by using an interferometer with a travelling microscope to measure the optical path difference by counting the fringes.

Main problem with radiations from Krypton lamp was its coherence length, which was not more than 50 cm, thus to get interference fringes over a distance of one metre was not possible. The metre, in terms of the specified radiation of krypton 86, is used to be scanned in two steps. But the lasers made it possible to have interference fringes over distances of more than one metre. In addition, it was also realized that due to highly monochromatic in nature, i.e. narrower bandwidth, less divergence and strong intensity, the lasers were found to be better reproducible and easy-to-use sources. Moreover, it was found that

1. Frequency of lasers can be maintained at a constant value.
2. Lesser relative uncertainty is possible in frequency measurement.
3. The measurement of frequency and wavelength of laser radiations has resulted in concordant determination of the speed of light whose accuracy was limited principally by the realization of the definition of metre.
4. Wavelengths determined from the frequency measurement and with a given value of speed of light gave a reproducibility superior to the one, which could be obtained by comparing with the wavelength standard radiations of krypton 86.
5. Scientists working in the field of astronomy and geodesy were measuring distances in terms of speed of light (electromagnetic waves) and time.

So it was thought prudent to define metre in terms of speed of light, which by definition is constant. 15th CGPM in 1975 accepted 299,792,458 ms^{-1} as the value of speed of light.

Based on this value, the 17th CGPM, in 1983 [7], defined metre as follows:

The metre is the length of the path travelled by light in vacuum during a time interval of 1/299,792,458 s.

Formal definition as approved by 26th CGPM (Nov. 2018) effective from 20 May 2019 is as follows:

The metre, symbol m, is the SI unit of length. Its magnitude is set by fixing the numerical value of the speed of light in vacuum c to be 299,792,458 when expressed in the unit m s^{-1}, where the second is defined in terms of the caesium frequency $\Delta\nu$Cs.

Please note that the effect of this definition is to fix c_0 the speed of light in vacuum at exactly 299,792,458 m s^{-1}. The original international prototype of the metre sanctioned by the 1st CGPM in 1889 [6] is still kept at the BIPM under conditions specified in 1889.

4.3.3   Unit of Mass

Lavoisier, a great scientist of his time, considered water as a natural standard. He proposed that unit of mass must be kilogram and it must be taken equal to mass of water of one cubic decimetre. Accordingly, a cylinder of pure sintered platinum was fabricated by French Academy. The mass of the cylinder was made equal to that of water at the temperature of its maximum density and occupying a volume of one cubic decimetre. This cylinder of sintered platinum was kept in the Archives de France on 22 June 1799. The cylinder was given the name "Kilogram de Archives" and was declared standard of kilogram on 10 December 1799.

4.3.3.1   International Prototype of Kilogram

In 1878, 3 years after BIPM was founded, several cylinders of platinum–iridium of nominal composition 90% platinum and 10% iridium were prepared. These were compared in 1880, with the Kilogram de Archives. The one, whose mass was closest to that of the Kilogram de Archives, was chosen as International Prototype by the CIPM in 1883 and a letter K was engraved on it. The same kilogram was approved as such by the 1st General Conference on Weights and Measures in 1889 as the International Prototype of Kilogram [6]. The 3rd CGPM, in 1901, declared that kilogram is the unit of mass rather than weight and is equal to the mass of the International Prototype of the Kilogram of 1889, kept in the custody of BIPM.

In 1989, CIPM took the following decision in respect of cleaning and washing of the prototypes:

(1)   That kilogram as defined in 1889 is the mass of the international prototype of kilogram just after cleaning and washing.
(2)   That the BIPM procedure given in document [2, 3, 8] should be used for cleaning and washing.
(3)   That to deduce the mass of the International Prototype of the Kilogram, at the time of using, the measured change in mass of +0.0368 μg per day must be used. Giving us

$$\text{Mass of the International Prototype Kilogram} = 1 \text{ kg} + 0.0368 \cdot d \ \mu\text{g},$$

where d is the number of days passed since last cleaning and washing.

The BIPM procedure for cleaning platinum–iridium weights has been given in references [2, 3, 8].

We know that Kilogram:

- The unit of mass is the only unit, which is being defined in terms of an artefact.
- All other units have been defined in terms of a physical or atomic phenomenon.

Considering the above facts, the 21st CGPM, in 1999 [6, p. 165] passed the following resolution:

The CGPM on considering

1. the need to assure the long-term stability of the SI,
2. the intrinsic uncertainty in the long-term stability of the artefact defining the unit of mass,
3. the consequent uncertainty in the long-term stability of the other three base units of the SI that depend on the kilogram, namely, the ampere, the mole and the candela,
4. the progress already made in a number of different experiments designed to link the unit of mass to fundamental or atomic constants and
5. the desirability of having more than one method of making such a link recommends that the national laboratories should continue their efforts to refine experiments that link the unit of mass to fundamental or atomic constants with a view to redefine the kilogram.

With regard to attaching a prefix to the unit of mass whose name, for historical reasons, contains a prefix, the 13th CGPM in 1968 [3] declared that names and symbols for decimal multiples and submultiples of the unit of mass are formed by attaching prefix names to the unit name "gram" and prefix symbols to the unit symbol "g".

It may be noted that it took some 14 years (from 1875 to 1889):

1. To identify the material suitable for the international prototype of kilogram, its copies and the national prototypes,
2. Preparing cylinders of this material,
3. Adjusting the mass value of these cylinders within ± 1 mg of the mass of kilogram de Archives and
4. Declaring one of them as the International Prototype of Kilogram, some as its official copies and others as national prototypes.

International Prototype of Kilogram is kept on a glass plate covered by three bell jars. The base has levelling screws to keep the base horizontal. The kilogram is shown in Fig. 4.5.

It follows that the mass of the International Prototype of the Kilogram is always 1 kg exactly, $m(K) = 1$ kg. However, due to the inevitable accumulation of contaminants on surfaces, the international prototype is subject to reversible surface contamination that approaches 1 µg per year in mass. For this reason, the CIPM declared that, pending further research, the reference mass of the international prototype is that immediately after cleaning and washing by a specified method [2, 3]. The reference mass thus defined is used to calibrate national standards of platinum–iridium alloy [9].

Notwithstanding with what is said above, International Prototype Kilogram will be no more the primary standards of mass from 20 May 2019 and its value is to be determined in terms of primary standard obtained by Kibble balance or XRCD (X-ray-crystal-density) method.

Fig. 4.5 International
Prototypeof Kilogram
(*Courtesy by BIPM*)

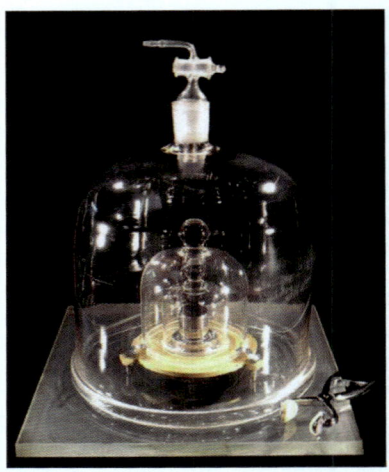

Note: The symbol, $m(K)$, is used to denote the mass of the International
Prototype of the Kilogram, the letter "K" is engraved on the cylinder.

**Formal definition as approved by 26th CGPM (November 2018) effective
from 20 May 2019 is as follows:**

**The kilogram, symbol kg, is the SI unit of mass. Its magnitude is set by
fixing the numerical value of the Planck's constant h to be $6.62607015 \times 10^{-34}$
when expressed in the unit J s, which is equal to kg m^2 s^{-1}, where the metre
and the second are defined in terms of c and ΔvCs.**

4.3.4   Unit of Electric Current

Electrical units with the name "international", for current and resistance, were
introduced by the International Electrical Congress held at Chicago in 1893, and
definitions of the "international" ampere and the "international" ohm were confirmed by the International Conference at London in 1908.

Although it was already obvious on the occasion of the 8th CGPM (1933) that
there was a unanimous desire to replace those "international" units by so-called "absolute" units, the official decision to abolish them was only taken by the 9th CGPM
(1948), which adopted the ampere for the unit of electric current and defined it as

**The ampere is that constant current which, if maintained in two straight
parallel conductors of infinite length, of negligible circular cross-section, and
placed 1 m apart in vacuum, would produce between these conductors a force
equal to 2×10^{-7} newton per metre of length.**

The expression "MKS unit of force" which occurs in the original text of 1946
has been replaced here by "newton", a name adopted for this unit by the 9th
CGPM (1948).

It will be shown later that the effect of this definition is to fix the permeability of vacuum at exactly $4\pi \times 10^{-7}$ H m^{-1}.

It may be noted that ampere has been defined by CGPM such that it is as close as possible to International Ampere and that International Ampere was taken as one-tenth of electromagnetic unit current (abampere).

Formal definition as approved by 26th CGPM (November 2018) effective from 20 May 2019 is as follows:

The ampere, symbol A, is the SI unit of electric current. Its magnitude is set by fixing the numerical value of the elementary charge e to be 1.602176634 × 10^{-19} when expressed in the unit C, which is equal to A·s, where the second is defined in terms of $\Delta \nu$Cs.

4.3.5 Unit of Temperature

Though temperature is nothing but the average energy of a molecule so could be expressed in terms of energy, for the sake of simplicity and ease it has been separately taken as one of the base units.

In 1948, 9th CGPM decided the following in respect of measurement of temperature and heat:

1. The zero of the centesimal thermodynamic scale was defined as the temperature 0.01° below that of the triple point of water.
2. An absolute thermodynamic scale with a single fundamental fixed point, at present provided by the triple point of pure water, the absolute temperature of which will be fixed at a later date.
3. The unit of heat quantity was assigned the name joule.
4. Out of three possible names {degree centigrade, centesimal degree and degree Celsius}, the name of degree Celsius was adopted.

4.3.5.1 Unit of Thermodynamic Temperature (Kelvin)

The definition of the unit of thermodynamic temperature was given in substance by the 10th CGPM (1954), which selected the triple point of water as the fundamental fixed point and assigned to it the temperature 273.16 K so defining the unit. The 13th CGPM (1967–1968) [10] adopted the name *kelvin* with symbol K. Earlier it was called "degree Kelvin" (symbol °K).

The unit of thermodynamic temperature is defined as follows:

The kelvin unit of thermodynamic temperature is the fraction 1/273.16 of the thermodynamic temperature of the triple point of water.

To make the definition more accurate, CIPM in 2005 affirmed that the water in the above definition is Vienna Standard Mean Oceans Water (V-SMOW) having the following isotopic compositions [5].

Deutron heavy hydrogen ^{2}H is 0.00015576 ^{2}H mol per mole of ^{1}H

Oxygen of atomic mass 18 ^{18}O is 0.0020052 mol of ^{18}O per mole ^{16}O

And oxygen of atomic mass 17 ^{17}O: 0.0003799 mol of ^{17}O per mole of ^{16}O.

Formal definition as approved by 26th CGPM (Nov. 2018) effective from 20 May 2019 is as follows:

The kelvin, symbol K, is the SI unit of thermodynamic temperature. Its magnitude is set by fixing the numerical value of the Boltzmann constant k to be 1.380649 x 10^{-23} when expressed in the unit J K^{-1}, which is equal to kg m^2 s^{-2} K^{-1}, where the kilogram, metre and second are defined in terms of h, c and ΔvCs.

Following the normal practice of expressing the temperature scales, a thermo-dynamic temperature, symbol T, is also expressed in terms of its difference from the reference temperature $T_0 = 273.15$ K, the ice point. This temperature difference is called the Celsius temperature, symbol t, and is defined by the quantity equation

$$t(^\circ C) = T_{90}(K) - T_0.$$

The unit of Celsius temperature is the degree Celsius with symbol $^\circ$C, which by definition is equal in magnitude to the kelvin. A difference or interval of temperature may be expressed in kelvin or in degree Celsius. The numerical value of a Celsius temperature t expressed in degree Celsius is given by

$$t(^\circ C) = T_{90}(K) - 273.15.$$

Here T is expressed in kelvin.

The kelvin and the degree Celsius are also the units of the International Temperature Scale of 1990 (ITS-90) adopted by the CIPM in 1989 [13].

The two names associated with unit of temperature are those of Lord Kelvin and Celsius.

4.3.6   Unit of Amount of Substance (Mole)

On the advice of

- The International Union of Pure and Applied Physics,
- The International Union of Pure and Applied Chemistry and
- The International Organization for Standardization.

14th CGPM, in 1971, [5, 12] decided to include mole as the seventh base unit and defined it as follows:

1. **The mole with symbol "mol" is the amount of substance of a system which contains as many elementary entities as there are atoms in 0.012 kg of carbon 12.**
2. **When the mole is used, the elementary entities must be specified which may be atoms, molecules, ions, electrons, other particles or specified groups of such particles.**

It follows that the molar mass of carbon 12 is exactly 12 g/mol,

$$M\left(^{12}C\right) = 12 \text{ g/mol}.$$

In 1980, the CIPM approved the report of the CCU (1980) which specified that in this definition, it is understood that unbound atoms of carbon 12, at rest and in their ground state, are referred to.

The definition of the mole also determines the value of the constant that relates the number of entities to amount of substance for any sample. This constant is called the Avogadro constant, symbol N_A or L. If $N(X)$ denotes the number of entities X in a specified sample and $n(X)$ denotes the amount of substance of entities X in the same sample, the two are related to N_A as follows:

$$n(X) = N(X)/N_A.$$

One may note that since $N(X)$ is dimensionless and unit of $n(X)$ is mole, coherent SI unit of the Avogadro constant is reciprocal mole with symbol mol^{-1}.

In any particular application, for simplicity and better understanding, the word substance should be replaced by its chemical name. For example, talk of "amount of hydrogen chloride, HCl", or "amount of benzene, C_6H_6". It is important to always give a precise specification of the entity involved (as emphasized in the second sentence of the definition of the mole); empirical chemical formula of the material involved should be given. Although the word "amount" has a more general dictionary definition, this abbreviation of the full name "amount of substance" may be used for brevity. This also applies to derived quantities such as "amount-of-substance concentration", which may simply be called "amount concentration". However, in the field of clinical chemistry, the name "amount of substance concentration" is generally abbreviated to "substance concentration". **Formal definition as approved by 26th CGPM (November 2018) effective from 20 May 2019 is as follows:**

The mole, symbol mol, is the SI unit of amount of substance. Its magnitude is set by fixing the value of Avogadro constant N_A to be $6.02214076 \times 10^{23}$ elementary entities, when N_A is expressed in the unit mol^{-1} and is called the Avogadro number.

4.3.7 Unit of Luminous Intensity

The unit of luminous intensity was initially based on flame or incandescent fil-
ament lamps. These standards continued to be used in various countries till
1948. Then these were replaced by the "new candle" based on the luminance of
a blackbody radiator at the freezing point of platinum. Though the definition of
new candle was prepared by the International Commission on Illumination (CIE)
and by the CIPM before 1937, CIPM took the decision to promulgate it in 1946.
However, it was ratified by CGPM only in 1948 in its 9th CGPM, which adopted a
name "new candle" for this unit and defined it as given below:

New candle (unit of luminous intensity): the value of the new candle is such
that the brightness of the full radiator at the temperature of solidification of platinum is 60 new candles per square centimetre.

Similarly, new lumen is the unit of luminous flux which was defined as the
luminous flux emitted in unit solid angle (steradian) by a uniform point source
having a luminous intensity of 1 new candle.

13th CGPM 1968 not only changed the wordings of the definition of new candle but also changed its name also, the name given was candela. The definition of
candela given was as follows:

The candela is the luminous intensity, in the perpendicular direction, of a surface of 1/600,000 m^2 of a blackbody at the temperature of freezing platinum under
normal standard pressure of 101,325 newton per m^2.

The definition of "new candle" was abrogated in 1968.

Later on, in 1979, the 16th CGPM, considering that

1. Despite the notable efforts of some laboratories there remain excessive diver-
   gences between the results of realizations of the candela based upon the blackbody as primary standard.
2. Radiometric techniques are developing rapidly, allowing precisions that are
   already equivalent to those of photometry and that these techniques are already
   in use in national laboratories to realize the candela without having to construct
   a blackbody.
3. The relation between luminous quantities of photometry and radiometric quantities, namely, the value of 683 lumens per watt for the spectral luminous efficacy of monochromatic radiation of frequency 540×10^{12} Hz, has been adopted
   by the CIPM in 1977.
4. This value has been accepted as being sufficiently accurate for the system of
   luminous photopic quantities, and it implies a change of only about 3% for the
   system of luminous scotopic quantities and
5. It, therefore, ensures satisfactory continuity and applies to both photopic and
   scotopic photometric quantities and to quantities yet to be defined in the mesopic field.

Decide to give the candela a definition that will allow an improvement in both the
ease of realization and the precision of photometric standards.

Hence, the candela was redefined by the 16th CGPM, in 1979, in terms of frequency and power [10] instead of the source at the freezing point of platinum.

Formal definition as approved by 26th CGPM (November 2018) effective from 20 May 2019 is as follows:

"The candela, symbol cd, is the SI unit of luminous intensity in a given direction. Its magnitude is set by fixing the numerical value of the luminous efficacy of monochromatic radiation of frequency 540×10^{12} Hz, Kcd, to be 683 when expressed in the unit $l\,mW^{-1}$".

It may be mentioned that unlike ampere, the unit of electric current, candela is not after the name of any scientist, but candela is the Latin word for "candle".

4.3.8   Dependence of Base Units

It was made clear that four quantities and their units are sufficient for describing a system of units. However, International System of Units contains seven base quantities with specific unit for each. Seven base units describe other units more compactly and conveniently. Obviously, all base units are not independent of each other, there dependence is shown in Fig. 4.6. Except base units of mass and time all other base units are inter-related.

Their dependence is shown by arrows emanating from base units of mass, length and time. The temperature is independent of any other base unit.

Fig. 4.6 Dependence of base units

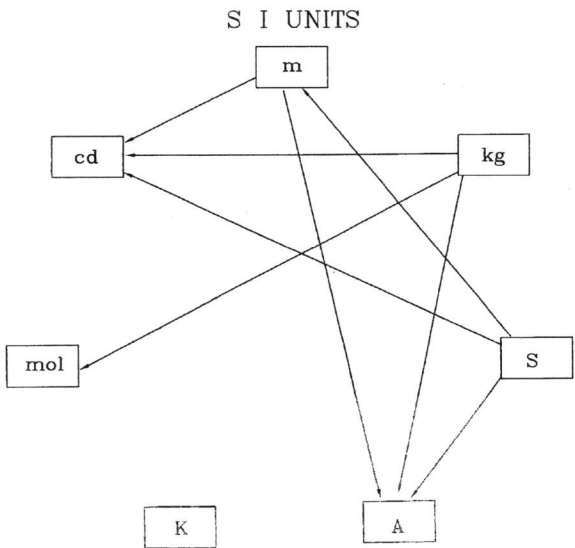

S I UNITS

References

1. BIPM, Proc.-Verb. Com. Int. Poids et Mesures, **31**, 97 (1963)
2. BIPM, Proc.- Verb.Com. Int. Poids et Mesures **57**, 104–105 (1989)
3. BIPM, Proc.- Verb.Com. Int. Poids et Mesures **58**, 95–97 (1990)
4. BIPM, Proc.-Verb. Com. Int. Poids et Mesures, **64**, 124 (1996)
5. BIPM, Le Systeme Internatinal d'Unites, 8th Edition, BIPM, Sevres, France (2006)
6. CIPM, Definitions of metre and kilogram Comptes Rendus 34–38 (1889)
7. P. Giacomo, News from BIPM. Metrologia **20**, 25 (1984)
8. G. Girard, The washing and cleaning of kilogram prototypes at the BIPM (1990), 19 pp.
9. G. Girard, Third periodic verification of national prototype of kilogram (1988–1992). Metrologia **31**, 317–336 (1994)
10. P. Giacomo, News from BIPM. Metrologia **16**, 56 (1980)
11. J. Terrian, News from the BIPM. Metrologia **4**(41-45), 45 (1968)
12. J. Terrian, News from BIPM. Metrologia **8**, 32–36 (1972)
13. J. Quinn, News from BIPM. Metrologia **27**, 11–13 (1990)

Chapter 5
New Definitions of SI Base Units

5.1 Seven Defining Constants and SI Base Units

There are seven base units in International System of Units (SI). Seven fundamental physical constants have been chosen to define the base units. These are also called as defining constants. The nature of the defining constants ranges from fundamental constants of nature to technical constant. For example, Planck's constant h is a fundamental constant while K_{cd} luminous efficacy is a technical one, and it refers to special application. The use of constant to define a unit disconnects definition from realization. The uncertainty to realize a unit may change with the advance technology, but definition will not change. Each base unit is defined so that defining constant has a specified magnitude when expressed in SI units.

A technical constant such as luminous efficacy (Kcd) refers to a special application. It can in principle be chosen freely, such as to include conventional physiological or other weighting factors. In contrast, the use of a fundamental constant of nature, in general, does not allow this choice because it is related to other constants through the equations of physics. The set of seven defining constants has been chosen to provide a fundamental, stable and universal reference that simultaneously allows for practical realizations with the smallest uncertainties.

Both the Planck's constant h and the speed of light in vacuum c are properly described as fundamental. They determine quantum effects and space–time properties, respectively, and affect all particles and fields equally on all scales and in all environments.

© Springer Nature Switzerland AG 2020
S. V. Gupta, *Units of Measurement*, Springer Series in Materials Science 122,
https://doi.org/10.1007/978-3-030-43969-9_5

5.2   Importance of Defining Constants

5.2.1   Caesium Frequency

The caesium frequency Δv_{Cs}, the unperturbed ground-state hyperfine transition frequency of the caesium-133 atom, has the character of an atomic parameter, which may be affected by the environment, such as electromagnetic fields. However, the underlying transition is well understood, stable and a good choice as a reference transition. The choice of an atomic parameter like Δv_{Cs} does not disconnect definition and realization in the same way that h, c, e or k do, but specifies the reference.

5.2.2   Velocity of Light

Velocity of light is a maximum in vacuum and is the limiting value of any matter can move. Equivalence of mass and energy is established by the relation $E = mc^2$. It determines space–time properties.

5.2.3   Planck's Constant

Planck's constant is properly described fundamental constant which gives the equivalence in particle and wave nature of electromagnetic waves.

5.2.4   Elementary Charge

The elementary charge e corresponds to a coupling strength of the electromagnetic force via the fine structure constant $\alpha = e^2/(2c\cdot\varepsilon_0\cdot h)$ where ε_0 is the vacuum electric permittivity or electric constant. Some theories predict a variation of α over time. The experimental limits of the maximum possible variation in α are so low, that it can be ignored.

5.2.5   Boltzmann Constant

The Boltzmann constant k corresponds to a conversion factor between the quantities temperature (unit is kelvin) and energy (unit is joule), whereby the numerical value is obtained from historical specifications of the temperature scale. The temperature of a system scales with the thermal energy, but not necessarily with the internal energy of a system. In statistical physics, the Boltzmann constant connects the entropy S with the number Ω of quantum mechanically accessible states, $S = k \ln \Omega$.

5.2.6 Avogadro Constant

The Avogadro constant N_A corresponds to a conversion factor between the quantity amount of substance (with unit mole) and the quantity for counting entities (with unit one, symbol 1). Thus, it has the character of a constant of proportionality similar to the Boltzmann constant k.

5.2.7 Luminous Efficacy

The luminous efficacy Kcd is a technical constant that gives an exact numerical relationship between the purely physical characteristics of the radiant power stimulating the human eye (W) and its photo-biological response defined by the luminous flux due to the spectral responsivity of a standard observer (lm) at a frequency of 540×10^{12} hertz.

5.3 Magnitude of Defining Constant in SI Units

The defining constants, their magnitudes with symbols and corresponding SI base unit are expressed in Table 5.1.

5.4 Formal Definitions of SI Units

Though the formal definitions of SI base units in terms of defining constant are formally given at the end of paragraphs of evolution of base units in Chap. 4, here they are repeated keeping in view the continuity and completeness.

Table 5.1 Seven defining constants and SI base units

Defining constant	Magnitude in SI units	SI base unit
Unperturbed ground-state hyperfine frequency transition of ^{133}Cs atom Δv_{Cs},	$9192\ 631\ 770\ \text{s}^{-1}$	Second
Velocity of light in vacuum c	$299\ 792\ 458\ \text{m·s}^{-1}$	Metre
Planck's constant h	$6.626\ 070\ 15 \times 10^{-34}\ \text{kg· m}^2\ \text{·s}^{-1}$	Kilogram
Elementary charge e	$1.602\ 176\ 634 \times 10^{-19}\ \text{A·s}$	Ampere
Boltzmann constant k	$1.380\ 649 \times 10^{-23}\ \text{kg·m}^2\text{·s}^{-2}\text{·K}^{-1}$	Kelvin
Avogadro number N_A	$6.022\ 140\ 76 \times 10^{23}$	Mole
Efficacy of monochromatic radiation of frequency 540×10^{12} Hz, Kcd	$683\ \text{lm W}^{-1}$, cd·sr· $\text{kg}^{-1}\text{·m}^{-2}\text{·s}^3$	Candela

5.4.1   The Second

The second, symbol s, is the SI unit of time. Its magnitude is set by fixing the numerical value of the caesium frequency $\Delta \nu_{Cs}$, the unperturbed ground-state hyperfine transition frequency of the caesium-133 atom, as 9,192,631,770 when expressed in the unit Hz, which is equal to s^{-1}.

5.4.2   The Metre

The metre, symbol m, is the SI unit of length. Its magnitude is set by fixing the numerical value of the speed of light in vacuum c to be 299,792,458 when expressed in the unit m s^{-1}, where the second is defined in terms of the caesium frequency $\Delta \nu_{Cs}$.

5.4.3   The Kilogram

The kilogram, symbol kg, is the SI unit of mass. Its magnitude is set by fixing the numerical value of the Planck's constant h to be 6.626 070 15 $\times 10^{-34}$ when expressed in the unit J s, which is equal to kg m^2 s^{-1}, where the metre and the second are defined in terms of c and $\Delta_{\nu Cs}$.

5.4.4   The Ampere

The ampere, symbol A, is the SI unit of electric current. Its magnitude is set by fixing the numerical value of the elementary charge e to be 1.602 176 634 $\times 10^{-19}$ when expressed in the unit C, which is equal to A·s, where the second is defined in terms of $\Delta \nu Cs$.

5.4.5   The Kelvin

The kelvin, symbol K, is the SI unit of thermodynamic temperature. Its magnitude is set by fixing the numerical value of the Boltzmann constant k to be 1.380 649 $\times 10^{-23}$ when expressed in the unit J·K^{-1}, which is equal to kg·m^2·s^{-2}·K^{-1}, where the kilogram, metre and second are defined in terms of h, c and $\Delta \nu Cs$.

5.4.6 The Mole

The mole, symbol mol, is the SI unit of amount of substance. Its magnitude is set by fixing the value of Avogadro constant N_A to be $6.022\ 140\ 76 \times 10^{23}$ elementary entities, when N_A is expressed in the unit mol^{-1} and is called the Avogadro number.

The amount of substance, symbol n, of a system is a measure of the number of specified elementary entities. An elementary entity may be an atom, a molecule, an ion, an electron, any other particle or specified group of particles.

5.4.7 The Candela

The candela, symbol cd, is the SI unit of luminous intensity in a given direction. Its magnitude is set by fixing the numerical value of the luminous efficacy of monochromatic radiation of frequency 540×10^{12} Hz, Kcd, to be 683 when expressed in the unit lmW^{-1}, which is equal to cd srW^{-1}, or cd· sr· kg^{-1} ·m^{-2} ·s^3, where the kilogram, metre and second are defined in terms of h, c and $\Delta \nu$Cs. It may be noted that steradian with symbol sr has unity as its symbol.

5.5 Effect of the New Definition

5.5.1 Second

This definition of second means that the second is equal to the duration of 9,192,631,770 periods of the radiation corresponding to the transition between the two hyperfine levels of the unperturbed ground state of the ^{133}Cs atom.

The phrase "unperturbed atom" is used to make it clear that the definition of the SI second is based on an isolated caesium atom that is unperturbed by any external field, such as ambient blackbody radiation.

The new definition of second is the unit of proper time in the sense of the general theory of relativity. To provide coordinated time scale, the signals of different primary clocks in different locations are combined, which are corrected for relativistic caesium frequency shifts.

The CIPM has adopted various secondary representations of the second, based on a selected number of spectral lines of atoms, ions or molecules. The unperturbed frequencies of these lines can be determined with a relative uncertainty higher or equal to the uncertainty of the realization of the second based on the ^{133}Cs hyperfine transition frequency, but some can be reproduced with superior stability.

5.5.2 Metre

The effect of the new definition is that one metre is the length of the path travelled by light in vacuum during a time interval with duration of 1/299 792 458 of a second.

5.5.3 Kilogram

The unit of "action" and "angular momentum" is kg m^2 s^{-1}, so while defining the unit of kilogram, the unit of action and angular momentum is automatically defined which may be written as

$$\frac{h}{6.62607015 \times 10^{-34}}.$$

Together with the new definitions of the second and the metre this leads to a definition of the unit of mass expressed in terms of the value of the Planck's constant h.

The previous definition of the kilogram fixed the value of the mass of the international prototype of the kilogram, $m(K)$, to be equal to one kilogram exactly and the value of the Planck's constant h has to been determined experimentally taking mass of international prototype kilogram as one kilogram exact. However, the present definition fixes the numerical value of h exactly so now the mass of the prototype has to be determined by experiment.

The magnitude of the Planck's constant in this definition is such that at the time of its adoption, the kilogram was equal to the mass of the international prototype, $m(K) = 1$ kg, with a relative standard uncertainty of 1×10^{-8}, which was the standard uncertainty of the combined best estimates of the value of the Planck's constant at that time.

It may be noted that with the present definition, primary realizations can be established, in principle, at any point in the mass scale that is at h/2 (500 g), h/5 (200 g, h/10(100 g) levels.

5.5.4 Ampere

The previous definition of the ampere was based on the force between two current-carrying conductors given by the formula $F_{per\ unit\ length} = \frac{\mu_0}{2\pi}\frac{I_1 I_2}{R}$.

The value assigned to F was 2×10^{-7}. The definition had the effect of fixing the value of the vacuum magnetic permeability μ_0 (also known as the magnetic constant) to be exactly $4\pi \times 10^{-7}$ H m$^{-1} = 4\pi \times 10^{-7}$ N A^{-2} where H and N denote the coherent derived units henry and newton, respectively. The new definition of the ampere fixes the value of e instead of μ_0. As a result, μ_0 must be determined experimentally.

It also follows that since the vacuum electric permittivity ε_0 (also known as the electric constant), the characteristic impedance of vacuum Z_0 and the admittance of vacuum Y_0 are equal to $1/\mu_0 c^2$, $\mu_0 c$ and $1/\mu_0 c$, respectively, the values of ε_0, Z_0 and Y_0 must now also be determined experimentally and are affected by the same relative standard uncertainty as μ_0 since c is exactly known. The product $\varepsilon_0\mu_0 = 1/c^2$ and quotient $Z_0/\mu_0 = c$ remain exact. At the time of adopting the present definition of the ampere, μ_0 was equal to $4\pi \times 10^{-7}$ H/m with a relative standard uncertainty of 2.3×10^{-10}.

5.5.4.1 Effect of Taking H and E as Exact Value

Besides decreasing uncertainty of many physical constant, the value of Josephson constant $K_j = 2e/h$ for voltage standard and von Klitzing constant $R_k = h/e^2$ for resistance standard have also become exact.

5.5.5 The Kelvin

The new definition fixes the numerical value of k instead of T_{TPW} (triple point of specific water), the latter must now be determined experimentally. Presently, one kelvin is equal to the change of thermodynamic temperature that results in a change of thermal energy kT by $1.380\,649 \times 10^{-23}$ J.

The previous definition of the kelvin set the temperature of the triple point of water, T_{TPW}, to be exactly 273.16 K. At the time of adopting the present definition, T_{TPW} was equal to 273.16 K with a relative standard uncertainty of 3.7×10^{-7}.

5.5.6 The Mole

It means that the mole is the amount of substance in a system that contains 6.022 140 76 $\times 10^{23}$ specified elementary entities.

The previous definition of the mole fixed the value of the molar mass of carbon 12. That is, $M(^{12}C)$ was taken 0.012 kg/mol exactly. Now $M(^{12}C)$ is no longer known, it is to be determined experimentally. The value chosen for N_A is such that at the time of adopting the present definition of the mole, $M(^{12}C)$ was equal to 0.012 kg/mol with a relative standard uncertainty of 4.5×10^{-10}.

The molar mass of any atom or molecule X may still be obtained from its relative atomic mass from the equation

$$M(X) = Ar(X)\,[M(^{12}C)/12] = Ar(X)M_u$$

and the molar mass of any atom or molecule X is also related to the mass cf the elementary entity $m(X)$ by the relation

$$M(X) = N_A m(X) = NA \, Ar(X) m_u.$$

In these equations, M_u is the molar mass constant equal to $M(^{12}C)/12$ and m_u is the unified atomic mass constant equal to $m(^{12}C)/12$. They are related to the Avogadro constant through the relation

$$M_u = N_A \, m_u.$$

In the name "amount of substance", the word "substance" will typically be replaced by specific name of the substance like hydrogen chloride (HCl). It is important to give a precise definition of the entity involved (as emphasized in the definition of the mole); this should preferably be done by specifying the molecular chemical formula of the material involved. Although the word "amount" has a more general dictionary meaning, the abbreviation of the full name "amount of substance" to "amount" may be used for brevity. This also applies to derived quantities such as "amount-of-substance concentration", which may simply be called "amount concentration". In the field of clinical chemistry, the name "amount-of-substance concentration" is generally abbreviated to "substance concentration".

5.5.7 The Candela

It means the candela is the luminous intensity of a source radiating monochromatic radiation of frequency 540×10^{12} Hz and has a radiant intensity of (1/683) W/sr in that direction.

5.6 Expressing SI Base Units in Defining Constants

For the purpose of brevity, let numbers involved in the formal definitions be, respectively, denoted by

$$9\,192\,631\,770 = N1; \ 299\,792\,458 = N2; \ 6.626\,070\,15 \times 10^{-34}$$
$$= N3; \ 1.602\,176\,634 \times 10^{-19} = N4 \ 1.380\,649 \times 10^{-23}$$
$$= N5; \ 6.022\,140\,76 \times 10^{23} = N6; \text{ and } 683 = N7.$$

5.6.1 The Second in Terms of $\Delta \nu Cs$

From Sect. 5.4.1, the second

$$\Delta \nu Cs = N1 \, Hz = N1 \, s^{-1}.$$

Writing in terms of second, we get

$$s = N1/\Delta\nu Cs = 9\,192\,631\,770/\Delta\nu Cs. \tag{5.1}$$

5.6.2 The Metre in Terms of C and S

From Sect. 5.4.2, the metre

$$c = 299\,792\,458\,\text{ms}^{-1} = N2\,\text{ms}^{-1}.$$

Expressing above in terms of m, we get

$$m = \frac{c}{N2}\frac{N1}{\Delta\nu Cs} = 30.663\,319\frac{c}{\Delta\nu C_s}. \tag{5.2}$$

5.6.3 The Kilogram in Terms of H

From Sect. 5.4.3, the kilogram

$$h = 6.62607015 \times 10^{-34}\,\text{Js} = N3\,\text{kg} \cdot \text{m}^2 \cdot \text{s}^{-1}.$$

Writing in terms of kg, we get

$$kg = \frac{h}{N3}m^{-2} \cdot s$$

$$kg = \frac{h}{N3}\frac{N2^2}{c^2}\frac{\Delta\nu Cs}{N1} = \frac{N2^2}{N1 \cdot N3}\frac{h\Delta\nu Cs}{c^2} \tag{5.3}$$

$$= 1.4755214 \times 10^{40}\frac{h\Delta\nu Cs}{c^2}.$$

5.6.4 The Ampere in Terms of E and S

From 5.4.4, the ampere

$$e = 1.602176634 \times 10^{-19}\,\text{A} \cdot \text{s} = N4\,\text{A} \cdot \text{s}$$

$$A = \frac{e}{N4}s^{-1} = \frac{e}{N4}\frac{\Delta\nu Cs}{N1} \tag{5.4}$$

$$6.78968710^8 e\Delta\nu Cs.$$

5.6.5 The Kelvin in Terms of K

$$k = 1.380649 \times 10^{-23}\,\text{JK}^{-1} = N5\text{kg} \cdot \text{m}^2 \cdot \text{s}^{-2} \cdot \text{K}^{-1}$$

$$K = N5\frac{N2^2}{N1 \cdot N3}\frac{h \cdot \Delta\nu Cs}{c^2}\left(\frac{c}{N2 \cdot}\frac{N1}{\Delta\nu Cs}\right)\left(\frac{c}{N2 \cdot}\frac{N1}{\Delta\nu Cs}\right)\frac{\Delta\nu Cs}{N1}\frac{\Delta\nu Cs}{N1} = \frac{N5}{N3 \cdot}\frac{N2}{N1}\frac{h \cdot \Delta\nu Cs}{k}$$

$$K = 2.2666653\frac{h \cdot \Delta\nu Cs}{k}.$$

$$\tag{5.5}$$

5.6.6 Mole in Terms of N_A

From Sect. 5.4.6, the mole

$$N_A = 6.02214076 \times 10^{23} \text{mol}^{-1}.$$

Transposing mol^{-1} and $\underline{N_A}$, we get

$$mol = \frac{6.022\,140\,76\,10^{23}}{N_A}. \tag{5.6}$$

5.6.7 Candela in Terms of K_{cd}

From Sect. 5.4.7, the candela
$K_{cd} = 683 \text{ cd} \cdot \text{kg}^{-1} \cdot \text{m}^{-2} \cdot \text{s}^{-3} = \text{N7 cd} \cdot \text{kg}^{-1} \cdot \text{m}^{-2} \cdot \text{s}^{-3}$ giving us
Or $cd = \frac{Kcd}{N7} \text{kg} \cdot \text{m}^2 \cdot \text{s}^{-3}$.
But $\text{kgm}^2 \text{s}^{-1} = h/N3$ and $\text{s}^{-2} = \frac{\Delta v \cdot Cs^2}{N1^2}$.
Hence

$$cd = \frac{Kcd}{N7}\frac{h}{N3}\frac{\Delta K v Cs^2}{N1^2} = 2.614830 \times 10^{10} h \cdot (\Delta v Cs)^2 . Kcd. \tag{5.7}$$

5.7 Relationship Matrix

We have seen above that every SI base unit can be defined as product of powers of defining constants. As a corollary, every SI unit whether base or derived can be expressed in terms of defining constants.

Similarly, any defining constants may be defined as a product of powers of base units. The tables of their relationships are described in following paragraphs. Powers of base unit/defining constant is given in the cell intersection of the unit and the constant. The sequence of the seven defining constants in the left column of Table 5.2 follows the order in which they are presented in the CGPM resolution. The sequence of base units in the top row of Table 5.2 follows the order in which these units are defined. In Table 5.3, the sequence of defining constants is given in first row while the base units are given in first column.

Table 5.2 Defining constants in terms of base unit

	s	m	kg	A	K	mol	cd
$\Delta v Cs$	−1	0	0	0	0	0	0
c	−1	1	0	0	0	0	0
h	−1	2	1	0	0	0	0
e	1	0	0	1	0	0	0
k	−2	2	1	0	−1	0	0
N_A	0	0	0	0	0	−1	0
Kcd	3	−2	−1	0	0	0	1

Table 5.3 Base units in terms of defining constants

Base units	ΔνCs	c	h	e	k	N	Kcd
s	−1	0	0	0	0	0	0
m	−1	1	0	0	0	0	0
kg	1	−2	1	0	0	0	0
A	−1	0	0	1	0	0	0
K	1	0	1	0	−1	0	0
mol	0	0	0	0	0	−1	0
cd	2	0	1	0	0	0	1

Defining constants can be expressed as a product of powers of base units and vice versa, [7]. (Davis R S, 2018, How to define the base units of the revised SI, Rapport BIPM-2018/02.)

5.7.1   Defining Constants in Terms of Base Units

The relations between defining constants and SI base units are given in Table 5.2.

5.7.2   Base Units in Terms of Defining Constants

The relations between base units and defining constants are given in Table 5.3.

5.7.3   Use of the Matrix

Any defining constant/base unit given in the first column can be expressed as a product of the base unit/defining constant each raised to the power indicated in the cell at the intersection of unit and the constant.

Example from Table 5.2
Boltzmann constant $k = s^{-2} \cdot m^2 \cdot kg \cdot K^{-1} = $ Joule per kelvin.
Example from Table 5.3
Base unit mass $kg = \Delta \nu Cs \cdot c^{-2} \cdot h$.

5.8   Inter-Dependence of Base Units

Even before defining base units in terms of fundamental constants, base units were not independent of each other. So it is prudent to give the dependence of base units before and after their new definitions.

5.8.1 New SI Units

The redefined system of base units is depicted in Fig. 5.1. Defining constants are shown in outer grey circles. The symbol k_B in outer grey circle represents Boltzmann constant.

We may observe from the above figure that

- The ground-state hyperfine transition frequency of the caesium-133 atom $\Delta\nu$Cs is needed in definition of all base units except the mole.
- The speed of light in vacuum c is needed *only* in the definitions of the metre and kilogram.
- The Planck's constant h is needed *only* in the definitions of the kilogram, kelvin and candela.

The elementary charge e, the Boltzmann constant k, the Avogadro constant N_A and the luminous efficacy of a specified wavelength Kcd are each needed to define a single base unit. These defining constants are, respectively, used for ampere, kelvin, mole and candela.

5.8.2 Old SI Units

In Fig. 5.2, inter-dependence of base units is depicted before new definitions

Fig. 5.1 Inter-dependence base units

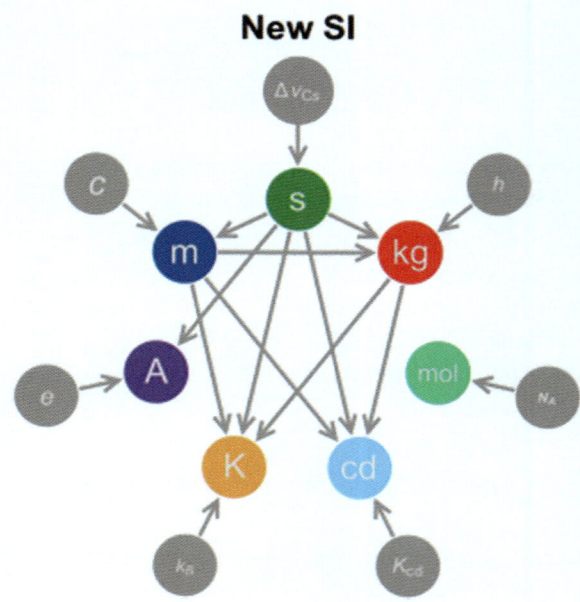

Fig. 5.2 Inter-dependence
base unit

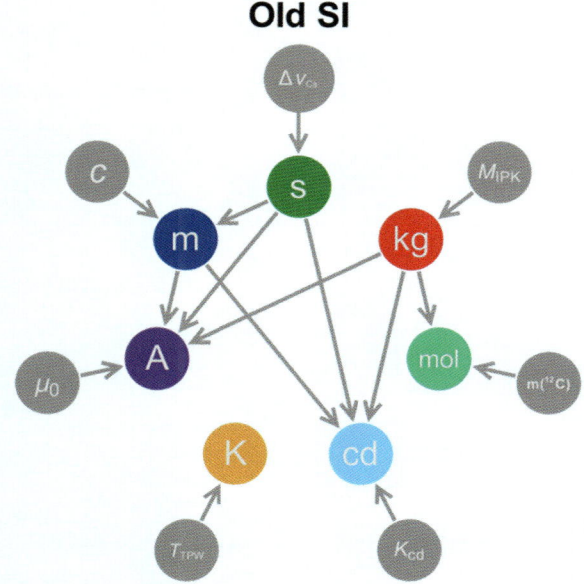

- The base unit second is needed to define three units, namely, metre, ampere and candela.
- The base unit metre is needed to define ampere and candela.
- The base unit kilogram is needed to define two units, namely, candela and mole.

The units are written in two circles. In outer circle are the defining constants according to the old definitions. Ampere is defined by taking μ_0 the permeability of free space equal to $4\pi \cdot 10^{-7}$ in the formula of force per unit length between two parallel wires of infinitely small cross-section and of infinite length placed at a distance R apart (definition of ampere)

$$F_{per\ unit\ length} = \frac{\mu_0}{2\pi} \frac{I_1 I_2}{R}.$$

Chapter 6
Realization of the SI Base Units
(S, M, Kilogram)

6.1 Practical Realization of the Unit of Time

The second is the base unit effectively defined as the duration of 9 192 631 770 periods of the radiation corresponding to the transition between hyperfine levels of the ground state (0 K) of the caesium atom ^{135}Cs.

6.1.1 Atomic Clocks

The definition of the second should be understood as the definition of the unit of proper time: it applies in a small spatial domain which shares the motion of the caesium atom used to realize the definition.

In a laboratory small enough to allow the effects of the non-uniformity of the gravitational field to be neglected when compared to the uncertainties of the realization of the second. The proper second is obtained after the application of the special relativistic correction for the velocity of the atom in the laboratory. It is wrong to correct for the local gravitational field.

Similarly, the definition has to be understood as referring to atoms free of any perturbation, i.e. at rest and at zero kelvin.

6.1.2 Primary Frequency Standards

Primary frequency standards are designed and built that produce electric oscillations at a frequency whose relationship to the transition frequency of the atom of caesium ^{133}Cs is known with a very low uncertainty. For such primary frequency

© Springer Nature Switzerland AG 2020
S. V. Gupta, *Units of Measurement*, Springer Series in Materials Science 122,
https://doi.org/10.1007/978-3-030-43969-9_6

standards, the various frequency shifts, including those due to the relativistic Doppler effect linked to the atomic motion, the thermal radiation of the environment (blackbody shift) and several other effects related to the clock design and operation, are estimated and corrected for.

In 2013, the best of these primary standards produces the SI second with a relative standard uncertainty of some parts in 10^{16}. At such a level of accuracy, the effect of the non-uniformity of the gravitational field over the size of the device is taken into account. The standard is then be considered in the framework of general relativity in order to provide the proper time at a specified point, for instance, a connector.

6.1.3 Secondary Representations of the Second

A list of frequencies recommended for secondary representations of the second is maintained since 2006 and is available at International Bureau of Weights and Measures.

These secondary frequency standards are accurate at the level of a few parts in 10^{18}; however, the uncertainties provided in the list are in the range of parts in 10^{14} or 10^{15} since they are limited by linking to a caesium primary standard.

All these methods of time comparison are subject to relativistic effects typically of several tens of nanoseconds, so corrections must be applied to take them into account.

Standard frequencies for practical realization of the metre and secondary representations of the definition of the second as approved by the CCTF in June 2017 and updated August 2018 are given in Table 6.1.

6.1.4 International Atomic Time (TAI)

National laboratories usually operate a number of clocks. These are run independently of one another and their data are combined to generate a perennial

Table 6.1 Frequency of standard radiation

Ion or element	Frequency (Hz)	Uncertainty	Recommended for second
^{115}In+	1 267 402 452 901 050	1.6×10^{-14}	–
^{199}Hg	1 128 575 290 808 154.4	1.6×10^{-14}	–
^{171}Yb	518 295 836 590 863.6	5×10^{-16}	Second
^{88}Sr+ ion	444 779 044 095 486.5	1.5×10^{-15}	Second
^{88}Sr neutral atom	429 228 066 418 007.0	6×10^{-16}	–
^{87}Sr neutral atom	429 228 004 229 873.0	4×10^{-16}	Second
^{40}Ca+ ion	411 042 129 776 399.8	2.4×10^{-15}	–
^{87}Rb	6 834 682 610.904 312 6	6×10^{-16}	Second

time scale. This scale is more stable and more accurate than that of any individual contributing clocks. The scale is based on the results of local clock comparisons in the laboratory. These atomic time scales are generally designated TA(k) for laboratory k.

Optimal combination of all the results of comparisons between the clocks maintained in the national time-service laboratories results in a world reference time scale, International Atomic Time (TAI). Responsibility for TAI was accepted by the CIPM and transferred from the Bureau International de l'Heure to the BIPM on 1 January 1988.

6.1.5   Terrestrial Time (TT), Geocentric Coordinate Time (TCG)

TAI is a coordinate time scale defined in a geocentric reference frame with the SI second as realized on the rotating geoid as the scale unit. This definition was amplified by the International Astronomical Union in 1991, as TAI is a realized time scale whose ideal form, neglecting a constant offset of 32.184 s, is Terrestrial Time (TT). This is related to the time coordinate of the geocentric reference frame, Geocentric Coordinate Time (TCG), by a constant rate.

TAI (International Atomic Time) is processed in two steps:

1. A weighted average based on some 420 clocks maintained under metrological conditions in about 70 laboratories is first calculated. The algorithm used is optimized for long-term stability, which requires observation of the behaviour of clocks over a long duration. In consequence, TAI is a deferred-time time scale, available with a delay of a few weeks. In 2013, the relative frequency stability of TAI was estimated to three parts in 10^{16} for mean duration of 1 month.

2. The frequency accuracy of TAI is then evaluated by comparing the TAI scale unit with various realizations of the SI second produced by primary frequency standards. This requires the application of a correction to compensate for the relativistic frequency shift between the location of the primary standard and a fixed point on a conventional surface of equal gravity potential, very close to the rotating geoids. Between points fixed on the surface of the Earth, the magnitude of this correction is of the order of 1 part in 10^{16} per metre of altitude. During 2013, the fractional deviation between the TAI scale unit and the SI second on the rotating geoid was a few parts in 10^{16}, and was known with a standard uncertainty of about 3×10^{-16}. Both numerical values change slightly from month to month and are reported in the BIPM *Circular T*. This difference is monthly reduced whenever necessary by steering the frequency of TAI through the application of corrections, of magnitude a few parts in 10^{16}. This method improves the accuracy of TAI while not degrading its middle-term stability.

6.1.6   Coordinated Universal Time (UTC)

TAI is not distributed directly in everyday life. The time in common use, broadcast by radio, television, the speaking clock, etc., is referred to a time scale called Coordinated Universal Time (UTC). UTC differs from TAI by a whole number of seconds, for example, $UTC - TAI = -35$ s, until at least 1 January 2014. This difference can be modified in steps of 1 s, using a positive or negative leap second, in order to keep UTC in agreement with the time defined by the rotation of the Earth such that, when averaged over a year, the Sun crosses the Greenwich meridian at noon UTC to within 0.9 s. In addition, the legal time of most countries is offset from UTC by a whole number of hours to establish time zones and summer time.

National time-service laboratories, which contribute to the formation of TAI at the BIPM, maintain an approximation of UTC, known as UTC(k) for laboratory k, which in some cases represents the basis of the legal time in those countries. UTC is disseminated monthly through the publication of the offsets $[UTC - UTC(k)]$ at 5-day intervals. These offsets amount to only a few tens of nanoseconds for about 20 of the 70 laboratories involved. Since January 2005, the uncertainties on these offsets have also been given in the BIPM *Circular T*.

6.2   Practical Realization of the Metre

Consultative Committee for length (CCL) recommended that the metre be realized by one of the following methods:

1. By means of the length l of the path travelled by a plane electromagnetic wave in the time t, this length is obtained from the measured value of time t, taking the velocity of light in vacuum c as exact and using the relation

   i.   length $= c \cdot t$,
   ii. where $c = 299\ 792\ 458$ ms^{-1} exact.

2. By means of wavelength in vacuum λ of a plane electromagnetic wave of frequency f, this wavelength is obtained from the measured frequency f, using the relation

3. $\lambda = c/f$.

4. By means of any one of the radiations given in Table 6.2 whose stated wavelength in vacuum or whose frequency can be used with uncertainty shown in column 5 of Table 6.2, provided that the given specifications and accepted good practices are followed.

In all cases, every necessary correction should be applied to take into account actual conditions such as diffraction, gravitation or imperfection in vacuum.

Taking wavelength λ in terms of the metre amounts to the definition that one metre will contain $1/\lambda$ number of waves of a particular radiation. For example,

Table 6.2 Standard radiations recommended by CCL

Element	Absorbing ion	Frequency kHz	Wavelength fm	Uncertainty
Indium	^{115}In	1 267 402 452 899.92	236 540 853.549 75	3.6×10^{-13}
Hydrogen	^{1}H	1 233 030 706 593.55	243 134 624.626 04	2.0×10^{-13}
Mercury	^{199}Hg	1 064 721 609 899. 143	281 568 867.591 969	1.9×10^{-14}
Ytterbium	^{171}Yb	688 358 979 309. 312	435 517 610.739 69	2.9×10^{-14}
Ytterbium	^{171}Yb	642 121 496 772.3	466 878 090.060 7	1.6×10^{-12}
Iodine	^{127}I$_2$	582 490 603 442	514 673 466.368	1.8×10^{-11}
Iodine	^{127}I$_2$	563 260 223 513	532 245 036.104	8.9×10^{-12}
Iodine	^{127}I$_2$	551 580 162 400	543 515 663.608	4.5×10^{-11}
Iodine	^{127}I$_2$	520 206 808.4 MHz	576 294 760.4	4×10^{-10}
Krypton	^{86}Kr	–	605 780 210.3	1.3×10^{-9}
Iodine	^{127}I$_2$	489 880 354.9 MHz	611 970 770.0	3×10^{-10}
Iodine	^{127}I$_2$	473 612 353 604	632 991 212.58	2.1×10^{-11}
Iodine	^{127}I$_2$	468 218 332.4 MHz	640 283 468.7	4.5×10^{-10}
Calcium	^{40}Ca	455 986 240 494. 150	657 459 439.291 67	1.1×10^{-13}
Strontium	^{88}Sr	444 779 044 095.5	674 025 590.863 1	2.2×10^{-13}
Rubidium	^{85}Rb	385 285 142 375	778 105 421.23	1.3×10^{-11}
C_2H_2	13C_2H_2	194 369 569 385	1 542 383 712.37	5×10^{-11}
CH_4	CH_4 molecule	88 376 181 600.18	3 392 231 397.327	3×10^{-12}
Osmium tetroxide	OsO_4 molecule	29 054 057 446. 579	10 318 436 884.460	1.4×10^{-13}

wavelength of ^{86}Kr is 605 780 210.3 fm giving us 1650 763.73 wavelengths make a metre, same definition as that of 11th CGPM (1960). But the uncertainty of measurement in using ^{86}Kr definition was only 10^{-9}. Taking velocity of light as exact and measuring frequency, uncertainty decreases by several orders of magnitude. For example, by measuring frequency of a particular transition of ^{198}Hg, wavelength comes 281 568 867.591 969 fm defining one metre equal to 3551 529.006 wavelengths of that radiation but with an uncertainty of 1.9×10^{-14}, which is the measurement uncertainty of frequency. This is five orders of magnitude better than metre was defined in terms of a particular radiation of ^{86}Kr. This is the clear advantage of taking velocity of light as exact and measuring the frequency and deriving wavelength from the relation.

$$\lambda = c/f.$$

6.2.1 Standard Radiations

The Consultative Committee on length (CCL) recommended a number of radiations covering the entire range from ultraviolet ($\lambda = 237$ nm) to far infrared ($\lambda = 10.3$ μm). The frequency of these radiations is measured with a very small uncertainty and their wavelengths are calculated by taking the fixed value of velocity of light.

A list of radiations recommended by the Consultative Committee on Length (CCL) as on 2006 is given in Table 6.2 [1]. Column 1 gives the element and column 2 the absorbing ion. Measured frequency of the radiation and measurement uncertainty are, respectively, given in columns 3 and 5. Calculated wavelength is given in column 4.

6.3 Practical Realization of the Kilogram (via Kibble Balance)

Having defined the kilogram so that the Planck constant h has a specified magnitude in SI base units, it has become necessary to describe methods of realization of kilogram in terms of h with the required uncertainty. There are two independent methods which can be used for this purpose. One method is through the use of electromechanical including Kibble balance [2] and the other is to compare the unknown mass to the mass of a single crystal with known isotopic composition and lattice constant. The method is termed as XRCD method [3].

6.3.1 Electromechanical (Kibble) Balances

The mass of an artefact A is determined in two modes: the weighing mode and the moving mode. Depending upon the design of the electromechanical balance, the two modes may occur successively or simultaneously. The observations relate mechanical to electric power from where we get the mass of standard mass piece in terms of uniform velocity, Josephson constant, von Klitzing constant and acceleration due to gravity.

The two modes of operations are illustrated in Figs. 6.1 and 6.2.

In the weighing mode, the weight mg of the artefact is balanced by the electromagnetic force produced on a circular coil of wire length l immersed in a radial magnetic field of flux density B when a current I_1 flows through the coil. The magnet and coil geometries are designed to produce a force that is parallel to the local gravitational acceleration. The acceleration of gravity g acting on the mass and the current I_1 flowing in the coil are measured simultaneously so that

$$mg = I_1 Bl. \tag{6.1}$$

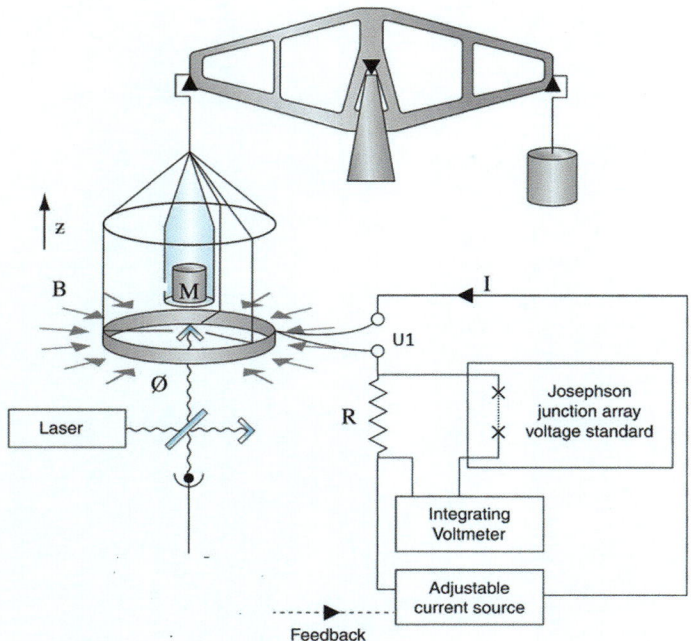

Fig. 6.1 Kibble balance weighing mode

In the moving mode, the voltage V, which is induced across the terminals of the same coil moving vertically at a velocity u through the same magnetic flux density, is measured, so that

$$U_2 = uBl. \tag{6.2}$$

Eliminating Bl from the two equations, we get

$$mgu = I_1 U_2. \tag{6.3}$$

Thus, power of a mechanical nature is equated to power of an electromagnetic nature. The powers are manifestly "virtual" in this method of operation because power does not figure in either mode of this two-mode experiment.

The current I_1 can, for example, be determined using Ohm's law by measuring the voltage drop U_1 across the terminals of a stable resistor of value R. Both voltages, U_1 and U_2, are measured in terms of the Josephson constant, K_J. The K_J is taken as twice the ratio of charge e to the Plank constant h, i.e.

$$K_J = 2e/h.$$

Here e is the elementary charge. Similarly, R can be measured in terms of the von Klitzing constant R_K which is taken equal to h/e^2. The quantities u and g are measured in their respective SI units, m·s^{-1} and m·s^{-2}.

It may be noted that $K_J^2 \times R_K = 4/h$, thus allowing (6.3) to be rewritten as

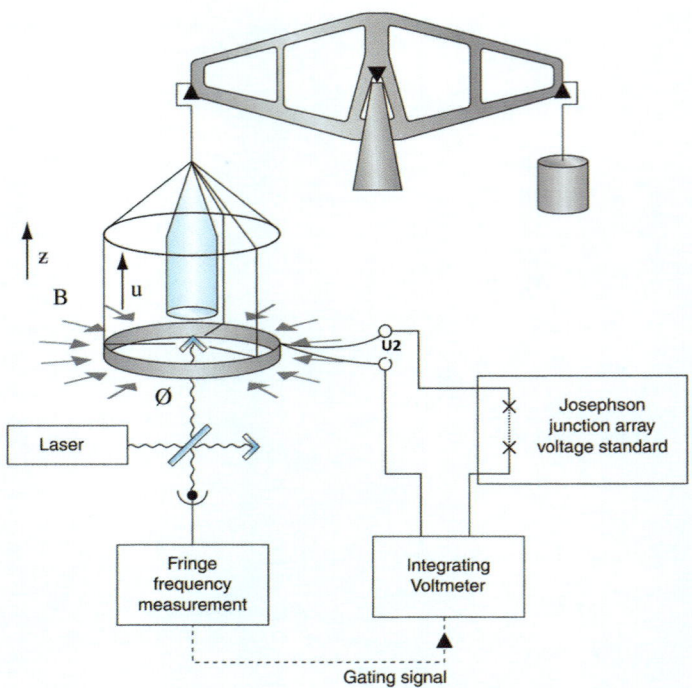

Fig. 6.2 Kibble balance moving mode

$$m = h\frac{bf^2}{4}\frac{1}{gu}.\tag{6.4}$$

Here f is an experimental frequency and b is a dimensionless experimental quantity, both associated with the required measurements of electrical current and voltage. All relevant influences on the mass, m, as derived from (6.4) must be considered for the realization, maintenance and dissemination of the unit of mass.

Other electromagnetic and electrostatic realizations have been proposed, such as the joule-balance and volt-balance methods. These may well be perfected in future.

However, to achieve an uncertainty 1 in 10^8, lot of equipment is needed and necessary precautions and corrections are to be applied. These are taken up along with measurement of parameter described below.

6.3.1.1 Measurement of Velocity (U)

- Normally the nominal value of u is 0.1 mm·s^{-1}, but this needs to be known with a uncertainty of one in 10^{-8}, and hence displacement should be measured with a precision of 3 nm. So naturally a good fringe counting interferometer is required.
- The correction to wavelength must be applied if measurement of u is carried out in air or in partial vacuum.
- The frequency of laser light should be stabilized.

6.3.1.2 Measurement of Mass

- Normally mass of the weight used in Kibble balance is measured in air, if a Kibble balance is operated in air, the apparent weight of the mass is compared to the force generated by the coil. So an upward buoyancy force will act along the electromagnetic force. Under these circumstances, the effects of air buoyancy do not cancel and the results must be corrected for its full effect which is approximately 500 parts in 10^6 for a silicon mass.
- For a beam balance, the mass pan is suspended at the end of the beam by a flexure or a knife-edge. If the mass piece is not centred on the mass pan, a torque will work to this pivot. Due to the finite stiffness of real pivots, a fraction of this torque is transmitted to the beam. This torque can cause a measurement bias, referred to as corner loading error. This error can be reduced by implementing multiple pivot points between the mass pan and the beam. With each pivot point the amount of torque that is transmitted up the linkage is substantially lowered.
- The mass pan can be designed such that the mass piece on it is self-centring. Then the mass slides to the centre of the balance pan with each mass exchange. A couple of weighings using such a design will reduce the corner loading effect.
- A pendulum motion of the mass pan can increase the noise of the watt balance, substantially increasing the number of cycles required for the mass self-centring action described above and possibly introduce a measurement bias. Therefore, it is desirable to damp the pendulum motion of the mass pan. An interesting possibility to damp the mass pan motion is to use sloshing liquids in a sealed ring channel mounted to the mass pan.
- For the correct operation, the mass comparator needs to be aligned with respect to the vertical. Otherwise, the weighing cell will become sensitive to horizontal forces. This sensitivity can be used to align the weighing cell.

6.3.1.3 Measurement of g

- To derive the mass m from the weight mg, it is necessary to know the value of the acceleration due to gravity g at the centre of gravity of the mass during the weighing phase of the measurement. The corrections due to its variability are also applied, for which we need instruments and actions.

- **Absolute gravimeters**

The absolute gravimeters measure g in SI units with an uncertainty of a few parts in 10^9. Such absolute gravimeters are expensive instruments and are time-consuming to set up and operate. Thus, a number of procedures are described below to avoid absolute gravimeters.

- **Relative gravimeters**

These instruments are small, easy to move, easy to operate and are usually used for three-dimensional gravity surveys of Kibble balance laboratories.

- **Gravity surveys**

It is important to carry out a gravitational survey to determine the vertical and horizontal gravitational gradients at the location where a Kibble balance is to be installed. A more thorough survey will provide a three-dimensional map of the site from which the optimum locations of the Kibble balance and gravimeter can be determined.

6.3.1.4 Corrections

A number of corrections must be applied when an accurate value of g at the centre of gravity of the mass from a set of raw measurements of g made by an absolute gravimeter.

- *Speed of light correction*: This correction is applied in the gravimeter software and reflects the fact that, at the required uncertainty of the measurement, the speed of light cannot be considered to be infinite with respect to the velocity of the falling object.
- *Horizontal correction*: This correction is determined by the survey and should be taken stable unless significant masses have been moved in the vicinity of the gravimeter or Kibble balance. Ideally it should be zero but in practice, due to the location of masses such as room walls, it is often a few parts in 10^9.
- *Vertical correction*: Part of this correction arises from gradients measured during the survey. It is useful to design the Kibble balance so that the height of the mass pan is close to part of the drop of the gravimeter which reduces the height difference, the size of the vertical correction and thereby its uncertainty.

The final correction will depend on the value determined from the survey, any change to the height of the reference plane of the mass pan and the height of the centre of gravity of the mass above the reference plane of the mass pan.

- *Atmospheric pressure*:

The measured value of *g* will be decreased if the local barometric pressure increases. Usually a single coefficient is used to calculate the correction to *g* from the measured barometric pressure. This assumes that the pressure in the region a few kilometres around the Kibble balance is uniform which is usually reasonable except under stormy conditions. Some modern laboratories have air conditioning systems which raise the pressure inside the laboratory. Under these circumstances, it is necessary to ensure that the barometer used for the measurements is recording the outside air pressure.

- *Ocean loading correction*

The Earth is an elastic body and due to high tides the Earth expands, and hence a correction due to change in height caused by the tidal motion of seawater is applied. The correction depends on the location of the Kibble balance with respect to large bodies of tidal water. In many cases, the correction is small and can be ignored.

- *Earth rotational axis (polar motion) correction*

The rotation of the Earth about its axis provides an acceleration of the laboratory frame of reference which affects the measured value of *g*. If the Earth rotated about a fixed axis, the effect would be constant. Unfortunately, the point at which the instantaneous rotational axis of the Earth intersects the surface of the Earth moves very slowly in a spiral pattern. The location of this point is monitored and its location is published online by the International Earth Rotation and Reference Systems Service (IERS) from which a correction can be calculated. This effect is also referred to as polar motion.

- *Self-mass correction*

Both the gravimeter and the Kibble balance contain parts which have significant masses. For a typical gravimeter, the associated correction of *g* is a few parts in 10^9 but for a Kibble balance the correction associated with the magnet can easily be 20 parts in 10^9 and other parts of the apparatus will have smaller effects. There are presently two ways to achieve a low uncertainty due to this correction. A finite element model can be used to calculate the gravitational field and its gradient near the mass pan to allow the appropriate correction to be applied at the centre of gravity of the working mass. Alternatively, a relative gravimeter can be placed in the area usually occupied by the mass pan to measure the difference in *g* from a local reference point and the vertical gradient near the pan. This technique depends on having a sufficiently low magnetic field in the vicinity of the mass pan to operate the gravimeter and a large enough space to accommodate the instrument.

- Pressure effect

At a room temperature of 22 °C and an atmospheric pressure of 100 kPa, the density of air is 1.2 kg m^{-3} approximately and the density of a silicon mass standard (one of the lowest density mass standards) is 2300 kg m^{-3}. The buoyancy correction which is about 500 parts in 10^6 is to be applied. However, this correction is difficult to calculate accurately because the density of the air is dependent on its temperature, pressure and composition. By reducing the air pressure to below 0.1 Pa, the buoyancy correction is much less than 1 part in 10^9. Most Kibble balances, therefore, are operated at such pressures to ensure that both the buoyancy and refractive index corrections become negligible. The reduction in pressure also affects the surface films on the mass and the resulting changes in mass are time dependent and may exhibit hysteresis with variations of pressure.

- *Magnetic forces on the mass*

All mass standards, including platinum–iridium and stainless steel, have a finite magnetic susceptibility, which can affect their apparent weight when in the spatially varying magnetic field of a Kibble balance. If the effect cannot be shown to be negligible, then it should require correction, which if estimated correctly and applied would decrease the uncertainty of the measured mass. To minimize this effect, many recent Kibble balances use magnets having a closed magnetic circuit which reduces both the stray field and its gradient, thereby reducing the effect considerably. Also research has been carried out to find materials with low magnetic susceptibilities which have the correct mechanical properties to make excellent mass standards. The application of both of these techniques can reduce corrections for the magnetic susceptibility to much less than 20 parts in 10^9.

The Kibble balance operates under vacuum and it takes many hours for a freshly pumped balance to stabilize. The pumping can produce temperature changes in the magnet and the moving parts of balance outgas at different, but slowly reducing, rates both of which disturb the weighing measurements. If the balance has to be opened every time the working mass has to be changed, much time can be lost via this mechanism. Some Kibble balances [4] now incorporate mechanisms for storing a number of working masses inside the vacuum chamber and provide mechanisms for loading a selected mass into the balance. Such a mass exchanger allows many comparative investigations to be carried out relatively rapidly.

These days load locks are provided in Kibble balance. The load locks allow only selected mass to go into the balance chamber, and the rest remain stored on the mass exchanger. This allows a large number of masses to be measured by the Kibble balance in an efficient manner which is a great advantage for routine operation.

The NIST Kibble balance is fitted with both a mass exchanger and a load lock to aid its use in maintaining national and international standards of mass. Both of these are likely to become far more common features of Kibble balances in the near future.

6.3.2 Constant Magnetic Field (Generation)

A fairly strong, radial magnetic field of say 0.9 T (Tesla) is required. Moreover, the magnetic flux density B should remain constant within a few parts in 10^9 throughout the duration of the two operating modes of Kibble balance. It is, therefore, necessary to discuss about the magnets used in the Kibble balance.

6.3.2.1 Magnets

In general, a magnetic field can be produced by a polarized ferromagnetic material or by a current. In the latter case, the current can flow through either a conventional or a superconducting coil. All three types of sources have been used to build Kibble balances. However, most of the laboratories used permanent magnets. The designs of permanent magnets are, generally cheaper, simpler and easier to use. The main disadvantage of using the permanent magnets is that the magnetic flux density cannot be varied over a large range. It can be useful for the experimenter to change the magnitude of the field to study systematic effects. Electromagnets, on the other hand, can be easily changed to different values by adjusting the current in the coils. However, they require a proper feedback system to give sufficiently constant current during normal operations. This is not a trivial task to keep current stability of 10^{-8}.

6.3.2.2 Design for the Magnet System

Every current Kibble balance uses a magnetic field for its operation. In the ideal case, the field is purely radial at the weighing position, i.e. it has no vertical component

$$B_z = 0. \tag{6.5}$$

The purpose of the magnet system is to provide the magnetic field at the weighing position of the coil and a few centimetres above and below this position. As discussed above, the radial component B_r is only weakly dependent on the vertical coil position z, and in the ideal case $\delta B_r / \delta z = 0$.

Most efficient way to generate a magnetic field is through a permanent magnet system. A permanent magnet system is typically constructed of two different materials, namely, (i) an active magnetic material, such as Samarium–Cobalt and (ii) a material that guides the flux. Mild steel is often used for this purpose. The magnetic flux is concentrated into an annular gap that houses the coil. Currently, all existing Kibble balances use one or more circular coils with a vertical axis of symmetry. The NPL/NRC Kibble balance uses two circular coils mounted on a single former. The two coils are connected in series opposition and are vertically displaced in two different air gaps.

Four different arrangements of the yoke and the active magnetic material are in use today. It is shown in Fig. 6.3. The two designs shown on the left of Fig. 6.3, the NPL design and the LNE design, allow access to the complete gap from the top. The coil can easily be inserted into the gap. In the BIPM and MSL designs, the coil is completely surrounded by the magnet; therefore, holes in the top or bottom yoke piece allow the penetration of rods that connect the coil to the balance and stirrup system. After the coil has been placed into the magnet system during construction, it needs to be closed. Different strategies are used to close the magnet. The top plate of the original BIPM magnet consists of sectors. After the coil is placed in the gap, the sectors are put in place, completing the magnetic circuit on the top. Using sectors instead of a monolithic top plate keeps the magnetic forces at a manageable level. The researchers at NIST completely split the magnet into two parts, insert the coil and rejoin the magnet.

All magnets exhibit rotational symmetry around the dashed line in the centre. The grey-shaded parts concentrate the flux and are typically manufactured of

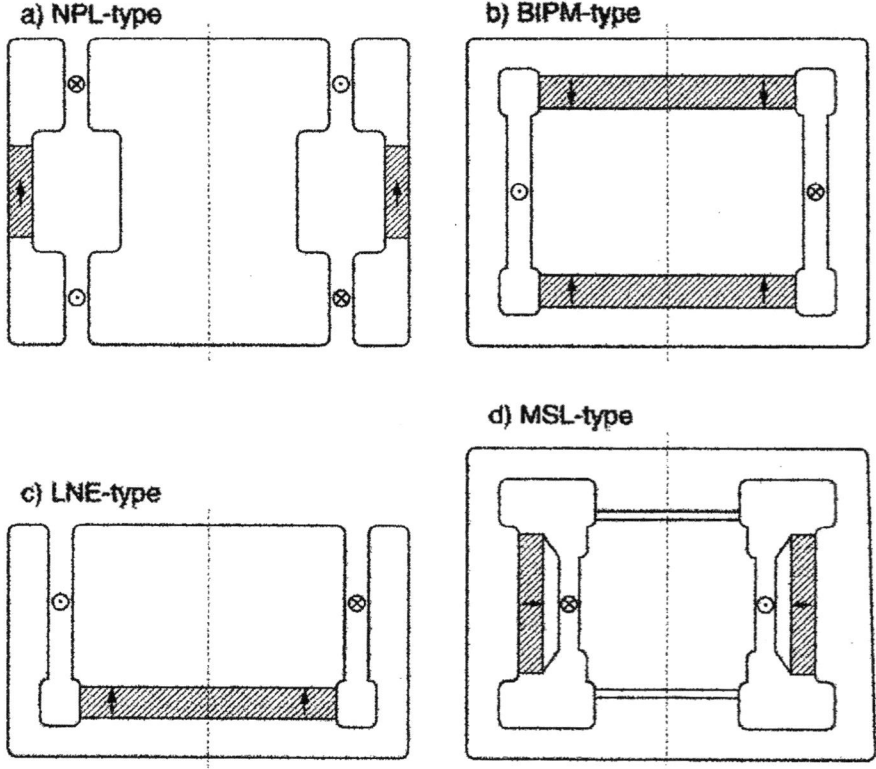

Fig. 6.3 Schematic drawings of four types of permanent magnets

mild steel. The hatched parts represent the active magnetic material. The arrows indicate a possible direction of the magnetic polarization of the material: (a) NPL type, (b) BIPM type, (c) LNE type and (d) MSL type.

This procedure needs a dedicated sturdy device because the magnetic forces can be quite large, in excess of 10 kN. The BIPM and MSL designs achieve a flat field at the weighing position because this position is in a horizontal plane of mirror symmetry.

In the NPL and LNE design, a flat field can be achieved by carefully engineering the width of the gap as a function of vertical position.

Besides the arrangement of the active magnetic material and yoke, other design parameters are as follows:

- the useful height of the gap, (gh);
- the width of the gap, (gw);
- the mean radius of the coil rc and
- the strength of the magnetic flux density at the coil position $\frac{\partial \emptyset}{\partial z}$.

Note. The column labelled Bg gives the magnetic flux density along the radial direction in the centre of the gap. The details of magnets used by different laboratories are given in Table 6.3.

One can observe from Table 6.3 that

- The magnetic flux density at the mean radius of the coil varies from 0.42 T to 0.95 T. The gap width ranges from 8 mm to 30 mm. The smallest usable height of the coil is 34 mm and the largest is 100 mm. The nominal coil radius is between 72 and 215 mm. The geometric factor,
- $BL = \frac{\partial \emptyset}{\partial z}$, approximately the product of the coil's nominal circumference, the magnetic flux density at this position and the number of turns. For the available data, the geometric factor ranges from 300 T· m to 1250 T· m.
- The flatness of the field at the weighing position, $\frac{\partial B_r}{\partial z}$ at $z = 0$, is an important concern.

Typically two measurements are performed in the weighing mode, named mass off and mass on. Depending on the compliance of the coil support and the details

Table 6.3 Parameters of the magnets of eight different laboratories

Laboratory	Bg T	gw mm	gh mm	rc mm	$\frac{\partial \emptyset}{\partial z}$ Tm	Type	References
BIPM	0.6	13	80	125	500	BIPM	[118]
KRISS	0.73	25	60	208	462	BIPM	[14]
LNE	0.95	9	60	134	536	LNE	[79]
METAS	0.64	8	50	100	757	BIPM	[83]
MSL	0.6	16	100	120	420	MSL	[119]
NRC	0.42	24	102	170	300	NPL	–
NIST	0.55	30	80	215	710	BIPM	[81]
UME	0.55	10	34	72	1250	BIPM	[31]

of the balance control, the coil can be at two different vertical positions for each of these two measurements. The substitution measurement that is carried out during force mode can be written in one equation as

$$I_{\text{off}} L\, B(z_{\text{off}}) = I_{\text{On}} LB(z_{\text{On}}) - Mg. \tag{6.6}$$

Instead of using the positions of the coil coordinates during mass on and mass off, the difference and mean values have been used. These are

$$\bar{z} = \left(z_{on} + z_{off}\right)/2 \tag{6.7}$$

$$\Delta z = (Z_{\text{on}} - Z_{\text{off}}) \tag{6.8}$$

$$I_A = (I_{on} + I_{off})/2 \tag{6.9}$$

and

$$\delta I = \left(I_{On} - I_{Off}\right)/2. \tag{6.10}$$

Here, I_A, the current amplitude, is a large positive number and ΔI is a small number which indicates how symmetric the mass-on and mass-off currents are about zero current. Replacing these variables and solving (6.4) for the weight of the test mass yields after expanding the result in a Taylor series up to second order in Δz and δI,

$$Mg = I_A LB(z) \left\{ 1 + \frac{\partial I}{\partial z} \frac{\partial B/\partial z}{B(\bar{z})} + \frac{(\Delta z)^2}{2} \frac{\partial^2 B}{\partial z^2} \right\}. \tag{6.11}$$

The second term in the parenthesis on the right side of the above equation can be made zero by adjusting the currents such that they are equal and opposite, $\delta I = 0$. In traditional Kibble balances, the current offset δI is adjusted by adding or removing a small amount of mass on the tare side of the balance.

Assuming a finite Δz the third term can only be made zero if the second derivative of the radial field with respect to z is zero. The effect of the third term is usually negligible as it contains the square of Δz which is small. According to recent reports on watt balances, typical relative changes of the magnetic flux over the height of the gap to be about 10^{-4}. Assuming a quadratic profile and a gap height of 8 cm, $(\delta^2 B/\delta z^2)/B$ is 0.125 m^{-2}. Combining this value with $\Delta z = 10\ \mu$m, third term in the parentheses on the right side of (6.9) yields 6.3×10^{-12} This number is more than three orders of magnitude smaller than the typical uncertainties achieved by Kibble balances. In conclusion, the field flatness does not play a major role in the weighing mode as long as the weighing currents are symmetric about zero.

A flat field is also desired for the moving mode. The electrical measurements benefit if the induced electromotive force (EMF) stays constant as a function of time. In this case, an equal and opposite voltage can be added to the EMF and a null measurement with high gain can be made. If the profile is flat, it is easy to achieve a constant EMF by moving the coil with constant velocity. If the field changes significantly over the region where measurements take place, the coil velocity may have to be varied slightly to maintain a constant EMF. This is not difficult but the variation can often be absorbed by the dynamic range of the voltmeter used for the measurement.

6.3.2.3 Effect of the Weighing Current on the Magnetic Flux Density

One important assumption for the two-mode two-measurement-phase Kibble balances is that the geometric factor is the same in the weighing and the moving mode. However, in the weighing mode, the coil carries a current and in the moving mode it does not. The current causes ohmic heating and a magnetic field. Both effects can change the BL between the modes. A popular model for the dependence of the magnetic field on the current has been introduced by researchers at NPL [5].

The magnetic flux density is written as

$$B(I) = Bo\left(1 + \alpha I + \beta I^2\right).$$ (6.12)

Rewriting (6.4) to reflect the change in B as a function of current is

$$I_{\text{Off}} LB(I_{\text{Off}}) = I_{\text{On}} LB(I_{\text{On}}) - Mg.$$ (6.13)

Using

$$I_{\text{On}} = \delta I + I_A$$

and

$$I_{\text{Off}} = \delta I - I_A$$

yields

$$Mg = 2LB_o I_A \left(1 + 2\alpha \delta I + 3\beta \delta I^2 + \beta I_A^2 I\right).$$ (6.14)

There are three correction terms to the unbiased term, $2B_o I_A$.

The first two terms are proportional to the current asymmetry. These vanish, if the weighing current for the mass-off state is exactly equal and opposite to the current in the mass on state. The final term, βI_A^2, is proportional to the current amplitude squared. This term can introduce a serious bias to the Kibble balance experiment but its magnitude can be estimated by using test masses with different mass values. For example, the relative size of this effect would quadruple, if a 0.5 kg test mass is replaced by a 1 kg test mass. Note that introducing another odd term in (6.10) yields another term proportional to δI. Only even powers of I produce bias terms which depend on I_A.

While the methods above provide an experimental way to estimate the magnet non-linearity, they do not provide a reason for the effect. Several possibilities exist to provide an explanation.

6.3.2.4 Demagnetization of the Rare Earth Magnets

The current in the coil adds or subtracts, depending on the sign of the current, a magnetic field to the demagnetizing field in the magnet. This shifts the working point along the recoil curve of the material, which can change the magnetic flux density in the gap of the permanent magnet. By using a symmetrical design, two permanent magnets or two coils, this effect can be reduced. This effect is mostly proportional to I since the recoil curve is very linear for rare earth magnets.

6.3.3   Change of the Reluctance of the Yoke

The magnetic field produced by the coil adds to the magnetic field produced by the permanent magnet and can change the relative permeability of the yoke material, which depends on a non-linear function on the magnetic field. Consequently, the reluctance of the yoke changes, which causes a change in magnetic flux density in the air gap. This effect is, of first order, proportional to I^2.

6.3.3.1   The Reluctance Force

An iron core gets pulled inside a solenoid if it is energized, because in this position the magnetic energy of the system is minimal and so is the reluctance of the field path. The same is true for a coil inside a yoke. It experiences a force towards the point where the reluctance of the yoke completing the magnetic circuit of the coil is minimal [5]. This effect does not change BL; instead, it generates a force. This force is proportional to I^2; hence, it would cancel if the currents were symmetric about zero. However, it is more complicated, because the coil moves between the mass-on and mass-off states due to the suspension's finite spring constant. Hence, this effect can produce a different force on the coil, even if the current is absolutely symmetric.

6.3.4   Temperature Change of the Rare Earth Magnet

The magnetic material gets heated up due to the current passing through the coil. With increasing temperature, the remanence of the material decreases causing a decrease of the magnetic flux density in the air gap.

There are two ways of mitigating this effect: (1) by engineering a better magnet and (2) by actively heating the magnet in moving mode to keep the thermal load on the magnet constant during all modes of the Kibble balance experiment. This effect is proportional to the ohmic heating, i.e. I^2.

6.3.5 Temperature Change of the Yoke Material

This effect is much smaller than the effect of changing the temperature of the active magnetic material, but it is listed for completeness. A changing temperature of the magnet system can change the reluctance of the yoke material and the geometry of the yoke, e.g. the width of the gap, through thermal expansion. Both effects change the magnetic flux density in the gap. This effect is also proportional to I^2.

6.3.6 Engineering of Magnets with Smaller Temperature Coefficients

The preferred active magnetic material is samarium–cobalt, Sm_2Co_{17}, a rare Earth magnet. A typical energy density of this sintered material is about 250 kJ m^{-3}. Double this energy density is provided by neodymium–iron–boron magnets.

However, for neodymium magnets, the Curie temperature, the temperature where a magnetic material loses its magnetization, is low, about 310 °C. Consequently, it has a large temperature coefficient of its remanence (of order 10^{-3} K^{-1}). In contrast, samarium–cobalt has a Curie temperature of about 800 °C and its temperature coefficient is about a third of that of neodymium.

For a typical Sm_2Co_{17} magnet, the temperature coefficient of the flux density is about -3×10^{-4} K^{-1}. If the magnet changes its temperature by -1 mK, the magnetic flux density changes by 3×10^{-7}, a number that is about a 10 times larger than the relative uncertainty reached with Kibble balances. This is only acceptable, because the temperature drift is usually very slow compared to the cadence of taking data. By using an appropriate data sequence and data analysis, most of the drift can be rejected in the final result. In recent years, magnet designs with much smaller temperature coefficients have been proposed. The data collected with these magnets will be quieter and it is less probable that the result includes a bias caused by temperature drift.

Researchers at METAS have designed a magnet system that uses gadolinium–samarium–cobalt [6] instead of samarium–cobalt as the active magnetic material. Alloying gadolinium to the samarium–cobalt reduces the temperature coefficient from -3×10^{-4} K^{-1} to -1×10^{-5} K^{-1} at the expense of reducing the remanence by 30%. Besides using a better magnet alloy, another technique has been implemented in the METAS magnet system: temperature compensation with a shunt. This idea has previously been suggested by LNE [7]. The magnet system has a second return path for the magnetic flux. In the first path, the flux goes through the air gap, and in the second path, the flux goes through a magnetic shunt made from an iron–nickel alloy with very low Curie temperature. Both flux paths are in parallel to each other. With rising temperature, the reluctance of the shunt path increases, which forces a larger fraction of the magnetic flux through the air gap. The thickness of the shunt can be finely tuned such that the increase in flux through the air gap is exactly equal and opposite to the loss of magnetization in the magnetic material. Hence, the magnetic flux density in the air gap remains constant, independent of the magnet temperature provided that no significant temperature gradients exist within the magnet. With this technique, it seems possible to build a magnet system with a relative temperature coefficient of the magnetic field in the gap within $\pm 10^{-6}$ K^{-1}.

6.3.7   Actively Controlling the Temperature

The relative change of the magnetic field inside the gap is the product of the temperature coefficient and the temperature change. The above section focused on minimizing the temperature coefficient. However, a similar end result can be achieved by reducing the temperature change of the magnet. A temperature change that is coherent with the sequence of the Kibble balance measurements is especially troublesome. Coherent temperature change can arise from several causes. For example, there is ohmic heating by the weighing current in the force mode, while there is none in the velocity mode. Hence, the heating power is modulated in phase with the experiment.

Researchers at NPL have implemented a simple but effective way to cancel this possible systematic effect [8]. The coil former carries a heater coil with the same resistance as that of the moving coil. During moving mode, a current equal to that of the weighing current is passed through the heater coil. The heater is a bifilar coil which does not generate an external magnetic field and therefore does not produce a force on the coil former or an external magnetic field. Besides temperature changes due to power fluctuations inside the Kibble balance experiment, temperature changes from the environment (laboratory) can couple into the measurement.

6.3.8   Voltage Measurements

Voltage measurements are vital for the successful operation of both measurement phases of a Kibble balance. In the weighing phase, it is necessary to measure the 5–20 mA current in the coil by measuring the voltage drop across a resistor.

Usually the resistor is chosen to be between 200 and 50 Ω to generate a voltage of order of 1 V. In the moving phase, most existing Kibble balances move the coil at approximately 1 mm·s^{-1}. This speed is chosen to take a sufficient number of voltage measurements over a practical moving range of around ± 20 mm. The voltage generated by the coil is usually chosen to be around 0.5 V.

In the moving phase, ground vibrations affect the apparent motion of the coil with respect to the magnet; this induces noise voltages in the coil [9, 10]. The interferometer system measures this motion and, in a well-designed system, the voltage and velocity will be precisely correlated. If the measurements of both velocity and voltage are made with a bandwidth greater than that of the interfering ground vibrations, their ratio can be free of vibration-generated noise.

This condition sets a lower limit to the bandwidth of the input stage of the voltage measuring system of a few 100 Hz to 1 kHz. Usually the velocity and voltage signals are integrated over the same period and the ratio of average voltage to average velocity is determined by least-squares data fitting. The joule balance uses the same technique of integrating the velocity and voltage signals over the same time but extends the integration time to points at which the coil is stationary.

For the weighing phase, there are no critical requirements for measurement bandwidth and voltage averages obtained by integration over a few seconds usually provide sufficient resolution.

6.3.8.1 Measurement Techniques

A conventional voltmeter can measure voltages with an uncertainty of a few parts in 10^7. To relate the measured voltages to fundamental constants with an uncertainty approaching 1 part in 10^9, the measurements are usually made by connecting an accurate, Josephson-effect-based reference voltage in opposition to the majority of the voltage to be measured and measuring the difference, either directly with a digital voltmeter or, to reduce measurement noise, by a combination of a low-noise amplifier and digital voltmeter. The voltmeter/amplifier is calibrated at the expected values of the difference voltage using the voltage reference. By measuring differences in this way, the combination of voltmeter/reference can measure voltages which are stable at the 0.1–1% level to a few parts in 10^9.

6.3.8.2 Josephson Reference

The Josephson effect allows the construction of extremely precise voltage references by illuminating weak links between superconductors with microwave radiation of frequency f. The voltage generated is a multiple of $hf/2e$. In carefully fabricated and operated devices, the uncertainty of the voltage generated can be much better than 1 part in 10^9. These references are commonly operated at frequencies of either 16 or 75 GHz with associated voltages of 33 μV and 155 μV, respectively. These voltages are too small for practical use at room temperature. However, arrays of these junctions, with output voltages up to 10 V, are available from several laboratories [11–14]. Two types of array have been used for Kibble balance work.

6.3.8.3 Hysteretic Arrays

The hysteretic array uses insulating junctions and can be set to any multiple of $hf/2e$ within its operating range [14]. However, such an array is very sensitive to electrical noise and interference which can cause it to suddenly change its voltage to a different (usually lower) multiple of $hf/2e$ requiring extreme care in its use. Only one Kibble balance (the NPL Mark II [15]) has made direct measurements using such an array.

6.3.8.4   Programmable Arrays

All existing Kibble balances either use or intend to use the programmable Josephson array [16–18] which consists of a string of Josephson junctions with a normal metal substituted for the insulator.

Connections are made to the array to divide it into segments containing numbers of junctions that are usually related in a binary manner. Bias currents of $\pm$ a few mA can be applied to individual segments to generate positive or negative voltages equal to the number of junctions in the segment multiplied by $hf/2e$.

This allows the array to generate any voltage up to $\pm$ its maximum voltage in steps of $hf/2e$. Theoretically, a 75 GHz array can be set to match the voltage to be measured within $155/2 \cong 80\ \mu V$ requiring only a modest linearity and accuracy of the voltmeter measuring the difference.

The programmable array can change its voltage rapidly and this property can be used to simplify the voltage measurement procedure during the moving phase. A good approximation to the voltage generated by the coil can be calculated from the velocity of the coil and the magnetic flux density. This allows the array voltage to be continuously adjusted to null the input to the voltmeter during the acceleration and deceleration of the coil. This eliminates errors due to transient thermal EMFs generated by the switches which would otherwise be necessary to protect the voltmeter/amplifier from overload.

The output voltage of the array is not well defined during the time that it is switching from one voltage state to another so, to ensure the accuracy of the measured voltage, once the coil has reached its target speed [19], the voltage from the array is fixed and any changes are measured via the voltmeter/amplifier.

6.3.9   Voltmeter

In theory, a voltmeter of fairly modest linearity and stability could be used to measure the difference voltages. In practice, the coil voltage noise is dominated by the effects of ground vibrations. In the weighing mode, the resistor voltage contains noise components from the servo system which keeps the balance in equilibrium. These noise sources limit, to around 1000, the gain of the amplifier which amplifies the difference voltage between the voltage source and voltage reference. Therefore, the voltmeter must achieve part in 10^6 level calibration, linearity and stability to achieve an overall measurement uncertainty of a part in 10^9. Modern voltmeters can easily achieve this level of performance but often need time for carrying out internal "auto-zero" procedures to eliminate the effects of drifts in their circuitry. This is not a major problem in the weighing phase of the measurement but does introduce problems in the moving phase where it is desirable to measure the voltage and velocity continuously over identical time intervals. The problem can be addressed by the NIST technique [20] which uses three voltmeters in a cyclic fashion where one is measuring, another is performing auto-zero functions and the third is preparing to measure.

Another way of achieving the same end is to use a single voltmeter preceded by a highly stable preamplifier [8]. This can eliminate the need for auto-zeroing as the effective drift of the voltmeter is reduced by the gain of the preamplifier which becomes one part of the unavoidable linear temporal drifts in the measurement system. The reversals inherent in the measurement procedure allow such drifts to be removed from the measurement in the post-processing calculations. The only problem with the use of a preamplifier is that most preamplifiers with 10^{-9} V level drifts have low bandwidths which may be incompatible with the need to eliminate noise from the moving phase by correlation between the weighing and moving measurements.

6.3.9.1 Amplifiers

Most highly stable 10^{-9} V level DC amplifiers [21, 22] are intended for use in measurements taking many seconds and have low bandwidths. Integrated circuit operational amplifiers can have much higher bandwidths but have unacceptable low-frequency performance: they drift with time. By combining the two types of amplifier, it is possible to assemble a composite amplifier which has a bandwidth of several hundred Hz and 10^{-9} V level drift [8]. This can be achieved by using the low drift amplifier to monitor the difference in voltage between the inverting and non-inverting input pins of the high bandwidth amplifier. A simple servo loop feeding the offset annulling input of the high bandwidth amplifier drives the input voltage to zero ensuring that the composite amplifier is close to the performance of an ideal amplifier at low frequencies. Extreme care must be taken to minimize the effects of thermal EMFs in critical parts of the circuit [8].

6.3.9.2 Synchronization of the Voltmeter and Counter

To eliminate correlated noise between the average voltage and average velocity measurements in the moving phase, it is necessary for the signals to be integrated over the same time and for the bandwidths of both signal channels to be greater than the bandwidth of the noise signal. The velocity signal is a frequency, generated by the laser interferometer, which is measured using a frequency counter. By using passive noise isolation techniques, such as resilient pads in parts of the support structure of the balance, it is possible to limit the bandwidth of vibrational noise to a few hundred hertz. Under these circumstances, differences in the integration times of less than 1 ms will have little effect on the elimination of correlated noise. Many methods of achieving this aim are possible and indeed have been implemented. For illustration, we will describe a method similar to the one used on the NPL Mark II balance [8] but employing a different form of frequency counter. It provides simple and accurate measurements of velocity and voltage with the caveat that the integration times are not identical. The technique uses a charge balance voltmeter and a time interval analyser. Both of these instruments possess the great advantage that they measure continuously. The charge balance voltmeter can be considered to be an integrator with two inputs. The first is connected directly to the voltage to be measured and the second is connected alternately to positive and negative reference voltages. The reference input polarity is switched whenever the output of the integrator reaches one of two fixed limits. The times for which each reference is applied are accumulated and, upon receipt of a trigger pulse, the analogue-to-digital converter (ADC) waits until a whole number of reference switching cycles has taken place and reports the accumulated data. The average value of the input voltage can be calculated from this data and calibration information. The period of the reference switching cycle is chosen to be around 200 μs and varies about this value.

The time interval analyser counts events and notes the time of the first and last event. This allows the average frequency of the events to be calculated but, as the last event of one measurement corresponds to the first event of the next, the counter, like the voltmeter described above, measures its input continuously. Whenever it notes a time it generates an output pulse. This "gate pulse" is used to trigger the voltmeter which will take approximately 200 μs to respond so, on average, the times of the integrals will be shifted by 100 μs with a jitter of ±200 μs. This may cause a slight decrease in the correlation between voltage and velocity signals but both integrals will be correct. There is a further advantage to the back-to-back data collection in that no part of either signal is lost and, if desired, the integration time can be increased in post-processing, giving the ability to analyse and correlate the data at both higher and lower frequencies.

6.3.10   Current Generation and Measurement

In weighing mode, a current is passed through the coil to generate the electromagnetic force. The current continues on through a resistor and the potential difference across this resistor is measured precisely, in a four-terminal geometry, using the techniques described in Sect. 6.3.3. Figure 6.4 shows a simplified circuit diagram of a Kibble balance in weighing mode. Typically, the electromagnetic force is half the weight of the mass standard used in the experiment and the current is reversed, such that the difference of the two electromagnetic forces corresponds to the weight of the mass. In this section, we discuss the current sources, the measurement resistor and the process required to calibrate the measurement resistor using the quantum Hall effect.

Fig. 6.4 Typical circuit
topology during force mode

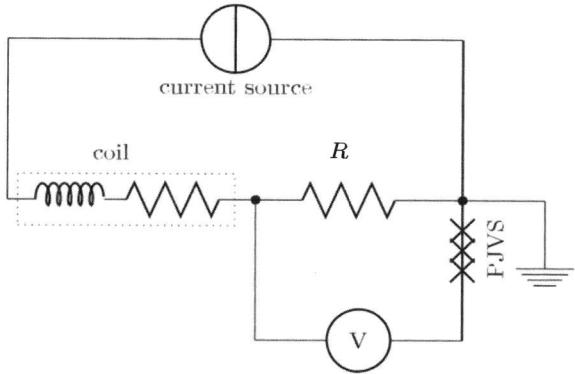

DVM (Digital Voltmeter)
The current is passed through the coil, drawn as an inductive and a resistive element and a measurement resistor. The voltage drop across the measurement resistor is compensated with a programmable Josephson voltage system (PJVS) and the residual voltage is measured with a digital voltmeter (DVM).

6.3.10.1   Current Sources

Typical weighing currents range from a few milliamperes to about 20 mA, given by the quotient of the geometric factor (see column 6 of Table 14.3) and half the weight of the test mass. The current source needs to be able to generate a bi-directional current since the force reverses between the mass-on and mass-off measurements. Properties to consider designing a current source are (1) the impedance to ground, (2) the update rate, (3) the resolution of the digital-to-analogue converter (DAC) and (4) the noise of the current source. Details to each of these design considerations are discussed below. Descriptions of current sources for Kibble balances can be found in [8, 23].

   The current source should be fully isolated to allow the experimenter to choose the point at which the Kibble balance measurement circuit will be connected to the mains ground wire. If the circuit is connected to mains ground at more than one point, parasitic currents can flow which can introduce a bias to the experiment if they flow through the coil or resistor, but not both. For example, a current flowing through the coil but not through the resistor will contribute to the electromagnetic force, but it will not be measured, resulting in a bias in the experiment. In order to avoid such parasitic currents, all elements of the electrical measurement circuit should have a high resistance to ground. High in this context is approximated by dividing the resistance in the measurement circuit by the maximum acceptable bias. For example, the current measurement requires a relative uncertainty of 1 part in 10^9 and a 100 Ω resistor, the resistance to ground should be more than 100 GΩ and would usually be at least 1 TΩ. One possible path of parasitic resistance is via the cables that carry the control signals from the control computer to the current source.

A good way to minimize this leakage path is to employ fibre optical communications between the controller and the current source. Another leakage path is via the power supply for the circuit. This leakage can be eliminated either by powering the current source with batteries or by using a mains power supply which has been carefully isolated. Such a supply is described in [24].

As a rule of thumb, the update rate of the current source should be at least an order of magnitude faster than the closed-loop bandwidth. This reasoning gives a lower bound for the update rate of the current source. The faster the update rate of the current source the better it is. However, the closed-loop system in the weighing mode contains at least two low-pass filters, attenuating the effect of changes at the current set points at high frequencies. The resonance frequency of the mechanical system of the Kibble balance depends on the design but is in the ball park of tenths of Hz to tens of Hz. This leads to an attenuation of the quotient of balance position and coil current at high frequencies. The second low-pass filter is electrical and is given by the inverse of the time constant of the system composed of the self-inductance of the coil and the series resistance of the measurement resistor and the coil, i.e. $\_ = L/R$. For example, a self-inductance of 1 H and a total resistance of 100 Ω yield a time constant of 10 ms. A Kibble balance coil in a permanent magnet has typically an inductance of a few henries. The total resistance is typically below 1 kΩ. Hence, this low-pass filter attenuates the quotient of coil current to applied voltage for frequencies above 1 kHz. This effect can be modified by the internal feedback of the current source.

The simplest design of the current source is a variable voltage source followed by a transconductance amplifier. In this case, the resolution of the current source is given by the resolution of the voltage source. Naively, one would think that in order to measure the current with a relative uncertainty of 10^{-9}, a resolution of 10^{-9} is required. However, this requirement calls for a digital-to-analogue converter (DAC) with 30-bit resolution, which is not commercially available. One technique to obtain sufficient resolution is to add two voltages together with a summing amplifier, where one voltage is attenuated by a voltage divider. In the NPL balance [8], for example, two 16-bit DAC outputs are combined with a relative gain of $-2000:1$. In the NIST Kibble balance [23], two 20-bit DAC outputs are combined with a ratio of 1000:1.

The ADC with the larger gain is used for coarse control of the balance and the one with the smaller gain for fine control. Since the current source is in a closed-loop feedback system, a higher resolution than the nominal resolution will be achieved, because the Kibble balance will average or integrate the applied current with a time constant given by the differential equation of the balance. Hence, the output rate multiplied with this characteristic time gives an effective increase in resolution of the DAC.

The combination of the two DACs will not be linear to their combined resolution but, if the control software is written to minimize unnecessary changes in the output of the more significant DAC, the resolution will, for most of the time, be equal to that of the less significant DAC. When it is necessary to change the

more significant DAC, it is set to centre the less significant DAC in its range; this
increases the time to the next change and its associated small glitch in the combined output. The noise of the current source is one contribution to the measurement noise in the weighing mode and ultimately the type A uncertainty. However,
this part is not likely to be the dominating factor in the measurement noise. In
this context, it is best to think about the current noise in the frequency domain.
Depending on the frequency, the noise level of the current source varies, achieving worst levels at low frequencies due to $1/f$ noise. However, this is not a problem. The critical time scale is given by the bandwidth of the weighing servo.
In weighing mode, the servo adjusts to keep the balance position constant over
many minutes without applying rapid changes of current which would be seen
by the measurement system as noise. In practice, the bandwidth of the servo is
of the order of 1 Hz. The action of the servo eliminates the need for excessive
low-frequency stability in the current source. For some balances, e.g. METAS,
BIPM, a fixed current is required and such circumstances often require a highly
stable current source. However, care should be taken to minimize the noise of
the current source at frequencies higher than the bandwidth of the servo. As the
weighing data is usually taken by a series of averages, each lasting a few seconds,
the sensitivity of the integral used to form the average to high-frequency noise
drops linearly with the frequency of the noise. This indicates that close attention
should be paid to the noise of the source in the region around 1–100 Hz.

In a practical situation, the slow drifts in the balance due to outgassing and temperature changes usually dominate over random noise. If the dynamic range of the
less significant DAC is chosen to ensure that it is many times the change expected
over the duration of a single weighing, the weighing current should be glitch free
during each measurement.

To further reduce the mid-range noise, it is possible, once the balance has stabilized, to reduce the bandwidth of the more significant DAC. As it, and its reference, will contribute the majority of the current source noise, a significant
reduction in its bandwidth should result in a significant reduction in the critical
mid-range noise.

6.3.10.2 The Measurement Resistor

The measurement resistor in the Kibble balance is, typically, a conventional resistor (wire wound or thin film). This conventional resistor is calibrated against a
quantum Hall resistor (QHR) on a regular basis (see next section). It is used in
a four-terminal configuration: two terminals connect to the current leads and two
connect to the potential leads. The potential leads are connected to a voltmeter
with high input impedance. Ideally, no current is flowing in the potential lead, and
hence contact resistances in the potential leads do not bias the measurement.

The measurement resistor is kept either in an air or an oil bath with good temperature stabilization. Nevertheless, the temperature of the bath must be carefully monitored. Most resistors have a linear temperature coefficient of several $\mu\Omega\Omega^{-1}$ K^{-1}.

For certain resistors, in addition to the linear temperature coefficient, a quadratic temperature coefficient must be considered. Besides the temperature dependence, the resistance depends on the measurement current, mostly due to self-heating. A power coefficient, i.e. the change in relative resistance divided by the power dissipated in the resistor, is used to quantify this effect. If the calibration current is different from the current used in the Kibble balance, a power correction may become necessary. Some resistors, with a certain design, require an additional pressure correction which includes changes in the atmospheric pressure and the hydrostatic pressure, exerted by the oil above the resistive element. For these resistors, the ambient atmospheric pressure must also be monitored.

In some cases, the resistor can cause local heating of the oil surrounding it which can cause transient effects at the start of the weighing mode. If the element is surrounded by a can, the removal of the can may allow more efficient mixing of the oil which may reduce the heating effect to acceptable levels. Otherwise, it may be possible to use isolated heaters, near the resistance element, to keep the power dissipation in the oil bath constant.

6.3.10.3 Measurement of Resistance in Terms of QHE

To link mass to the Planck constant the resistor used in the Kibble balance measurement must be related to the quantum Hall effect (QHE). A QHE measurement system consists of a superconducting magnet, a QHE device and a cryogenic current comparator bridge. The QHE device is held in a low-temperature probe in the 5–14 T field of the superconducting magnet. The Hall resistance of the quantized Hall sample is compared to that of the Kibble balance resistor using a cryogenic current comparator [25, 26]. The voltages at the potential terminals of the two resistors are adjusted to be equal by passing different currents through them and the ratio of the resulting currents is measured using a technique which makes use of the Meissner effect. By this means, the Kibble balance resistor can be measured with an uncertainty of a few parts in 10^9.

As mentioned above, the value of the resistor will depend on the power dissipated in it. If possible, the resistor should be calibrated at the currents that are used in the Kibble balance measurements. If this is not possible, a power coefficient must be measured which can then be used to correct the value of the resistor to the operating power. The use of a power coefficient will, in general, increase the uncertainty associated with the resistor.

Ideally, the resistor should be measured in situ, either by using cables [8] over tens of metres or via a transportable QHR measurement system [27]. If it is necessary to transport the resistor to the quantum Hall effect system, extreme care should be taken in the transport arrangements. Mechanical shocks can alter the value of the resistor in an unpredictable way and would increase the uncertainty assigned to the resistance measurement. Extremely good temperature control and monitoring are also required. A thermal shock to the resistor, caused by changing thermal environments during transport, could permanently change its value or its temporal drift. In addition, if the temperature gradients in the enclosure varied from the location of use to the location of measurement, and this affected the temperature difference between the monitoring thermometer and the resistor, the resistor value corrected for temperature would be different at the two locations. The magnitude of this problem can be investigated by changing the temperature gradient across the resistor enclosure at a constant temperature as seen by the monitoring thermometer. There should be no significant correlated changes in the device resistance.

6.3.11   Results

Some results for determination of Planck constant h with the Kibble balance have been given in Table 6.4. First column contains the abbreviated name of the laboratory, while version of the balance used is given in second column, third column contains the values of h obtained with uncertainty, at one standard deviation level, in column 4. The relative deviations from the value of h obtained from $R_{k\text{-}90}$ and $K_{j\text{-}90}$ are given in column 5. Columns 6 and 7 indicate the year and reference of the result. At four laboratories (METAS, NPL, NIM and NIST), more than one balance have been built. To distinguish the results from different iterations, an incremental version number to the Kibble balance has been assigned. A new version number is assigned only when substantial changes were made. The early experiments were performed in air. The vacuum chambers were added later on. Eleven numerical values have been produced. But some of the results listed

Table 6.4   Results of Planck's constant measurement

Lab	ver	$h/10^{-34}$ Js	$\frac{\uparrow \Delta h}{h}/10^{-9}$	$(h/h_{90})/10^{-9}$	Year	References
BIPM	1				–	[28]
KRISS	1				–	[29]
LNE	1	6.6260688	302	–8	2015	[30]
METAS	1	6.6260691	302	37	2011	[31]
NPL	1	6.62606821	136	–97	1990	[32]
NPL	2	6.62607123	200	359	2012	[8]
NRC	1	6.62607011	19	189	2014	[33]
NIM	1	6.626104	8900	5300	2014	[34]
NIM	2	6.626069	2566	22	2016	[35]
NIST	1	6.62607039	1300	232	1989	[36]
NIST	2	6.62606839	87	8	1998	[37]
NIST	3	6.62606936	57	77	2015	[38]
NIST	4	6.62606983	34	148	2016	[39]

Note Several institutes have worked on different versions of the Kibble balance. This is the latest number obtained from the version of the balance indicated in the second column. The reference number indicated within square brackets gives the details of the papers published

in Table 6.4 can be discarded because new results from the same instrument have superseded older results. One example is the NPL-2 Kibble balance. This balance was transferred to the Canadian Metrology Institute (NRC) in 2009. Upon arrival in Canada, these effects were carefully studied and the corresponding entries in the uncertainty budget were considerably reduced. Hence, the NRC result can be considered to effectively supersede the NPL result. The seven most precise values agree reasonably well.

6.4   Practical Realization of the Kilogram (via XRCD Method)

The concept of the X-ray-crystal-density (XRCD) method comes from a classical idea where the mass of a pure substance can be expressed in terms of the number of elementary entities in the substance. Such a number can be measured by the XRCD method in which the volume of the unit cell and volume of an ideally perfect crystal are determined, e.g. by measuring the lattice parameter "a" and the mean diameter of a spherical object made of same pure single crystal, the number of unit cells can be determined. Single crystals of silicon are most often used in this method because large crystals can be obtained having high chemical purity and no dislocations. This is achieved using the crystal growth technologies developed for semiconductor industry.

The method described here was used to determine the value of the Avogadro constant N_A. The product of the Planck constant and the Avogadro constant is currently known to a relative standard uncertainty of 4.5 parts in 10^{10} from a physical connection via the Rydberg constant [1], so this relation can be used to calculate Planck constant from the knowledge of Avogadro number.

An accurate measurement of N_A was an essential contribution on the road for redefining the kilogram in terms of h by 26th CGPM in 2018. Further the ratio of atomic mass of ^{28}Si and Planck's constant, i.e. $m(^{28}\text{Si})/h$ is also a natural constant.

Note: Author appreciated the paper realization of kilogram through XRCD [2] by Kenichi Fujii et al. and used the material liberally.

6.4.1   Principle

Let us consider a sphere of pure silicon. Its total mass will consist of mass of its core and oxide layers. Let m_{sphere} be mass of sphere and m_{SL} be the mass of the surface layers on it, then m_{core}, the core mass will be given as

$$m_{\text{core}} = m_{\text{sphere}} - m_{\text{SL}}, \tag{6.15}$$

and the mean mass of a silicon atom $m(\text{Si})$ is obtained as

$$m(Si) = m_{core}/N = m_{core}a^3/(8V_{core}).$$

Here N is the total number of atoms and V_{core} is volume of the crystal. Each cell is cubical of *lattice a* with volume a3 and there are eight atoms associated with each cell, giving

$$m_{core} = (8V_{core}/a^3)(m(Si)). \tag{6.16}$$

Let mass of Si isotope with i as mass number be $m(^iSi)$. Expressing it in terms of electronic mass m_e and relative atomic ratio $Ar(^iSi)$, we get

$$m(^iSi) = m_eA_r(^iSi)/A_r(e). \tag{6.17}$$

In case of silicon crystal, i take values of 28, 29 and 30 and $A_r(e)$ is the relative atomic mass of electron.

Using the exact composition of isotopes of Si crystal, molar mass is given as

$$M(Si) = m_e \Sigma f(^iSi)A_r(^iSi)/A_r(e). \tag{6.18}$$

Replacing m_e by $2 h R_\infty/c\alpha^2$, $M(Si)$ by $\Sigma f(^iSi)A_r(^iSi)/A_r(e)$ in (6.16), mass of sphere m_{sphere} is given as

$$m_{sphere} = \{2hR_\infty/(c\alpha^2)\}\{\Sigma f(^iSi)A_r(^iSi)/A_r(e)\}\{8Vcore/a^3\} + m_{SL} - m_{Deficit}. \tag{6.19}$$

In this equation, $2 h_\infty/(c\alpha^2)$ is the mass of the electron, $m_e \Sigma f(^iSi)A_r(^iSi)/A_r(e)$ is the mean mass ratio of silicon to the electron and $8Vcore/a^3$ is the number of silicon atoms in the core. A new term $m_{deficit}$ is introduced to consider the influence of point defects (i.e. impurities and self-point defects in the crystal) on the core mass.

So we must have a sphere of enriched Si, must measure its volume V. Estimate the mass m_{SL} of surface layer, mass $m_{deficit}$ of the self-point defects and impurities. The term (m_{SL}) adds to the mass of the core sphere, while $m_{deficit}$ subtract from it. Measure accurately the lattice constant a, the values of $f(^iSi)Ar(^iSi)/Ar(e)$ and other constants. The mass of sphere is thus measured by means other than weighing. Hence, the sphere is a primary mass standard and is the unit of mass, namely, the kilogram.

Here we should understand that (6.19) is not exact because the right-hand side is reduced by the mass equivalent, E/c^2; E is the total binding energy of the atoms in the crystal and c is the speed of light in vacuum. The correction is about two parts in 10^{10}, which is insignificant compared with present experimental uncertainties and has been ignored. Additional energy terms (e.g. thermal energy) are even smaller than the binding energy and thus negligible.

So essentially what we need

1. Sphere of silicon of known volume.
2. Isotopic composition of silicon.
3. For isotopic composition, we need to know the production technology of single crystals and associated issues.
4. Lattice constant of the crystal.
5. Mass of surface layers on the silicon sphere.

6.4.2   Sphere

In XRCD method, a sphere of nominal mass of 1 kg is used. The balances have best resolution varying from $1\mu g$ to $0.1\mu g$ at 1 kg level and kg is the unit of mass. The material of the sphere is well-characterized enriched ^{28}Si. The silicon sphere should not have a shape deviation above 50 nm and the surface roughness should be below 0.2 nm. The sphere should show no subsurface damage.

6.4.2.1   Volume of Sphere

The volume V is calculated from the measured mean diameter D with special interferometer given in [3, 4]. Since silicon crystals are usually covered with thin oxide layers having a total thickness of around 2 nm, the "core" volume of the sphere without the surface layers has to be evaluated. Therefore, the surface of the sphere needs to be chemically and physically characterized on an atomic scale.

Even before making the sphere and carrying out measurement on it, getting the ^{28}Si-enriched single crystal is essential.

6.4.3   Obtaining 28Si-Enriched Polycrystal

A crystal is enriched with ^{28}Si by a chemical process involving several steps. First step is to obtain gaseous silicon tetrafluoride. Second step is to use cascade of centrifuges to give gaseous ^{28}Si F_4. It is treated with $Ca(OH)_2$ which result to get $^{28}SiH_4$. In fourth step, ^{28}Si is deposited on already existing thin (8 mm) ^{28}Si rod, giving polycrystalline ^{28}Si. The brief details are given below:

1. The production of highly enriched silicon is obtained from two materials, namely, sodium silicon fluoride and pure crystalline silicone. In each case, the aim is to get gaseous silicon tetrafluoride (SiF4)

   By decomposition of Na2SiF6 powder:

   $$Na2SiF6 = 2NaF \downarrow + SiF4 \uparrow .$$

   From highly pure crystalline silicon and gaseous fluorine

   $$Si + 2F_2 = SiF_4 \uparrow .$$

2. It is known that fluorine combines only with a single stable isotope of ^{28}Si, so the process of converting Si to silicone fluoride means obtaining $^{28}SiF_4$. The enrichment process is carried out by centrifugation. The enrichment technology uses cascades of hundreds of centrifuges and must be optimized to reach an extremely high chemical purity of the extracted $^{28}SiF4$. In particular, impurities

like Si2F6O and SiF3OH containing silicon with natural isotopic composition should be avoided.

3. Subsequently, ^{28}SiF4 is chemically transformed into silane (^{28}SiH4) using finely dispersed calcium hydride (CaH2) at a temperature of about 1800 °C by the following reaction:

$$^{28}\text{SiF}_4 + 2\text{CaH}_2 = \text{SiH}_4 + 2\text{CaF}_2.$$

To prevent contamination by carbon, the reaction is carried out in absence of organic solvents.

Fluorine-containing compounds like fluorosi oxanes and light hydrocarbons are the main contaminants in the produced silane. Silane is then preliminarily separated from the low-volatile impurities and finely suspended particles by cryofiltration with sub-cooled boiling.

Further rectification is carried out in a stainless steel column with a feeding reservoir placed in the centre. The fractions enriched with compounds having boiling points lower and higher than silane are simultaneously removed from the top and bottom parts of the column. The concentration of hydrocarbons in the selected fractions can be monitored, for example, by gas chromate-graphy.

Polycrystalline silicon is produced in a specially designed chemical or, more precisely, pyrolytic vapour deposition setup, characterized by a vertical cylindrical ^{28}Si rod.

The silane deposition starts on a ^{28}Si rod with a diameter of about 8 mm. This slim rod has to be grown from a previous batch of ^{28}Si.

In this way, a ^{28}Si-enriched cylindrical polycrystalline rod is produced as the starting material for subsequent single crystal growth.

6.4.4 Single Crystal Growth

The polycrystalline rod is purified by float-zone melting; first in vacuum (to evaporate oxygen) and then in argon, while preserving the low oxygen concentration. Carbon is reduced by segregation via multiple float zones. After float-zone purification, a single crystal is grown using a ^{28}Si seed oriented in the (1 0 0) direction, grown by a crucible-free pedestal method. After the purification, only 4.8 kg of the material is obtained. The material is designated as AVO-28. The 1 kg silicon sphere is produced from a cylinder with a diameter and height of at least 100 mm. Many other samples are required for the X-ray interferometers for lattice constant, for ensuring uniformity in density, molar mass measurements and impurity evaluation.

The other new crystal which was made in 2015 (Si28-23Pr1 1) has a simpler shape. Only the small terminal parts of the single crystals are disturbed by back-gliding dislocations and cannot be used for the XRCD method. The isotopic

Table 6.5 Fractional isotopic composition of the ^{28}Si-enriched single crystals

Isotope	AVO-28	Si28-Pr11
^{28}Si	0.999 958	0.999 984
^{29}Si	0.000 041	0.000 015
^{30}Si	0.000 001	0.000 001

compositions of the existing large ^{28}Si-enriched single crystals are shown in Table 6.5.

6.4.5   Isotopic Composition of Silicon

The isotope ratio measurements may be conducted in high mass resolution (HR) mode using an MC-ICP-MS Neptune™ instrument (Thermo Fisher Scientific GmbH, Bremen, Germany) with a modified sapphire torch and several parts almost free of natural silicon (perfluoroalkoxy alkane) (PFA) spray chamber. Typical machine parameters are reported in [5]. Isotopic composition for the two crystals designated as AVO28 and Si28-23Pr11 is given in Table 6.5.

6.4.6   Crystal Perfection: Evaluation of Point Defects

One of the key prerequisites for using the XRCD method is the existence of nearly perfect single crystals. Although large single crystals can be grown without any silicon dislocations, enriched ^{28}Si crystals contain point defects that should be known so that that the term m_{deficite} in (6.19) may be estimated appropriately.

The main impurities in silicon crystals are carbon (C), oxygen (O) and nitrogen (N). Their concentrations are measured by infrared absorption spectroscopy [5]. The C, O and N impurities are not electrically active, and their IR absorption is caused by excitation of the local oscillator formed by the impurity atom and the neighbouring silicon atoms.

Carbon and oxygen impurities get into the raw material (the polycrystalline rod) during the chemical vapour deposition step. The concentration of carbon can be reduced in most parts of the single crystal by multiple float-zone (FZ) refinement. The detection limit for carbon is about $5 \times 10^{14}\,\text{cm}^{-3}$.

Nitrogen is introduced intentionally during FZ growth as doping material to prevent agglomeration of vacancies such as swirls. It occupies interstitial lattice sites and suppresses the formation of swirl defects. The nitrogen concentration in crystals grown in argon containing 0.1% of N_2 amounts to about $2 \times 10^{14}\,\text{cm}^{-3}$. The detection limits of O and N are a factor of ten smaller than that of carbon, i.e. about $5 \times 10^{13}\,\text{cm}^{-3}$.

Two main factors contribute to the uncertainties of impurity concentration measurements: the conversion factor for the determination of the impurity concentration from the measured absorption coefficient and the determination of the absorption coefficient itself. In the case of carbon, the latter represents the dominant part of the uncertainty budget, whereas for all other impurities, the uncertainty is mainly caused by the conversion factors. These factors are taken from literature or semiconductor industry standards and have a rather large standard uncertainty, usually in the order of 10%. However, the uncertainty of the core mass due to this impurity correction is still at the level of only ~4 μg, being 3.8 μg for AVO28-S5 and 3.5 μg for AVO28-S8. The uncertainty in the determination of the absorption coefficient is due to the reproducibility of IR measurements, spectral interferences, the unknown impurity concentration in a nominally impurity-free reference sample and the evaluation procedure for the determination of peak height in IR spectra.

Boron (B), phosphorus (P), gallium (Ga), arsenic (As) and antimony (Sb) impurities are electrically active, and electronic inter-band transitions give rise to numerous absorption peaks in the far infrared spectral range. The detection limits for these impurities are about 10^{11} cm^{-3}, three orders of magnitude lower than those of local oscillators. Except for boron, the signals are normally near or below the detection limit and negligible for the XRCD method.

Deep-level transient spectroscopy (DLTS) was used to detect hydrogen in the AVO-28 crystal. The detection limit was 2×10^{13} cm^{-3}, and no hydrogen could be found.

Point defect concentrations and mass deficit of impurities are, respectively, given in Tables 6.6 and 6.7 for two spheres S5 and S8 carved out from silicon crystal AVO-28.

In principle, the presence of all chemical elements (except silicon) in the crystal has to be checked. For many elements, this can be performed by neutron activation [6].

Table 6.6 Point defect concentrations in the AVO28-S5 and AVO28-S8 spheres

Defect	Unit/cm^3	AVO28-S5	AVO28-S8
Carbon	10^{15}	0.40(5)	1.93(19)
Oxygen	10^{15}	0.283(63)	0.415(91)
Nitrogen	10^{15}	0.017(10)	0.138(30)
Boron	10^{15}	0.011(4)	0.031(18)
Vacancy	10^{15}	0.33(11)	0.33(11)

Table 6.7 Mass difference $m_{deficit}$ in AVO28-S5 and AVO28-S8 spheres

Defect due to impurity	AVO28-S5 in μg	AVO28-S8 in μg
Carbon	4.6(6)	22.0(2.2)
Oxygen	−3.2(7)	−4.8(1.1)
Nitrogen	−0.2(1)	−1.4(3)
Boron	0.1(1)	0.4(2)
Metals	−4.0 (3.0)	0.0(1.0)
Vacancy	6.6(2.2)	6.6(2.2)
Total	3.8(3.8)	22.7(3.5)

6.4.7   MSL Layers

Surface layer SF is composed of mainly three layers, namely, starting from top, water, carbonaceous contamination and SiO_2. Water layer itself is composed of two layers, physisorbed water (PWL) and chemisorbed water (CWL). Main layers from air interface to Si core of the silicon sphere are depicted in Fig. 6.5.

Normally the following methods are used for surface characterization of silicon sphere used in XRCD method:

Name	Abbreviation
Spectroscopic ellipsometry,	SE.
X-ray reflectometry,	XRR.
X-ray fluorescence analysis,	XRF.
X-ray photoelectron spectroscopy,	XPS.
Gravimetric.	Grav.

An overview of the different methods used for surface layers characterization of silicon is enumerated in Table 6.8.

Abbreviations used for heading Table 6.8 are SC: Screening, Qu: Quantitative, Pr: Primary, Acc: Accuracy, Pre: Precision. Thickness d is reported in nanometre (nm).

The dominant uncertainty sources in the determination of m_{SL} are m_{OL} and m_{CL}. Analysis of the present uncertainty in surface characterization and estimation of

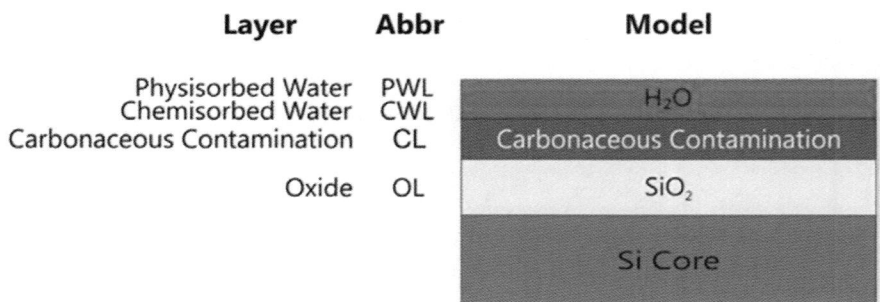

Fig. 6.5   Different layers on silicon sphere

Table 6.8   Different methods used for surface layers on silicon spheres

Method	Measure	SC	QU	Pr	Acc	Pre	Speed
SE	Thickness	No	Yes	Yes	Medium	High	High
XRR	Thickness	No	Yes	Yes	High	High	Low
XRF	Area mass	Yes	Yes	Yes	High	High	Medium
XPS	Area mass	Yes	No	No	Low	Low	Medium
Grav	Mass	No	Yes	Yes	High	High	Slow

Table 6.9 Thickness measurement of different layers in nm (10^{-9} m)

Sphere	Lab	d_{CL}	d_{WL}	d_{PWL}	d_{OL}	d_{SL}
AVO-28 S5c	PTB	0.60(18)	0.28(8)	–	0.91(14)	1.79(24)
	NMIJ	0.60(18)	0.28(8)	0.39(9)	0.76(27)	1.64(33)
Average		0.60(18)	0.28(8)		0.88(12)	1.76(23)
AVO-28 S8c	PTB	0.49(16)	0.28(8)	–	1.17(13)	1.94(22)
	NMIJ	0.49(16)	0.28(8)	0.43(9)	0.64(25)	1.41(31)
Average		0.49(16)	0.28(8)		1.06(22)	1.83(28)

Table 6.10 Mass values of different layers in μg

Sphere	Lab	m_{CL}	m_{CWL}	m_{PWL}	m_{OL}	m_{SL}
AVO-28-S5c	PTB	16.6(5.7)	7.7(2.2)	–	55.2(8.9)	79.5(10.9)
	NMIJ	16.6(5.7)	7.7(2.2)	10.8(2.5)	46.1(16.5)	70.4(17.7)
Average		16.6(5.7)	7.7(2.2)		50.8(7.7)	74.9(10.0)
AVO28-S8c	PTB	13.5(5.2)	7.7(2.2)	–	71.0(8.5)	92.2(10.2)
	NMIJ	13.5(5.2)	7.7(2.2)	11.9(2.7)	38.9(15.3)	60.0(16.3)
Average		13.5(5.2)	7.7(2.2)	–	64.3(13.7)	85.5(14.8)

further uncertainty reduction indicate that the carbonaceous contamination would be the defining parameter. Hence, improvement of the carbon content measurement would contribute to reducing the uncertainty in realizing the kilogram. To reduce the contributions of these uncertainty sources, new surface analysis apparatuses are being developed at PTB, Germany (Table 6.9).

The thickness d_{CL} measured by XRF at PTB was based on the assumption that the density of CL is 1.1 g cm^{-3}. The uncertainty of this thickness was estimated using the results of surface analysis from the previous measurement [7] and calculated from data reported by Mizushima [8].

The data for d_{PWL} came from comparison of weighing results of the two spheres in nitrogen gas (at a pressure of ~1200 Pa) and in water vapour (at a pressure of ~1200 Pa) [9]. The density of PWL was assumed to be 1.0 g cm^{-3}. This value does not include the thickness of PWL.

The Birge ratio of the oxide layer thickness values for AVO28-S8c is 1.8. Therefore, the uncertainty of the weighted mean was multiplied by 1.8. A possible reason for the difference in the oxide layer determinations may be that NMIJ used the CL thickness value of PTB, while the surface cleaning procedures were not identical at PTB and NMIJ.

Mass values of different layers for sphere AVO-28-S5c and AVO-28-S8c were measured at PTB, Germany and NMIJ, Japan. These are given in Table 6.10. The results of the two laboratories agree extremely well.

The mass layer m_{PWL} is not included in m_{SL} to deduce the mass of the sphere in vacuum.

6.4.8   Molar Mass

The molar mass M of silicon is deduced from the respective molar masses of silicon $M(^iSi)$ and the amount of substance $f(^iSi)$ using the relation $\Sigma\{f(^iSi).M(^iSi)\}$. The $f(^iSi)$ is determined by measuring isotopic ratios.

However, to obtain relative uncertainty in N_A less than 2×10^{-8}, a sufficiently small uncertainty of M is tolerable. The ratios $f(^iSi)/f(^{28}Si)$ have too large uncertainty to fulfil this requirement. Therefore, a modified isotope dilution mass spectrometric (IDMS) technique has been developed to overcome this problem [10–12]. The solvents initially NaOH and later on TMAH (Tetramethylammonium hydroxide) mentioned at several places were used for getting the solution of ^{29}Si and ^{30}Si. The IDMS technique is based on the introduction of a "virtual element" (VE), treating silicon as a matrix containing the VE (^{29}Si and ^{30}Si). In the VE-IDMS, only the isotope ratios $R_{30,29} = f(^{30}Si)/f(^{29}Si)$ have to be measured, giving relative uncertainties $u_{rel}(R_{30,29}) < 1\%$, sufficient for $u_{rel}(M) = 1 \times 10^{-8}$.

Experimentally, the VE-IDMS approach is performed using high-resolution multi-collector inductively coupled mass spectrometry (MC-ICP-MS). The $R_{30,29} = f(^{30}Si)/f(^{29}Si)$ have to be measured.

Here $f(^iSi) = R_i/\Sigma R_j$.

Here i takes value of 28, 29 and 30, similarly j takes values 29 and 30.

The VE-IDMS method has been successfully applied by several other national metrology institutes (NMIs), namely, the National Research Council (NRC, Canada) [13], National Metrology Institute of Japan (NMIJ, Japan) [14], the National Institute of Standards and Technology (NIST, USA) [15] and the National Institute of Metrology (NIM, People's Republic of China) [16]. A typical set of values of amount of substance $f(^{28}Si)$, $f(^{29}Si)$ $f(^{30}Si)$ and molar mass AVO-28 crystal are given in Table 6.11.

It may be noted that measurements prior to 2013 were carried out using aqueous solution of sodium hydroxide (NaOH), while all subsequent measurements used aqueous TMAH (Tetramethylammonium hydroxide).

Table 6.11   Molar fractions and molar mass of AVO28

NMI	$f(^{28}Si)$	$f(^{29}Si)\ 10^{-5}$	$f(^{30}Si)\ 10^{-6}$	Molar mass g	Solvent
PTB2011	0.999 957 50(17)	4.121(15)	1.29(4)	27.97697027(23)	NaOH
NRC2012	0.999 958 79(19)	4.054(14)	0.067(6)	27.97696839(24)	NaOH
NMIJ2014	0.999 957 64(3)	4.114(7)	1.22(4)	27.97697009(14)	TMAH
NIST2014	0.999 957 701(41)	4.1223(41)	1.076(88)	27.976969880(41)	TMAH
PTB2015	0.999 957 52(12)	4.136(11)	1121(14)	27.97697012(12)	TMAH

6.4.9   Lattice Parameter

Lattice parameter paragraph is essentially based on the paper by Masa et al. [17–19]. Bonse and Hart [20] in 1960 developed a first X-ray interferometer, to determine the lattice constant "*a*" of a silicon crystal. The method is based on interferometry in the optical wavelength region. According to this principle, evaluation of the X-ray wavelength and measurement of the corresponding diffraction angle are not necessary.

In 1980, using the X-ray interferometer, Becker et al. [21] reported a reliable value of the Si crystal lattice constant with a relative standard uncertainty of 6.2×10^{-8}. The lattice spacing of silicon has been measured using technologies developed in X-ray and optical interferometry. These technologies are improved day in and day out. This leads to the improvement of relative uncertainty in measurement of lattice constant from 5.10^{-5} in 1960 to a few parts in 10^{-10} in 2015.

Mainly the measurements of lattice constant have been carried out at NIST, USA; PTB, Germany; NMIJ, Japan and INRIM, Italy. The uncertainties are indicated by Circles for NIST, Squares for PTB, Diamonds for NMIJ and Triangles for INRIM. The gradual decrease in magnitude of relative uncertainty in lattice parameter measurement by various laboratories has been shown in Fig. 6.6.

6.4.9.1   Experimental Apparatus

The latest apparatus, combined X-ray and optical interferometer used by Masa et al. [17–19], is shown in Fig. 6.7 It consists of three crystal blades, 1.20 mm thick. They are so cut that the {2 2 0} planes are orthogonal to the crystal. The first one may be called diffraction. Second one as transmission and third as analyser.

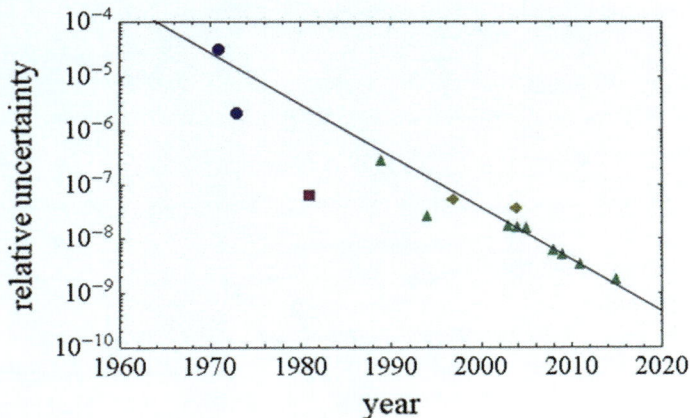

Fig. 6.6 Reduction in magnitude of uncertainty

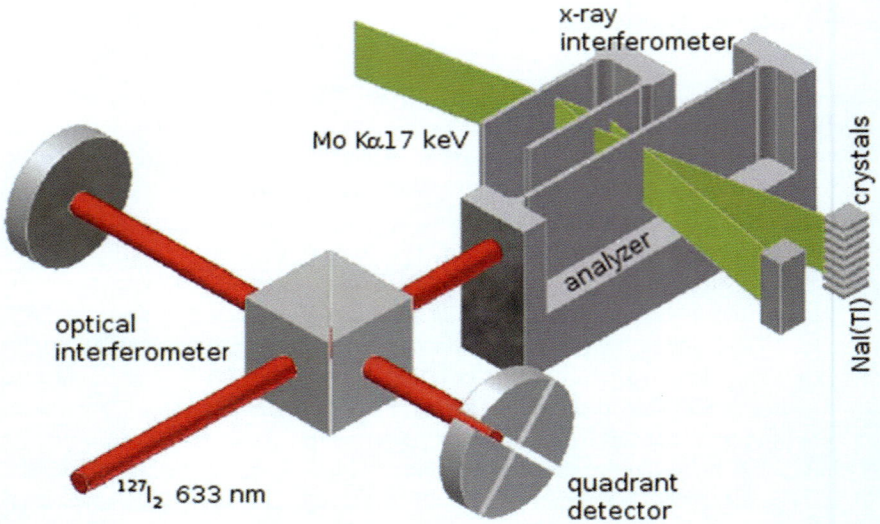

Fig. 6.7 Combined X-ray and optical interferometer

The {2 2 0} diffracting planes are chosen on the basis of their greatest reflectivity. X-ray source is a Mo Kα. The X-rays are split by the first crystal and recombined, via two transmission crystals. The interference pattern was imaged onto a multi-anode photomultiplier tube through a pile of eight NaI(Tl) scintillating crystals. The equivalent pixel size projected on the interferometer is (1×1.8) mm^2.

The analyser crystal moves in a direction parallel to the laser beam and its displacement is measured by the optical interferometer and each passing diffracting plane is counted. Both the X-ray and optical interference patterns are imaged into position-sensitive detectors to sense lattice strain and parasitic rotations of the analyser.

In other words, when the analyser is moved along a direction orthogonal to the {22 0}-diffracting planes, a periodic variation in the transmitted and diffracted X-ray intensities is observed, the period being the diffracting-plane spacing. To cope with the highly demanding request of accuracy, the INRIM extended the crystal-displacement capabilities to 5 cm. This magnification made more numerous effects visible and reproducible. In addition, it allowed wider crystal parts to be surveyed, thus increasing confidence in the crystal perfection and in the mean lattice parameter value. The analyser movement is an extremely difficult task; it requires nano-radian (10^{-9} rad) attitude-control and picometre (10^{-12}m) vibration and position controls. The analyser displacement and rotation are measured by optical interferometry; the necessary picometre (10^{-12} m) and nano-radian resolutions are achieved by polarization encoding and phase modulation.

6.4.9.2 Measurement Procedure

The measurement equation is $a = \sqrt{8}d2\ 2\ 0 = \sqrt{8}\ m\lambda/(2n)$, where d2 2 0 is the spacing of the {2 2 0} planes, the $\sqrt{8}$ factor accounts for the different spacing and orientations of the {1 0 0} and {2 2 0} planes and n is the number of X-ray fringes observed in a displacement of m optical fringes having a period of $\lambda/2$. The laser source operates in single mode and its frequency is stabilized against that of a transition of the $^{127}I_2$ molecule. This ensures the calibration of the optical interferometer with a negligible uncertainty. To eliminate the adverse influence of the refractive index of air and to ensure temperature uniformity and stability of 10^{-3} K (mK), the experiment is carried out in a thermo-vacuum chamber.

In practice, $d220$ is determined by comparing the unknown period of the X-ray fringes against the known period of the optical ones. This is done by measuring the X-ray fringe fraction at the end of increasing displacements $m\lambda/2$, where $m = 1, 10, 100, 1000, 3000$ and $30,000$. The time required for counting each X-ray fringe is rather too large. Therefore, we started from the approximation $\lambda/(2d220) = n/m = 1648.28$ and measured the fringe fraction only at the displacement ends with accuracy sufficient for predicting the integer number of fringes in the next displacement over the increasing sequence. Consequently, the $\lambda/(2d220)$ ratio is updated and its accuracy increases at each step.

The least-squares method is applied to reconstruct X-ray fringes and to determine their phases at the displacement ends [22]. The input data are about 300 subsequent photon counts made over 100 ms windows and at about 4 pm displacement intervals; a typical sample contains six X-ray fringes, covers a distance of 1.2 nm and lasts 30 s. Each $d220$ measurement is the average of about nine values collected in measurement cycles during which the analyser is repeatedly moved back and forth along the selected displacement. The visibility of the X-ray fringes approached 50% with a mean brilliance of 500 counts s^{-1} mm^{-2}.

The symmetric analyser shape allows it to be reversed; measurements were carried out with the X-rays crossing the crystal in both directions so that surface effects, as well as other systematic effects, could be investigated.

Note: The concentrations of carbon and oxygen in the interferometer crystals are kept as low as $1.07(10) \times 10^{15}$ cm^{-3} and $0.369(33) \times 10^{15}$ cm^{-3}, respectively [23]. The concentration of vacancy-related defects is $0.33(11) \times 10^{15}$ cm^{-3}.

6.4.9.3 Results

The spacing of the {22 0} lattice planes of a ^{28}Si crystal, used to determine the Avogadro constant by counting silicon atoms, was measured by combined X-ray and optical interferometry to a relative accuracy of 3.5×10^{-9}.

The result is $d220 = (192\ 014\ 712.67 \pm 0.67)$ am $(10^{-18}$ m) at 20.0 °C and 0 Pa.

Table 6.12 Lattice constants

S. No	Sample	Institute	Value in fm (10^{-15} m)
1	WASSO 4.2	PTB	192015.563 (12)
2	Mo*4	IMGC	192015.551(6)
3	SHI	NMIJ	192015.587(11)
4	PFX	NIST	192015.54(2)
5	WASO04	PTB	192015.566(12)
6	WASO 17	PTB	192015.566(12)
7	Si 5	PTB	192015.568(12)
8	Mo*4	IMGC	192015.562(12)
9	WG	IMGC	192015.568(12)
10	W3	IMGC	192015.566(12)
11	SHI	NMIJ	192015.565(12)
12	PFX	NIST	192015.570(12)
13	ISCX	NIST	192015.544(18)

Table 6.13 Relative standard uncertainty

Quantity (parameter)	Relative standard uncertainty in 10^9
Planck's constant	0
h/m(28Si)	<1
Lattice parameter	5
M/M_r Σf(iSi)/Ar(iSi)	5
Point defects	3
Surface layer mass	13
Volume of sphere	20
Total uncertainty	25

This value is greater by $(1.9464 \pm 0.0067) \times 10^{-6}$ $d220$ than the spacing in natural silicon, a difference which confirms quantum-mechanics calculations. This result is a key step towards a realization of the mass unit based on a conventional value of the Planck or the Avogadro constant. Some older values of lattice constant of ^{28}Si are given for comparison purposes in Table 6.12.

6.4.9.4   Uncertainty in XRCD Method

The relative uncertainties in mass of sphere shown in Table 6.13 are when the same institute measures volume of sphere and the mass of surface layers [23].

References (Kibble Balance)

1. http://bipm.org/en/si/si-brochure/appendix2/
2. A.I.A. Robinson, S. Schlamminger, Metrologia **53**, A46–A58 (2016)

3. K. Fujii, H. Bettin, P. Becker, E. Massa, O. Rienitz, A. Pramann, A. Nicolaus, N. Kuramoto, I. Busch, M. Borys, Realization of the kilogram by the XRCD method. Metrologia **53**(6), A19–A145 (2016)
4. R.L. Steiner, E.R. Williams, R. Liu, D.B. Newell, Uncertainty improvements of the NIST electronic kilogram. IEEE Trans. Instrum. Meas. **56**, 592–596 (2007)
5. S. Schlamminger, Design of the permanent-magnet system for NIST-4. IEEE Trans. Instrum. Meas. **62**, 1524–1530 (2013)
6. F. Jones, M. Tokunaga, Low temperature coefficient cobalt-rare earth magnets. IEEE Trans. Magn. **12**, 968–970 (1976)
7. P. Gournay, G. Geneves, F. Alves, M. Besbes, F. Villar, J. David, Magnetic circuit design for the BNM watt balance experiment. IEEE Trans. Instrum. Meas. **54**, 742–745 (2005)
8. I.A. Robinson, Towards the redefinition of the kilogram: a measurement of the Planck constant using the NPL Mark II watt balance. Metrologia **49**, 113–156 (2012)
9. X. Jiang, W. Zeng, I.M. Smith, P. Scott, F.X. Maletras, The detection of transient behaviour in environmental vibration for the watt balance. Meas. Sci. Technol. **18**, 1487–1494 (2007)
10. W. Zeng, X. Jiang, I.M. Smith, P. Scott, Transient signal separation in watt balance experiments. Phys. Lett. A **374**, 1301–1306 (2010)
11. S.P. Benz, C.A. Hamilton, Application of the Josephson effect to voltage metrology. Proc. IEEE **92**, 1617–1629 (2004)
12. R. Behr, O. Kieler, J. Kohlmann, F. Müller, L. Palafox, Development and metrological applications of Josephson arrays at PTB. Meas. Sci. Technol. **23**, 124002 (2012)
13. Y. Tang, V.N. Ojha, S. Schlamminger, A. Rüfenacht, C.J. Burroughs, P.D. Dresselhaus, S.P. Benz, A 10 V programmable Josephson voltage standard and its applications for voltage metrology Metrologia **49,** 635–643 (2012)
14. S. Solve, R. Chayramy, M. Stock, A bias source for the voltage reference of the BIPM watt balance. IEEE Trans. Instrum. Meas. **62**, 1594–1599 (2013)
15. I.A. Robinson, B.P. Kibble, An initial measurement of Planck's constant using the NPL Mark II watt balance. Metrologia **44**, 427–440 (2007)
16. J. Kohlmann, R. Behr, T. Funck, Josephson voltage standards. Meas. Sci. Technol. **14**, 1216–1228 (2003)
17. S.P. Benz, C.A. Hamilton, C.J. Burroughs, T.E. Harvey, L.A. Christian, Stable 1 volt programmable voltage standard. Appl. Phys. Lett. **71**, 1866–1868 (1997)
18. C.A. Hamilton, Josephson voltage standards. Rev. Sci. Instrum. **71**, 3611–3623 (2000)
19. S. Topcu, L. Chassagne, D. Haddad, Y. Alayli, P. Juncar, High accuracy velocity control method for the French moving-coil watt balance *Rev.* Sci. Instrum. **75**, 4824–4827 (2004)
20. R.L. Steiner, D. Newell, E.R. Williams, Details of the 1998 watt balance experiment determining the Planck constant. J. Res. Natl Inst. Stand. Technol. **110**, 1–26 (2005)
21. EM Electronics A10 DC sub-nanovolt amplifier
22. D. Drung, J.-H. Storm, Ultralow-noise chopper amplifier with low input charge injection. IEEE Trans. Instrum. Meas. **60**, 2347–2352 (2011)
23. D. Haddad, B. Waltrip, R.L. Steiner, Low noise programmable current source for the NIST-3 and NIST-4 watt balance, in *2012 Conference on Precision Electromagnetic Measurements* (2012), pp. 336–337
24. B.P. Kibble, I.A. Robinson, Guidance on eliminating interference from sensitive electrical circuits Technical Report DES 129, NPL (1993)
25. I.K. Harvey, A precise low temperature dc ratio transformer. Rev. Sci. Instrum. **43**, 1626–1629 (1972)
26. P. Gutmann, H. Bachmair, *Cryogenic Current Comparator Metrology* (Springer, Berlin, 1989), pp. 255–268
27. C.A. Sanchez, B.M. Wood, R.G. Green, J.O. Liard, D. Inglis, A determination of Planck's constant using the NRC watt balance. Metrologia **51**, S5–S14 (2014)
28. H. Fang, A. Kiss, A. Picard, M. Stock, A watt balance based on a simultaneous measurement scheme. Metrologia **51**, S80–S87 (2014)

29. D. Kim, B.C. Woo, K.C. Lee, K.B. Choi, J.A. Kim, J.W. Kim, J. Kim, Design of the KRISS watt balance. Metrologia **51**, S96–S100 (2014)
30. M. Thomas, P. Espel, D. Ziane, P. Pinot, P. Juncar, F. Pereira Dos Santos, S. Merlet, F. Piquemal, G. Genevs, First determination of the Planck constant using the LNE watt balance. Metrologia **52**, 433–443 (2015)
31. A. Eichenberger, H. Baumann, B. Jeanneret, B. Jeckelmann, P. Richard, W. Beer, Determination of the Planck constant with the METAS watt balance. Metrologia **48**, 133–141 (2011)
32. B.P. Kibble, I.A. Robinson, J.H. Belliss, A realisation of the SI watt by the NPL moving-coil balance. Metrologia **27**, 173–192 (1990)
33. C.A. Sanchez, B.M. Wood, R.G. Green, J.O. Liard, D. Inglis, Corrigendum to the 2014 NRC determination of Planck's constant. Metrologia **52**, L23 (2015)
34. Z. Zhang, Q. He, Z. Li, B. Han, Y. Lu, J. Lan, C. Li, S. Li, J. Xu, N. Wang, G. Wang, H. Gong, The joule balance in NIM of China. Metrologia **51**, S25–S31 (2014)
35. J. Xu, Z. Zhang, Z. Li, Y. Bai, G. Wang, S. Li, T. Zeng, C. Li, Y. Lu, B. Han, N. Wang, K. Zhou, A determination of the Planck constant by the generalized joule balance method with a permanent-magnet system at NIM. Metrologia **53**, 86–97 (2016)
36. P.T. Olsen, R.E. Elmquist, W.D. Phillips, E.R. Williams, G.R. Jones, V.E. Bower, A measurement of the NBS electrical watt in SI units. IEEE Trans. Instrum. Meas. **38**, 238–244 (1989)
37. E.R. Williams, R.L. Steiner, D.B. Newell, P.T. Olsen, Accurate measurement of the Planck constant. Phys. Rev. Lett. **81**, 2404–2407 (1998)
38. S. Schlamminger, R.L. Steiner, D. Haddad, D.B. Newell, F. Seifert, L.S. Chao, R. Liu, E.R. Williams, J.R. Pratt, A summary of the Planck constant measurements using a watt balance with a superconducting solenoid at NIST. Metrologia **52**, L5–L8 (2015)
39. D. Haddad, F. Seifert, L.S. Chao, S. Li, D.B. Newell, J.R. Pratt, C. Williams, S. Schlamminger, Invited article: a precise instrument to determine the Planck constant, and the future kilogram. Rev. Sci. Instrum. **87**, 061301 (2016)

References (XRCD)

1. A. Pramann, K.-S. Lee, J. Noordmann, O. Rienitz, Probing the homogeneity of the isotopic composition and molar mass of the 'Avogadro'-crystal. Metrologia **52**, 800–810 (2015)
2. S.V. Gupta, Practical density measurements and hydrometry (IOP, UK, 2002), P. 47
3. R.A. Niclaus, G. Bonch, A novel interferometer for dimensional measurements of a Silicon sphere. IEEE Trans. Instrum. Meas. **46**, 54–56 (1997)
4. S. Zakel, S. Wundrack, H. Niemann, O. Rienitz, D. Schiel, Infrared spectrometric measurements of impurities in highly enriched 'Si28'. Metrologia **48**, S14–9 (2011)
5. G. D'Agostino, L. Bergamaschi, L. Giordani, G. Mana, M. Oddone, Elemental characterization of the Avogadro silicon crystal WASO 04 by neutron activation analysis. Metrologia **49**, 696–670 1 (2012)
6. B. Andreas et al, Counting the atoms in a ^{28}Si crystal for a new kilogram definition. Metrologia **48**, S 1–13 (2011)
7. S. Mizushima, Determination of the amount of gas adsorption on SiO2/Si(1 0 0) surfaces to realize precise mass measurement. Metrologia **41**, 137–144 (2004)
8. Y. Azuma et al, Improved measurement results for the Avogadro constant using a ^{28}Si-enriched crystal. Metrologia 360–375 (2015)
9. O. Rienitz, A. Pramann, D. Schiel, Novel concept for the mass spectrometric determination of absolute isotopic abundances with improved measurement uncertainty: part 1—theoretical derivation and feasibility study. Int. J. Mass Spectrom. **289**, 47–53 (2010)

10. A. Pramann, O. Rienitz, D. Schiel, B. Güttler, S. Valkiers, Novel concept for the mass spectrometric determination of absolute isotopic abundances with improved measurement uncertainty: part 3—molar mass of silicon highly enriched in ^{28}Si. Int. J. Mass Spectrom. **305**, 58–68 (2011)

11. A. Pramann, O. Rienitz, J. Noordmann, B. Güttler, D. Schiel, A more accurate molar mass of silicon via high resolution MC-ICP-mass spectrometry. Z. Phys. Chem. **228**, 405–419 (2014)

12. L. Yang, Z. Mester, R.E. Sturgeon, J. Meija, Determination of the atomic weight of ^{28}Si-enriched silicon for a revised estimate of the Avogadro constant. Anal. Chem. **84**, 2321–2327 (2012)

13. T. Narukawa, A. Hioki, N. Kuramoto, K. Fujii, Molar-mass measurement of a ^{28}Si-enriched silicon crystal for determination of the Avogadro constant. Metrologia **51**, 161–168 (2014)

14. R.D. Vocke Jr., S.A. Rabb, G.C. Turk, Absolute silicon molar mass measurements, the Avogadro constant and the redefinition of the kilogram. Metrologia **51**, 36 1–75 (2014)

15. T. Ren, J. Wang, T. Zhou, H. Lu, Y.-J. Zhou, J. Anal. At. Spectrom. **30**, 2449–2458 (2015)

16. E Massa, G Mana, U Kuetgens2, L Ferroglio, Measurement of the {2 2 0} lattice-plane spacing of a ^{28}Si x-ray interferometer. Metrologia 48, S37–S43 (2011)

17. E. Massa, G. Mana, C.P. Sasso, C. Palmisano, A more accurate measurement of the ^{28}Si lattice parameter. J. Phys. Chem. Ref. Data **44**, 031208 (2015)

18. E. Massa, G. Mana, E. Ferroglio, E.G. Kessler, D. Schiel, S. Zakel, The lattice parameter of the ^{28}Si spheres in the determination of the Avogadro constant. Metrologia **48,** S44–9 (2011)

19. U. Bonse, M. Hart, An x-ray interferometer. Appl. Phys. Lett. **6**, 155–156 (1965)

20. P. Becker, H. Bettin, L. Koenders, J. Martin, A. Nicolause, S. Rottger, The silicon path to the kilogram. PTB Mitteilungen **106**, 321–329 (1996)

21. A. Bergamin, G. Cavagnero, G. Mana, Accuracy assessment of a least-squares estimator for scanning x-ray interferometry. Meas. Sci. Technol. **2**, 725–734 (1991)

22. B. Andreas et al, Counting the atoms in a ^{28}Si crystal for a new kilogram definition. Metrologia 48, S1–13 (2011)

Chapter 7
Realization of SI Base Unit Ampere and Other Electric Units

7.1 Introduction

The following paragraphs are based on the Draft Mise en pratique for the definition of the ampere and other electric units in the SI. The draft is prepared by the Consultative Committee on Electricity and Magnetism of the International Committee of Weights and Measures (CIPM).

In general, the term "to realize a unit" means the establishment of the value and associated uncertainty of a quantity of the same kind as the unit that is consistent with the definition of the unit.

No experiment is needed to realize the unit of ampere. Any method capable of deriving an electric current value traceable to the set of seven reference constants could, in principle, be used. Thus, the list of methods given is not exhaustive.

A primary method is a method having the highest metrological properties, whose operation can be completely described and understood, for which a complete uncertainty statement can be written down in terms of SI units, and which does not require a reference standard of the same quantity.

7.2 Definition of the Electrical/Magnetic Units

7.2.1 Practical Realization of Ampere, SI Base Unit of Electric Current

Definition: The ampere, symbol A, is the SI base unit of electric current. It is defined by assigning the value $1.602\ 176\ 634 \times 10^{-19}$ to the magnitude of the elementary charge e, when expressed in the unit coulomb symbol C, which is equal to A·s, where the second is defined in terms of $\Delta\nu_{Cs}$.

© Springer Nature Switzerland AG 2020

S. V. Gupta, *Units of Measurement*, Springer Series in Materials Science 122, https://doi.org/10.1007/978-3-030-43969-9_7

Realization: In practice, the ampere A can be realized in following ways:

(a) By using Ohm's law, the unit relation A=V/Ω. The volt and ohm are, respectively, realized through Josephson junction and quantum Hall resistance or
(b) By using a single electron transport (SET) or similar device, the unit relation $A = C/s$, the value of e given in the definition of the ampere and a practical realization of the SI base unit the second s or
(c) By using the relation

$$I = C \cdot dU/dt, \tag{7.1}$$

where I is electric current, C is capacitance and dU/dt is rate of change in voltage.

Equation (7.1) gives the following unit relation:

$$A = F \cdot V/s. \tag{7.2}$$

Practically realized through the knowledge of SI derived units of the volt V and of the farad F, and of the SI base unit second s.

Single electron transport (SET) implementations still have technical limitations and often larger relative uncertainties than some other competitive techniques. However, SET implementations are included in this *Mise en pratique* because they offer unique and elegant approaches to realizing SI units, and their uncertainties have been improving in recent years, and likely to improve further in the future.

7.2.2   Derived Units

7.2.2.1   Practical Realization of the Volt, V, SI Derived Unit of Electric Potential Difference (Voltage) and Electromotive Force

The volt V can be realized using the Josephson effect and the following value of the Josephson constant K_J:

$$K_J = 483.597\ 848\ 416\ 984\ \text{THz} \cdot \text{V}^{-1}. \tag{7.3}$$

By taking the exact values of electronic charge and the Planck's constant, the value of K_J has been calculated to 15 significant digits.

The value of K_J is based on the assumption that the equation $K_J = 2e/h$ is correct, which is strongly supported by a large body of experimental and theoretical works. The values of h and e are taken from defining constants, Chap. 5. Although the quotient $2e/h$ can obviously be calculated with any number of digits, this truncated recommended value is in error by less than 1 part in 10^{15}, which is intended to be negligible in the vast majority of applications. In those rare cases where this error may not be negligible, additional digits should be employed. The advantage of recommending a particular value of K_J for practical use is that it ensures that virtually all realizations of the volt based on the Josephson effect employ exactly the same value.

It may be noted that the value of K_J in (7.3) is smaller than the value $K_{J\text{-}90} = 483.597\ 9$ THz V^{-1}, which the CIPM has adopted effective from 1 January 1990 for the international realization of the volt using the Josephson effect, by the fractional amount 106.665×10^{-9}. This implies that the unit of voltage realized using $K_{J\text{-}90}$ was larger than the present SI unit as realized using the value in (7.3) by the same fractional amount. Thus, the numerical value of a voltage measured in terms of $K_{J\text{-}90}$ would have been smaller by the same fractional amount as the numerical value of the identical voltage measured today in terms of the present SI volt realized using the value of K_J given in (7.3).

7.2.2.2 Practical Realization of the Ohm, Ω, SI Derived Unit of Electric Resistance and Impedance

The ohm Ω can be realized as follows:

(a) By using the quantum Hall effect in a manner consistent with the CCEM Guidelines [2] and the following value of the von Klitzing constant R_K:

$$R_K = 25\ 812.807\ 459\ 3045\ \Omega. \tag{7.4}$$

This value has been calculated to 15 significant digits.

The value R_K is based on the assumption that the equation $R_K = h/e^2$ is correct, which is strongly supported by a large body of experimental and theoretical works, and the values of h and e given in [1]. Although the quotient h/e^2 can obviously be calculated with any number of digits, this truncated recommended value is in error by less than 1 part in 10^{15}, which is intended to be negligible in the vast majority of applications. In those rare cases where this error may not be negligible, additional digits should be employed. The advantage of recommending a particular value of R_K for practical use is that it ensures that virtually all realizations of the ohm based on the quantum Hall effect employ exactly the same value or

(b) By comparing an unknown resistance to the impedance of a known capacitance using, for example, a quadrature bridge, where the capacitance is determined by means of a calculable capacitor and the value of the electric constant given by (7.5) in Sect. 7.2.2.10.

Note that the value of R_K in (7.4) is larger than the value $R_{K\text{-}90} = 25\ 812.807\ \Omega$, which the CIPM adopted effective from 1 January 1990 for the international realization of the ohm using the quantum Hall effect, by the fractional amount 17.793×10^{-9}. This implies that the unit of resistance realized using $R_{K\text{-}90}$ was larger than the present SI unit as realized using the value in (7.4) by the same fractional amount. Thus, the numerical value of a resistance measured in terms of $R_{K\text{-}90}$ would have been smaller by the same fractional amount as the numerical value of the identical resistance measured today in terms of the present SI ohm realized using the value of R_K given in (7.4).

7.2.2.3 Practical Realization of the Siemens, S, SI Derived Unit of Electric Conductance

The siemens S can be realized from a realization of the ohm, since S is related to Ω by the unit relation $S = \Omega^{-1}$.

7.2.2.4 Practical Realization of the Coulomb, C, SI Derived Unit of Electric Charge

The coulomb C can be realized as follows:

(a) By measuring the duration in terms of the SI unit of time, the second s, of the flow of an electric current known in terms of the ampere realized as indicated in Sect. 7.2.1 or

(b) By determining the amount of charge placed on a capacitance known in terms of the farad F realized by method (a) or (b), using the unit relation $C = F \cdot V$ and by measuring the voltage across the capacitance in terms of the volt V as realized by the Josephson effect and the value of the Josephson constant given in (7.3) or

(c) By using a SET or similar device to transfer a known amount of charge based on the value of e, given in the definition of the ampere, onto a suitable circuit element.

7.2.2.5 Practical Realization of the Farad, F, SI Derived Unit of Capacitance

The farad F can be realized as follows:

(a) By comparing the impedance of a known resistance obtained using the quantum Hall effect and the value of the von Klitzing constant given in (7.4), including a quantized Hall resistance itself, to the impedance of an unknown capacitance using, for example, a quadrature bridge or

(b) By using a calculable capacitor and the value of the electric constant given by (7.5).

7.2.2.6 Practical Realization of the Henry, H, SI Derived Unit of Inductance

The henry H can be realized as follows:

(a) By comparing the impedance of an unknown inductance to the impedance of a known capacitance with the aid of known resistances using, for example, a Maxwell–Wien bridge, where the known capacitance and resistances have been determined, for example, from the quantum Hall effect and the value of R_K given in (7.4) or

(b) By using a calculable inductor of, for example, the Campbell type of mutual inductor and the value of the magnetic constant μ_0 given by (7.8).

7.2.2.7 Practical Realization of the Watt, W, SI Derived Unit of Power

The watt W can be realized using electrical units by using the fact that electric power is equal to current times voltage, the unit relation based on Ohm's law, $W = V^2/\Omega$, and realizations of the volt and ohm using the Josephson and quantum Hall effects and the values of the Josephson and von Klitzing constants given in (7.3) and (7.4).

7.2.2.8 Practical Realization of the Tesla, T, SI Derived Unit of Magnetic Flux Density

The tesla T can be realized as follows:

(a) By using a solenoid, Helmholtz coil or other configuration of conductors of known dimensions carrying an electric current determined in terms of the ampere realized as discussed in Sect. 7.4 and the value of the magnetic constant μ_0 given in (7.8) in the calculation of the magnetic flux density generated by the current-carrying conductors or

(b) By using nuclear magnetic resonance (NMR) with a sample of known gyromagnetic ratio, for example, a spherical sample of pure H_2O at 25 °C and the most recent recommended value of the shielded gyromagnetic ratio of the proton γ_p given by CODATA.

7.2.2.9 Practical Realization of the Weber, Wb, SI Derived Unit of Magnetic Flux

The weber, symbol Wb, can be realized from the tesla based on the unit relation $Wb = T\ m^2$ or from the volt based on the unit relation $Wb = V\ s$. Use can also be made of the fact that the magnetic flux quantum Φ_0, which characterizes the magnetic properties of superconductors, is related to h and e as given in [1] by the exact relation $\Phi_0 = h/2e$.

7.2.2.10 Magnetic Constant μ_0 and Related Quantities

It may be noted that relationships among the magnetic constant (permeability of vacuum) μ_0, electric constant (permittivity of vacuum) ε_0, characteristic impedance of vacuum Z_0, admittance of vacuum Y_0 and speed of light in vacuum c have not changed due to the new definitions of the kilogram, ampere, kelvin and mole. Moreover, c has an exact value by new definition of the metre, m. The relationships among these constants are

$$\varepsilon_0 = 1/\mu_0 c^2 \tag{7.5}$$

$$Z_0 = \mu_0 c = (\mu_0/\varepsilon_0)^{1/2} \tag{7.6}$$

$$Y_0 = 1/\mu_0 c = (\varepsilon_0/\mu_0)^{1/2} = 1/Z_0. \tag{7.7}$$

However, the new definitions do affect the value of μ_0, and hence the values of ε_0, Z_0 and Y_0. In particular, μ_0 no longer has the exact value $4\pi \times 10^{-7}$ N A^{-2} and must be determined experimentally. The value of μ_0 can be obtained with a relative standard uncertainty, u_r, identical to that of the fine structure constant α from the exact relation

$$\mu_0 = \alpha \frac{2h}{ce^2}. \tag{7.8}$$

Since h, c and e have fixed numerical values, it follows from (7.5)–(7.8) relative uncertainty of these magnetic constants is same and equal to that of fine structure constant α.

$$u_r(\varepsilon_0) = u_r(\mu_0) = u_r(Y_0) = u_r(Z_0) = u_r(\alpha). \tag{7.9}$$

The recommended values of h, e, k and N_A resulting from the 2017 CODATA special least-squares adjustment of the values of the fundamental constants [3] were the basis of the exact values used for these four constants in the new definitions of the kilogram, ampere, kelvin and mole adopted by the 6th CGPM [1]. The 2017 special adjustment but with h, e, k and N_A taken to have the exact values used in the new definitions yields the following currently recommended value of the magnetic constant:

$$\begin{aligned} \mu_0 &= 4\pi \left[1 + 2.0(2.3) \times 10^{-10}\right] \times 10^{-7} \text{N A}^{-2} \\ &= 12.566\,370\,6169(29) \times 10^{-7} \text{NA}^{-2}. \end{aligned} \tag{7.10}$$

However, users should always compute the value from the most recent CODATA adjustment [4]. The values and uncertainties of the electric constant, characteristic impedance of vacuum and characteristic admittance of vacuum may always be obtained from the relationships of (7.5)–(7.8).

It should be recognized that the recommended values for μ_0, ε_0, Z_0 and Y_0 are expected to change slightly from one future CODATA adjustment to the next, as new data that influence the value of α become available. Users should, therefore, always employ the most up-to-date CODATA recommended values for these constants in their calculations. Of course, the values of h, e, k and N_A fixed by the new definitions will be unchanged from one adjustment to the next.

7.3 Mole

The mole, symbol mol, is the SI unit of amount of substance. Its magnitude is set by fixing the value of Avogadro constant N_A to be $6.022\ 140\ 76 \times 10^{23}$ elementary entities, when N_A is expressed in the unit mol^{-1} and is called the Avogadro number.

The amount of substance, symbol n, is a measure of the number of specified elementary entities, in the system. An elementary entity may be an atom, a molecule, an ion, an electron, any other particle or specified group of particles.

Thus, we have the exact relation

$$N_A = 6.022\ 141\ 29 \times 10^{23} \text{mol}^{-1}. \tag{7.11}$$

Inverting this equation gives an exact expression for the mole in terms of the defining constant

$$mol = \frac{6.022\ 141\ 28 \times 10^{23}}{N_A}. \tag{7.12}$$

The effect of this definition is that the mole is the amount of substance of a system that contains $6.022\ 141\ 29 \times 10^{23}$ specified elementary entities. So amount of substance, symbol n, is equal to multiple of mole giving

$$n = \frac{m \times 6.022\ 141\ 28 \times 10^{23}}{N_A} \text{mol} \tag{7.13}$$

or

$$n = \frac{N(X)}{N_A} \text{mol}. \tag{7.14}$$

Here $N(X)$ is the number of specific entity.

It may be noted that mole is no more connected with the unit of mass.

The previous definition of the mole fixed the value of the molar mass of carbon 12, i.e. $M(^{12}C)$ is 0.012 kg/mol, but now $M(^{12}C)$ is no longer taken as exact but is determined experimentally. However, the value chosen for N_A is such that at the time of adopting the new definition of the mole, $M(^{12}C)$ was equal to 0.012 kg/mol with a relative standard uncertainty of less than 1×10^{-9}.

The molar mass any atom or molecule X may still be obtained from its relative atomic mass from the equation

$$M(X) = Ar(X)[M(^{12}C)/12] = Ar(X)M\text{u} \tag{7.15}$$

and the molar mass of any atom or molecule X is also related to the mass of the elementary entity $m(X)$ by the relation

$$M(X) = N_A\, m(X) = N_A\, Ar(X)m\text{u}. \tag{7.16}$$

In these equations, Mu is the molar mass constant and is equal to $M(^{12}C)/12$, and mu is the unified atomic mass constant, which is equal to $m(^{12}C)/12$. They are related by the Avogadro constant through the relation

$$Mu = N_A mu. \tag{7.17}$$

In the phrase "amount of substance", the words "of substance" could simply be replaced by words to specify the substance concerned in any particular application, so that one may, for example, talk of "amount of sulphuric acid H_2SO_4", or "amount of benzene, C_6H_6". It is important to always give a precise specification of the entity involved. This should preferably be done by giving the molecular chemical formula of the material involved. Although the word "amount" has a more general dictionary definition, the abbreviation of the full name "amount of substance" to "amount" may often be used for brevity. This also applies to derived quantities such as "amount-of-substance concentration", which may simply be called "amount concentration". In the field of clinical chemistry, however, the name "amount-of-substance concentration" is generally abbreviated to "substance concentration".

7.4 Realization of Mole

The mole may be realized by a variety of primary methods. Three examples are discussed below.

7.4.1 Pure Sample

For a pure sample, the amount of substance n in the sample is the ratio of its measured mass m of the sample and the molar mass M, giving the relation:

$$n = m/M. \tag{7.18}$$

If the mass m is expressed in gram, and the molar mass M in g/mol, then the amount of substance n is obtained in mol. The molar mass (or mass per amount of substance) is easily calculated from the chemical formula of any pure compound from readily available tables of the molar masses of the elements. The molar mass of an element of naturally occurring isotopic composition is obtained from the molecular weight (i.e. relative molecular mass) by multiplying by the unit g/mol. The molar masses of all the nuclides are known and tabulated with a relative standard uncertainty of 10^{-7} or less, and for many elements less than 10^{-8}. For a naturally occurring sample of an element, it is generally necessary to calculate a weighted average over the isotopes using tables of relative abundance. Tabulated values of atomic weights are obtained in this way. This method of realizing the mole is generally the most precise method available, because measuring the mass of a sample is a relatively simple and accurate procedure. The mole may easily be realized with a relative standard uncertainty of less than 1 in 10^6 by this method. However, it is important to note that this procedure depends on having a pure sample of the material, which implies having a precise chemical analysis of the sample, and this will often be the limiting factor in an uncertainty evaluation.

7.4.2   Pure Gas

For a pure gas, the amount of substance may be determined from the equation of state for the gas in the form:

$$pV = nRT(1 + B(T)(n/V)\ldots) \tag{7.19}$$

where p and V are the pressure and volume, T is the temperature and R is the molar gas constant. The term involving the second virial coefficient $B(T)$ and possible higher terms involving the third viral coefficient are small corrections. When expressed in terms of pressure these corrections may be written in the form:

$$pV = nRT(1 + Bp(T)p\ldots) \tag{7.20}$$

where $Bp(T)$ is the second virial coefficient on a pressure basis. This shows that the correction terms may be eliminated by extrapolating to low pressure. For many purposes, at pressures below one atmosphere, the amount of substance may be calculated with sufficient accuracy from the ideal gas equation:

$$n = pV/RT. \tag{7.21}$$

Virial coefficients expressed in SI units are tabulated for a number of simple gases.

The molar gas constant R is known with a relative standard uncertainty of 1.7×10^{-6} (CODATA 2006) in the SI unit (Pa m^3 mol^{-1} K^{-1}), thus giving n in mol. The uncertainty in measurements of n made this way depend on the uncertainty in measuring p, V and T, and in correcting for gas imperfections. This method of realizing the mole for a gas is also dependent on the use of a pure sample of the gas.

7.4.3   Chemical Electrolysis

In chemical electrolysis, the amount of substance n liberated at an electrode is proportional to the charge Q passed through the system, and thus to the product of the electric current I multiplied by the time t for which it flows. The proportionality constant is the reciprocal of the charge number z of the ion that is liberated multiplied by the Faraday constant F, according to the following formula:

$$n = Q/zF = It/zF. \tag{7.22}$$

The Faraday constant F is known with a relative standard uncertainty of approximately 2.5×10^{-8} (CODATA 2006) in the SI unit (C/mol), thus giving n in mol.

7.5   Primary Method

A primary method of measurement is a method having the highest metrological qualities, whose operation can be completely described and understood, for which a complete uncertainty statement can be written down in terms of SI units, and whose results are, therefore, accepted without reference to a standard of the quantity being measured.

A primary direct method measures the value of an unknown without reference to a standard of the same quantity.

A primary ratio method measures the value of a ratio of an unknown to a standard of the same quantity; its operation must be completely described by a measurement equation.

The criteria used to determine whether a method has the potential to be primary are discussed in detail by Milton and Quinn [4].

References

1. 9th edition of the SI brochure, to be published. A draft is available on the BIPM web site
2. F. Delahaye, B. Jeckelmann, Revised technical guidelines for reliable dc measurements of the quantized Hall resistance. Metrologia **40**(5), 217–223 (2003)
3. D. Newell, F. Cabiati, J. Fischer, K. Fujii, S.G. Karshenboim, H.S. Margolis, E. de Mirandes, P.J. Mohr, F. Nez, K. Pachucki, T.J. Quinn, B.N. Taylor, M. Wang, B. Wood, Z. Zhang, The CODATA 2017 Values of h, e, k, and N A for the Revision of the SI. Metrologia **55**(1), L13–L16 (2018)
4. M.J.T. Milton, T.J. Quinn, Primary methods for the measurement of amount of substance. Metrologia **38**, 289–296 (2001)

Chapter 8
Boltzmann Constant Defining Kelvin K

8.1 Introduction to Boltzmann Constant

The Boltzmann constant k is a scaling factor between macroscopic (thermodynamic temperature) and microscopic (thermal energy) physics. Macroscopically, the ideal gas law states that, for an ideal gas, the product of pressure p and volume V is proportional to the product of amount of substance n (in moles) and absolute temperature T.

It is a fundamental constant of physics occurring in nearly every statistical formulation of both classical and quantum physics. The constant is named after Ludwig Boltzmann, a nineteenth-century Austrian physicist, who substantially contributed to the foundation and development of statistical mechanics, a branch of theoretical physics. Although Boltzmann published his famous definition of entropy in 1877, the constant of proportionality in Boltzmann's definition was not identified as Boltzmann's constant until 1900 when Planck published his analysis of blackbody radiation (1900a, 1900b), where he identified the constant and named it after Boltzmann.

Boltzmann constant has the same SI units as entropy in heat measurement. Its SI unit is JK^{-1}. It relates the average kinetic energy of a particle in a gas with the temperature of the gas. It is the gas constant R divided by the Avogadro constant N_A:

$$k = R/N_A$$

The physical significance of k is that it provides a measure of the amount of energy (i.e. heat) corresponding to the random thermal motions of the particles making up a substance. For a classical system at equilibrium at temperature T, the average energy per degree of freedom is $kT/2$. In the simplest example of a gas consisting of N non-interacting atoms, each atom has three translational degrees of

© Springer Nature Switzerland AG 2020
S. V. Gupta, *Units of Measurement*, Springer Series in Materials Science 122,
https://doi.org/10.1007/978-3-030-43969-9_8

freedom (it can move in the x-, y- or z-directions), and so the total thermal energy of the gas is $3NkT/2$. Here, N is the total number of entities in the gas.

We know that velocity of sound u_0 in a gaseous medium is given by

$$u_0 = \{\gamma p/\rho\}^{1/2} = \{\gamma p(/M/V)\}^{1/2} = \{\gamma V/M\}^{1/2} = \{\gamma RT/M\}^{1/2}. \quad (8.1)$$

Last equation shows that velocity of sound is independent of pressure of the ideal gas.

Here, p is a pressure on one mole of gas, and ρ is the molar density $= M/V$,

$$p\mathrm{V} = RT \text{ for one mole of gas} \quad (8.2)$$

γ is the ratio of two specific heats of gas at constant pressure and constant volume (C_p/C_V).

Replacing R by kN_A, we get square of the velocity of sound in an ideal gas

$$u_0^2 = \gamma \cdot k \cdot N_A \cdot T/M. \quad (8.3)$$

Here, γ is 5/3 for monotonic gases, but differ if gas is not perfectly a monotonic gas. We know the value of N_A Avogadro number a few parts in 100 million. So if u_0, T and M are measured, then k can be calculated. The method of determining k from the measurement of speed of sound is known as acoustic gas thermometry. In general, the methods of measurement of Boltzmann constant may be classified in the following groups.

- Acoustic gas thermometry AGT.
- Radiation thermometry: total radiation thermometry (TRT) and spectral-band-limited radiation thermometry (SRT).
- Thermal-equation-of-state methods: constant-volume gas thermometry (CVGT), dielectric-constant gas thermometry using audio frequency capacitance bridges (DCGT),
- Refractive-index gas thermometry applying optical resonators (RIGT) or microwave quasi-spherical cavity resonators (QSCR) and density measurement.
- Methods based directly on statistics and quantization: Johnson noise thermometry (JNT) and Doppler-broadening thermometry (DBT).

8.2 Acoustic Gas Thermometry AGT

The determination of the Boltzmann constant applying AGT is based on the relation

$$k = M u_0^2 / N_A \gamma T_{TPW}. \quad (8.4)$$

The formula is valid for an ideal gas, where M is the molar mass of the gas used; u_0 is the zero-frequency, zero-pressure limit of the speed of sound; and γ is the heat–capacity ratio of the specific heat capacities at constant pressure (c_p) and constant-volume (c_V), i.e. $\gamma = c_p/c_V$. The ratio of molar mass M to the Avogadro number N_A is the microscopic mass m of a gas particle, so (8.4) can be written in microscopic form as given below:

$$k = mu_0^2/(\gamma_0 T_{\text{TPW}}). \tag{8.5}$$

The pressure dependence of the speed of sound is of the second order, which is one main advantage of the AGT. In a real gas, it may be expressed by an expansion

$$u^2 = u_0^2\left(1 + \alpha p + \beta p^2 + \cdots\right). \tag{8.6}$$

The acoustic coefficients α and β can be expressed in terms of the temperature-dependent density virial coefficients $B(T)$ and $C(T)$. Applying (8.6), u_0 is determined by extrapolation to zero pressure, and k is calculated using (8.1). The main advantages of AGT are the second-order influence of pressure measurement and the low influence of the deformation of the apparatus under pressure. Compared with the other kinds of gas thermometry, it has quite different sources of error. Mainly two types of interferometers have been used to measure the speed of sound [1, 2]. Till recently, cylindrical interferometers with fixed frequency and variable paths were used. Nowadays, variable-frequency, fixed-path spherical or quasi-spherical resonators are preferred. The spherical resonators are 10 times better than cylindrical resonators. Furthermore, boundary-layer effects and the problems due to the excitation of different modes are smaller. The application of AGT with spherical or quasi-spherical resonators for primary thermometry in the temperature range from 7 to 505 K is described in [3–11].

Moldover et al. [12] assembled a 3-litre steel-walled spherical resonator. Its diagram is shown in Fig. 8.1. It is being used since 1986 to re-determine the gas constant R with a relative uncertainty of 1.7 ppm.

The resonance frequencies were measured by using electro-acoustic transducers T (black shade). The locations of the quite small capsule-type platinum-resistance thermometers are indicated by "PRT".

There are two advantages, of using helium gas over argon. First is that the number of necessary parameters in the virial expansion is smaller, and other is that the uncertainty of the molecular weight is negligible.

Presently, the dimensions of spherical or quasi-spherical resonators are determined by obtaining resonance with variable-frequency microwave sources. Earlier mercury was used to determine the volume of the resonators.

8.2.1 Measurement at NPL, UK

The researchers at NPL UK, in collaboration with Cranfield University and the Scottish Universities Environmental Research Centre (SUERC) [13] (see Metrologia, 2013, 50, 354–376), measured the value of k with an uncertainty of 0.7×10^{-6} with $k = 1.380 \times 6156 \ 10^{-23}$ JK^{-1}; they used acoustic gas

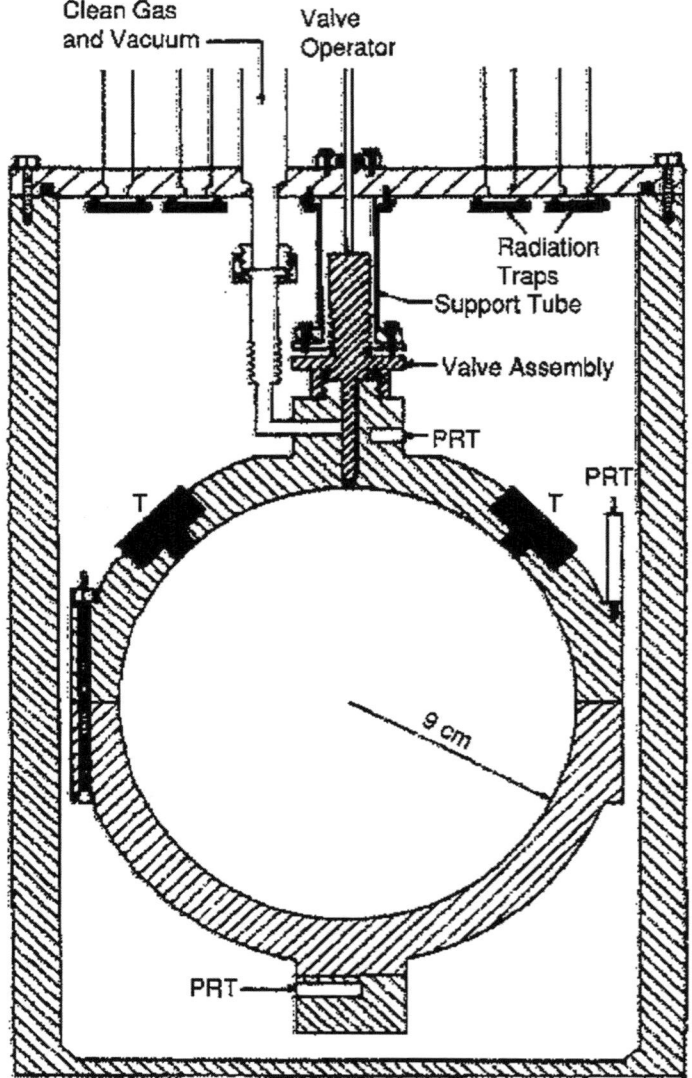

Fig. 8.1 Cross section of the 3-litre, steel-walled spherical resonator [12]

thermometry to make the measurement by building an acoustic resonator and making amazingly precise measurements of the speed of sound in argon gas.

The resonator cooled down to the temperature of the triple point of water, so the temperature is exactly known in the current definition of temperature and the resonator is filled with argon gas of known isotopic purity. There is a good facility at SUERC for analysing isotopic nature of gas filled in the resonator.

Then u_0 is calculated near zero pressure by extrapolating the required isotherm used the speed of sound measurement u_0 to calculate the average speed of the argon molecules to get the average amount of kinetic energy and hence the Boltzmann constant with an extremely high accuracy.

In order to achieve this high accuracy, the radius of the resonator is measured with equally high accuracy.

A single-crystal diamond cutting tool is used to produce four copper hemispheres. The best pair, when put together, formed a tri-axial ellipsoidal resonator that would be of the correct shape to within one-thousandth of a millimetre. The radius is then calculated using the specific frequencies at which the wavelength of microwaves exactly fits into the resonator and is measured with an overall uncertainty of 11.7 nm, which is the thickness of about 600 atoms.

To obtain low uncertainty in M, it requires meticulous gas handling and quantification of isotopic variations and chemical impurities, which can also affect γ. Low uncertainty in T is achieved by carrying out the experiment close to the temperature of the triple point of water, T_{TPW}. The entire experiment can be viewed as a primary measurement of the product $k_B T_{TPW}$, but because T_{TPW} is currently defined to be 273.16 K exactly, measuring the product allows a value of k.

The results of measurements of Boltzmann constant k by other national measurement institutes are summarized in Table 8.1.

8.2.2 Main Uncertainty Components

The main uncertainty components with the estimated limits of the standard uncertainty in parentheses are as follows:

1. determination of the dimensions of the spherical resonator (0.39 ppm),
2. traceability to the TPW (0.36 ppm),

Table 8.1 Values of k by acoustic gas thermometry AGT

Institute	Gas used	Ref.	Year	$k/10^{-23}$ JK^{-1}	Rel. uncertainty	Deviation from CODATA 2006
LNE- CNAM	Helium	[14]	2009	1.380×6495	2.7	−0.7 ppm
NPL	Argon	[16]	2010	1.380×6486	3.1	−0.6 ppm
INiRM	Helium	[17]	2010	1.380×6404	7.5	−7.3 ppm
LNE_CNAM	Argon	[15]	2011	1.380×6476	1.2	−2.0 ppm
NPL	Argon	[13]	2013	1.380×6156	0.7	−

Here
LNE-CNAM = Laboratoire National de Metrologie et d'Essais, France
NPL—National Physical Laboratory, UK
INiRM—Istituto Nazionale di Ricerca Metrologica, Italy

3. molecular weight of the measuring gas argon (0.42 ppm) and zero-pressure limit and
4. correction to frequency (0.69 ppm).

For the first component, it might be problematic that in finding out the volume of resonators, mercury has been used whose density values were determined many years ago. To avoid any doubt, it is intended to derive the dimensions of the spherical or quasi-spherical resonator from the resonance frequencies of microwave modes in the resonator without referring to the density of mercury. Indeed, it would be essential progress compared with the method used at NIST. Several microwave modes will be used to evaluate the perturbations of the modes due to different effects. In their talks, Marcarino and Gavioso described at the workshop that new AGT measurements to determine the Boltzmann constant will be performed in a collaboration of Istituto di Metrologia "Gustavo Colonnetti" (IMGC-CNR) and Istituto Elettrotecnico Nazionale Galileo Ferraris (IEN), Italy. These two institutes are recently merged into one institute called Istituto Nazionale di Ricerca Metrologica (INRiM).

8.3   Radiation Thermometry

Employing measurements of absolute blackbody radiation, i.e. primary thermometry, is based on Planck's law [18]. The principle of radiometric measurement is equating the electrical heat energy to the radiation energy absorbed by the detector for raising the same temperature in each case. From the Planck radiation law, we can have equation for the spectral radiance versus frequency v (8.7) or integral of this spectral distribution over the entire frequency which gives Stefan Boltzmann constant (8.8). *So* there are two methods of using radiation law for measurement of Boltzmann constant k. If we determine the integral of L_v over the entire frequency range, we get σ. This method is called as total radiometry or total radiation thermometry (TRT). If we use the spectral radiation law, then the method is called spectral-band-limited radiation thermometry SRT.

$$Lv = \frac{2hv^3}{c_0^2} \frac{1}{\left[\exp\left(\frac{2hv}{RT}\right) - 1\right]} \tag{8.7}$$

$$L = \int_0^\infty Lv dv_v = \sigma T^4/\pi. \tag{8.8}$$

Here, σ is Stefan–Boltzmann constant and

$$\sigma = 2\pi^5 k^4/15c_0^2 h^3. \tag{8.9}$$

8.3.1   Total Radiation Thermometry TRT (Stefan–Boltzmann Measurement)

The use of electrical substitution radiometer (ESR) was introduced in late 1970 with the prospect of attaining measurement uncertainties well below 0.1% or even below 0.01%. The ESR was first operated at cryogenic temperature at the National Physical Laboratory (NPL), UK [19]. This "cryogenic radiometer" was employed for a determination of the Stefan–Boltzmann constant [20].

The relative uncertainty in measurement of σ was 1.3×10^{-4}. As the k, Boltzmann constant raised to 4th power, is proportional to Stefan–Boltzmann constant, the relative uncertainty of the Boltzmann constant would come to 3.2×10^{-5}. The main contributions to this uncertainty are from the thermal radiation transfer function (25 ppm), diffraction (18 ppm), absorption of the aperture land (5 ppm) and scatter (5 ppm).

With a specialized device, its "absolute radiation detector", the NPL expects to measure L (and thus σ) at the triple point of water (TPW) with a relative uncertainty of 2×10^{-5}, which would in turn allow them to determine k with a relative uncertainty of 5×10^{-6}.

Strictly, exploitation of the Stefan–Boltzmann law in order to determine k should be done with a perfectly "black" radiation detector (inverse blackbody) with full absorption and emissivity (each being equal to 1) over the whole spectral range which contributes to the integral of $L\nu$.

It may be noticed that one thousand part of the total thermal radiation is emitted at wavelengths greater than about 200 μm at the triple point of water (TPW) and about one-millionth part of it have wavelengths greater than 2 mm. Cavity detectors of cryogenic radiometers can be designed to very nearly fulfil this condition over a wide spectral range, and absorption corrections can be determined with the help of Monte Carlo simulations. Nevertheless, the uncertainty of these corrections will become a hindrance if a relative uncertainty level of 10^{-5} is to be reached for σ.

Moreover, without imaging optics it is not L that is measured by a radiation detector, but rather the radiation power received. In order to have a well-defined relation of the power received by the detector to the radiance emitted by the blackbody, some "geometrical" system of apertures has to be mounted in between the detector and the blackbody. Determination of the effects of this system is no problem in the limit of geometrical optics, if all dimensions are exactly known. However, the uncertainties connected with the determination of "radiometric" aperture areas as well as corrections for diffraction and scattering by the aperture edges will also become very problematic at the 10^{-5} relative uncertainty level. Fox [3] analysed the potential to reach the envisaged uncertainties and reported especially how to solve the difficulties with the scattering in the radiation trap connecting the blackbody and the detector. The scattering needed in the past a significant correction of 2.3×10^{-4}.

Taking into account all of this information, a determination of the Boltzmann constant with a reliable relative uncertainty of 5×10^{-6} would certainly have to be considered a major advance in absolute radiation thermometry.

8.3.2 Spectral-Band-Limited Radiation Thermometry

As compared to total radiation thermometry, this method can be set up to operate only around v_{max}, i.e. around the maximum of radiation emission (Fig. 8.2a), thus reaching a better signal-to-noise ratio and avoiding the problem of very long-wavelength radiation. With a view to the propagation of uncertainty, it may be advantageous to perform the measurement at somewhat higher frequencies, where L_v does start to decrease sharply. The spectral band is defined by some filters. The additional uncertainty of the calibration of the filter transmission (or expediently of the spectral responsivity of the whole filter radiometer, i.e. the filter–detector assembly) is taken into account, which cannot be lower than the uncertainty of the cryogenic radiometer used for calibration. This results in the best relative uncertainties at the 10^{-4} level for this type of radiation thermometry and measurements at temperatures of about 500 oC and above [21, 22]. Since the uncertainty will not diminish with decreasing temperature, 5×10^{-5} is presently considered a realistic estimate for the relative uncertainty of k that can be reached by measurement at the *TPW*. Accordingly, spectral-band-limited radiation thermometry is not expected to contribute to an improvement of the present uncertainty of k. Nevertheless, spectral-band-limited radiation thermometry would be very useful for improved dissemination of a temperature scale based on a fixed value of k, in particular, at high temperatures.

Fig. 8.2 Spectral band radiation thermometry

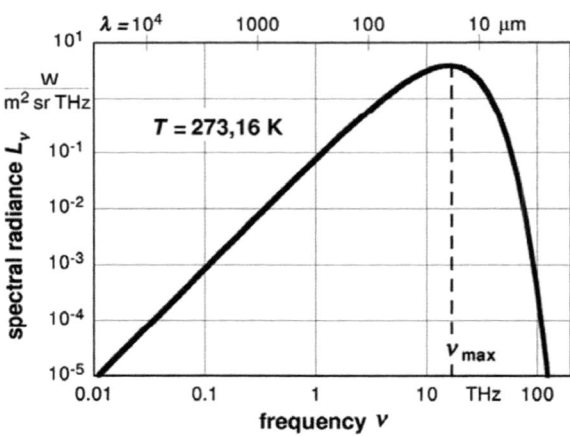

8.4 Thermal-Equation-of-State Methods

In general, there are three different methods of gas thermometry, namely,
method of constant volume gas thermometry (CVGT),
method of constant pressure (CPGT) and
method of constant bulb temperature (CTGT).
But nowadays, only CVGT is used because it yields the smallest uncertainty.

8.4.1 Constant-Volume Gas Thermometry (CVGT)

Equation of state for ideal gas is given as

$$pV = n_{\mathrm{m}}RT. \tag{8.10}$$

At finite pressures and densities, the behaviour of a real gas can be described by
the virial expansion

$$pV = n_m RT \left(1 + B(T)/V_m + C(T)/V_m^2 + \cdots \right), \tag{8.11}$$

where $B(T)$ and $C(T)$ are, respectively, the temperature-dependent second and third
density virial coefficients and $V_m = V/n_m$ is the molar volume.

Primary CVGT can be performed using either absolute or relative pV-isotherm
CVGT. For determination of Boltzmann constant k, in the technique of absolute
pV-isotherm (CVGT), the gas bulb is kept at a constant temperature T *and* is
filled with a series of increasing amounts of gas. This changes the pressure inside
the bulb and is measured as accurately to obtain a series of pressures p. The ratio
$pV/n_{\mathrm{m}} = pV_{\mathrm{m}}$ is plotted against $1/V_{\mathrm{m}}$. The isotherm will cut pV_{m} axis, giving the
value of RT. For this method, it is not necessary to know the virial coefficients
because the extrapolation to zero pressure is made by fitting a virial expansion
to the experimental data. Knowledge of RT and value of N_A gives the measured
value of k.

8.4.2 Dielectric-Constant Gas Thermometry

The basic principle of DCGT is to replace the density in the state equation of a gas
by the dielectric constant ε and to measure it by incorporating a capacitor in the
gas bulb. The dielectric constant of an ideal gas is given by the relation

$$\varepsilon = \varepsilon_0 + \alpha_0 N/V, \tag{8.12}$$

giving

$$\mathrm{N/V} = (\varepsilon - \varepsilon_0)/\alpha_0. \tag{8.13}$$

Ideal gas equation

$$p = (N/V)\,kT,$$

giving

$$p = kT(\varepsilon - \varepsilon_0)/\alpha_0, \tag{8.14}$$

where ε_0 is the exactly known electric constant (permittivity of free space) and is related with permeability of free space μ_0 by $\mu_0\,\varepsilon_0 = c^2$; here, c is the velocity of light, α_0 is the static electric dipole polarizability of the atoms and N/V is the number density;

Similar to Acoustic gas thermometry AGT, formula for DCGT also does not contain density term. Hence, its troublesome determination is not needed. In addition, the pressure-sensing tubes can be of any convenient size and the thermometric gas can be moved in or out of the bulb without the need to allow for the amount of gas involved.

A compensating disadvantage of DCGT is the need to measure a dielectric constant, which is very close to unity. Absolute DCGT requires knowledge of the static electric dipole polarizability α_0 with the necessary accuracy. Nowadays, this condition is fulfilled for helium, which has become a model substance for evaluating the accuracy of ab initio calculations of thermophysical properties. Recent progress has decreased the uncertainty of the ab initio value of α_0 well below one part in 10^6 [23–25]. The molar polarizability $A\varepsilon$ is defined as $A\varepsilon = N_A\alpha_0/(3\varepsilon_0)$, i.e. the Boltzmann constant is related to α_0, $A\varepsilon$ and the molar gas constant R by

$$k = (R/A_\varepsilon)\alpha_0/3\varepsilon_0. \tag{8.15}$$

The measurement of the ratio $A\varepsilon/R$ of two macroscopic quantities gives the value of k without knowledge of the Avogadro constant. The performed *ab initio* calculations yielded exactly the static electric dipole polarizability of the ^1S ground state of the ^4He atom in the ^4He reduced atomic unit of polarizability.

$$\alpha_0\left(^4He\right) = \alpha_0\left(^4He\right)/4\pi\,\varepsilon_0 a^3(1 + m_e/m_\alpha)^3. \tag{8.16}$$

Here,

a_0 is the Bohr radius and m_e/m_α is the electron to α particle mass ratio. With this relation, the complete expression for k becomes

$$k = (4\pi/3)\alpha_0^3(1 + m_e/m_\alpha)^3\alpha^*\left(^4He\right)/(A\varepsilon/R)_{4\,He}. \tag{8.17}$$

The standard uncertainty of a_0 is 3.3×10^{-9} and m_e/m_α is 4.4×10^{-10} as per 2002 CODATA [23]. For a real gas, the interaction between the particles has to be considered by combining the virial expansions of the state equation and the Clausius–Mossotti equation. When neglecting higher order terms and the very small dielectric virial coefficients, this yields

$$p \approx \{\chi/(3A_\varepsilon/RT + \kappa_{eff})\}\left[1 + B(T)\chi/3A_\varepsilon + C(T)\left(\chi 2/(3A_\varepsilon)^2 + \cdots\right], \tag{8.18}$$

where $\chi = (\varepsilon/\varepsilon_{0-1})$ is the dielectric susceptibility, considering the pair and triplet interactions, $B(T)$ and $C(T)$ are, respectively, the second and third density virial coefficients, and κeff is the effective compressibility of a suitable capacitor used to measure the susceptibility χ. For determining $3A_\varepsilon/RT$, isotherms have to be measured. Writing the relative change in capacitance—Rel(C(p)), we get

$$\mathrm{Rel}(C(p)) = (C(p) - C(0))/C(0) = \chi + (\varepsilon/\varepsilon 0)p\kappa_{\mathrm{eff}}. \tag{8.19}$$

Rel(p)) of the gas-filled capacitor is determined as a function of the pressure p of the gas by the capacitance $C(p)$ of the capacitor with the space between its electrodes filled with the gas at various pressures p and C(0) is capacity after evacuating the space between its electrode, i.e. $p = 0$. A polynomial fit to the between p versus Rel(C(p)) data points is established. With knowledge of the pressure dependence of the dimensions of the capacitor (effective compressibility κeff) yields $3A\varepsilon/RT$. Since the susceptibilities of gases are very small (for example, susceptibility of helium gas is 7×10^{-5} at the *TPW* and 0.1 MPa), they cannot be determined via absolute capacitance measurements. However, the necessary measurement of the relative capacitance changes with an uncertainty of a few parts in 10^9 causes extreme demands on the parameters of the audio frequency capacitance bridge.

8.4.3 Results

Gaiser et al. published an improved value of k as $1.380 \times 6509 \times 10^{-23}$ J K^{-1} in 2013 [26] at triple point of water TPW. The relative standard uncertainty is 4.3 parts per million (4.3 ppm)). By improving upon the design and assembly of the measuring capacitors, the determination of effective compressibility, the determination of their effective compressibility, the sensitivity of the capacitance bridge and the scattering and the evaluation of the data, the combination of these two values with the 2013 result, fully taking into account the correlations, has yielded a final result of $k = 1.380 \times 6482 \times 10^{-23}$ J K^{-1} with a relative standard uncertainty of 1.9 ppm. This value is about 0.2 ppm smaller than the CODATA 2014 one, which has a relative standard uncertainty of 0.57 ppm.

The Boltzmann constant k has been determined by dielectric-constant gas thermometry at PTB, Germany. In the pressure range from about 1 MPa to 7 MPa, 11 helium isotherms have been measured at the triple point of water (TPW) by applying a new special experimental setup consisting of a large-volume thermostat, a vacuum-isolated measuring system, stainless-steel 10 pF cylindrical capacitors, an autotransformer ratio capacitance bridge, a high-purity gas-handling system including a mass spectrometer and traceably calibrated special pressure balances with piston–cylinder assemblies having effective areas of 2 cm^2. The value of k has been deduced from the linear, ideal-gas term of an appropriate virial expansion fitted to the combined isotherms. The main uncertainty components result from the measurement of pressure and capacitance as well as the influence of the effective compressibility of the measuring capacitor and impurities contained in the helium gas. The combination of the results obtained at the triple point of water (TPW) $k_{TPW} = 1.380 \times 654 \times 10^{-23}$ JK^{-1} with relative standard uncertainty 9.2 parts per million with data measured earlier at low temperatures (21–27 K), $k_{LT} = 1.380 \times 657 \times 10^{-23}$ JK^{-1} with 15.9 parts per million, has yielded a value of $k = 1.380 \times 655 \times 10^{-23}$ JK^{-1} with uncertainty of 7.9 parts per million.

Michael de Podesta et al. [27) evaluated k from exceptionally accurate measurements of the speed of sound in argon gas which can be related directly to the mean molecular kinetic energy. Newly estimated $k = 1.380\ 651\ 56\ (98) \times 10^{-23}$ JK^{-1} with a relative standard uncertainty $u = 0.71 \times 10^{-6}$.

Pitre et al. [28] using AGT reported the value of R as 8.314 4614(50) J· mol^{-1}· K^{-1}. Using the best available value of the Avogadro constant, they obtained the value of k as 1.380 648 78(83) $\times 10^{-23}$ J· K^{-1} with $u(k)/k = 0.60 \times 10^{-6}$. This value is consistent with the previous determinations and with that of the 2014 CODATA published in 2016 *Rev. Mod. Phys.* **88** 035009.

Up till now, primary DCGT using conventional cylindrical capacitors for determining ε has been performed by two groups in the range from about 3 K to 27 K [29–31]. The obtained relative uncertainties are of the order of 10^{-5}. The results described in [31] yielded a value of k that has at present the smallest uncertainty for a direct determination (without knowledge of the Avogadro constant). A ratio $A\varepsilon/R$ of 6.221 12(19) $\times 10^{-8}$ K Pa^{-1} has been measured, leading to $k = 1.380$ 65(4) $\times 10^{-23}$ J K^{-1} applying (8.6), the values of a_0 and *me/mα* recommended in [2], and a copy of the gas thermometer scale NPL-75 as thermodynamic reference [32, 33]. This value of the Boltzmann constant differs relatively from the value recommended by CODATA (1.380 6505(24) $\times 10^{-23}$ J K^{-1} by no more than four parts in 10^7, which is well within the uncertainty level of about 30 parts per million. The main deficiency of the conventional cylindrical capacitors used to date is the fact that the whole length of the capacitor electrodes influences the effective compressibility κeff. For instance, for the system described in [31], the main uncertainty components result from the measurement of pressure p (5 ppm), relative capacitance changes *(C(p) − C(0))/C(0)* (3 ppm) and temperature (2 ppm).

8.5 Refractive-Index Gas Thermometry RIGT

Refractive-index gas thermometry (RIGT) was first suggested by Colclough in 1974 [34]. The method is based on the Lorentz–Lorenz law which expresses dielectric constant.

The Clausius–Mossotti **relation** expresses the dielectric constant (relative permittivity, ε_r) of a material in terms of the atomic polarizability α, of the material. Its equivalent is the Lorentz–Lorenz equation, where ε_r is replaced by square of refractive index n. The relation between relative permittivity and atomic polarizability is

$$\frac{\epsilon_r - 1}{\epsilon_r + 2} = \frac{N\alpha}{3\,\epsilon_0}. \tag{8.20}$$

Here

    ε_0 is the permittivity of free space,

    N is the number density of the molecules or entity and

    α is the molecular polarizability in SI units ($C \cdot m^2/V$).

The Lorentz–Lorenz equation is similar to the Clausius–Mossotti relation, except that it relates the refractive index rather than the dielectric constant of a substance to its polarizability. The Lorentz–Lorenz equation is named after the Danish mathematician and scientist Ludvig Lorenz who published it in 1869, and the Dutch physicist Hendrik Lorentz, who discovered it independently in 1878.

The most general form of the Lorentz–Lorenz equation is

$$\frac{n^2 - 1}{n^2 + 2} = \frac{4\pi}{3} N\alpha_m, \tag{8.21}$$

where n is the refractive index, N is the number of molecules or entity per unit volume and α_m is the mean polarizability. This equation is approximately valid for homogeneous solids as well as liquids and gases.

When for many gases the square of the refractive index is $n^2 \cong 1$, (8.10) reduces to

$$n^2 - 1 = 4\pi N\alpha_m \tag{8.22}$$

or simply

$$n - 1 = 2\pi\alpha_m. \tag{8.23}$$

For gases at ordinary pressures, the refractive index of the gas n can then be expressed in terms of the molar refractivity A as

$$n = \sqrt{1 + \frac{A \cdot p}{RT}}, \tag{8.24}$$

where p is the pressure of the gas, R is the gas constant and T is the (absolute) temperature.

Applying the virial expansion for a real gas, the law can be written in the form

$$\frac{n^2 - 1}{n^2 + 2} = A\epsilon\rho + B_R\rho^2 + C_R\rho^3 + \ldots \tag{8.25}$$

where n is the refractive index, $\rho = n_m/V$ is the molar density, and B_R and C_R are the second and third refractivity virial coefficients, respectively. For most of gases, n^2 is very nearly 1 so it may be replaced by 1 in the denominator. For ideal gas, i.e. taking B_R and C_R as zero and writing p/RT in place of ρ, (8.25) becomes

$$\left(n^2 - 1\right) = 3A\varepsilon(p/RT) = (p/kT)(\alpha_0/\varepsilon_0). \tag{8.26}$$

The above equation was tested, for the first time [35], with Michelson–Morley interferometer with one arm evacuated and the other filled with helium gas; Fringe counting system was applied to determine the change in the refractive index. This refractometer seems to have large uncertainties since its length and the pressure distortions were not experimentally determined accurately. Later on, a Fabry–Perot cavity (FPC) was used as the refractometer. A tunable laser is locked to the transmission maximum of the FPC to find the resonance frequency v_{reso} the specific state of the gas-filled cavity. In the first order, this frequency is connected with the refractive index according to

$$v_{res=q} \frac{c_0}{2.n.\delta},$$

(8.27)

where c_0 is the speed of light in the vacuum, δ is the length of the cavity and q is an integer for an FPC. The measured frequency has a sufficiently small uncertainty. The experiments of Stone and Stejskal [35] aimed at measuring the refractivity of nitrogen is a proof of principle. The pressure-induced distortions of the cavity caused the main uncertainty component.

May et al. [36] using quasi-spherical cavity (QSCR) measured relative permeability ε_r of helium gas at 289 K and pressures up to 7 MPa. The value of ε_r coincides within about 0.2 ppm. The Boltzmann constant k when calculated from the values ε_r yielded an uncertainty of about 40 ppm at the highest pressure. It may be noted that the dimensions of the QSCR were determined by a coordinate measurement machine with 10 ppm uncertainty level or better, depending on the properties of the surface under study.

8.6 Doppler-Broadening Thermometry

Joachim Fischer [37] described methods of determinations of Boltzmann constant in his paper of 2015. The one described here is more or less from his paper.

Consider a plane electromagnetic wave—a laser beam with frequency v and propagating along x-axis in the laboratory frame of reference, and an atom or molecule moving with constant velocity $v = c_0 \beta$ along the axis of laser beam. The frequency observed in the atomic rest frame is Doppler-shifted to

$$v_d = v(1 - \beta)/\left(1 - \beta^2\right)^{1/2}.$$

(8.28)

We are interested to thermal velocities at temperatures of about 300 K; this means typical values of $\beta = v/c_0$ are around 10^{-6}, so it may be sufficient to consider only the linear Doppler shift, i.e. neglecting the term $(1-\beta^2)$, the Doppler-shifted frequency is given by

$$v_d = v(1 - \beta).$$

(8.29)

Now let us consider the situation the other way round and assume that the atom has a sharp absorption resonance at a frequency which is v_d for an atom at rest, and that a tuneable laser at rest in the laboratory is used to irradiate the atom moving with velocity v. Then in a linear approximation, laser radiation will be absorbed if the laser is tuned to frequency v_d.

The Gaussian Maxwell probability density function for velocity V_x is proportional to

$$\exp\left[-(V_X/V_0)^2\right], \tag{8.30}$$

where
$V_0^2 = 2kT/m$ and m is the atomic mass of gas.

Around the absorption frequency ν_D, the profile of Doppler-broadened absorption line is proportional to

$$\left[\exp\left[-(\nu/\nu_D)^2\right], \tag{8.31}\right.$$

where

$$\nu = v - \nu_D, \text{ and} \tag{8.32}$$

$$\nu_D = \left(2kT/mc^2\right)^{1/2} \text{ is the Doppler width.} \tag{8.33}$$

This relation allows the determination of the Boltzmann constant by spectroscopic measurement of a Doppler-broadened absorption line profile and determination of its width. In principle, the measurement can be done using standard laser spectroscopic techniques. The main advantage of DBT compared to other optical methods, like absolute radiation thermometry, is that the Doppler profile can be determined by relative radiation measurements since only the width is of interest here. Moreover, laser frequencies can be controlled with extremely small uncertainties. However, at the 10^{-6} uncertainty level, various other sources of uncertainty will have to be investigated in detail. Apart from the quadratic Doppler effect, these include, among many others, the effects brought about by interatomic interactions, notably additional line-broadening mechanisms (collisional, transit time and saturation) and the reduction of Doppler broadening caused by a finite mean-free-path length (Dicke narrowing). Due to these effects, measurements have to be performed at a series of pressure values and extrapolated to zero pressure.

The DBT has several differences from other better-established methods of primary gas thermometry, besides the basic principles of operation. It can take advantage of recently developed technologies of optical-frequency metrology and from an extrapolation to zero pressure with the required uncertainty. The gas pressure varies from 0.1 Pa to 500 Pa, which is a few orders of magnitude smaller than the pressure of the AGT and DCGT experiments.

Therefore, this method is better in comparison to the other gas-based thermometers.

Laboratoire de Physique des Lasers (LPL) in cooperation with LNE-CNAM obtained in 2007 the value $k = 1.380\,65 \times 10^{-23}$ J K^{-1} with a relative uncertainty of 1.9×10^{-4} [38]. They used an ammonia line ($^{14}NH_3$) probed by a CO_2 laser spectrometer close to 30 THz corresponding to a wavelength of 10.35 μm. The absorption signal was recorded by splitting the laser beam into two, and then propagating one of the two beams through the ammonia cell for spectroscopy while the other was used as a reference beam. In further refinements, LPL evaluated a series of 1420 ammonia spectra and corrected it for the hyperfine structure of the absorption lines [39] and obtained the value of k as $1.380\,70\,4 \times 10^{-23}$ J K^{-1} with a relative uncertainty of 5×10^{-5} [40].

A second group at the Second University of Naples, in collaboration with the Polytechnic University of Milan and INRiM, has been performing DBT. They began by investigating a CO_2 line at a wavelength of 2 μm and obtained $k = 1.380\,58 \times 10^{-23}$ J K^{-1} with a relative uncertainty of 1.6×10^{-4} [40, 41]. Experiments were performed at pressures between 70 Pa and 130 Pa, a range for which Dicke-narrowing and speed-dependent effects could be neglected. By improving various aspects of Doppler broadening, new value of Boltzmann constant given by them is $1.380\,631 \times 10^{-23}$ J K^{-1} with a relative uncertainty of 24×10^{-6} [42]. The two single uncertainties with the largest contributions are type A (15.7×10^{-6}) and line shape modelling (14.9×10^{-6}).

8.7 Noise Thermometry

The average time of the square of noise voltage, $\langle U^2 \rangle$, developed in a resistor R_{el} is the basis of Johnson noise thermometer. Nyquist [43], from the thermodynamic principles, gave an expression between (U^2), thermodynamic temperature T, Boltzmann constant k, frequency- independent resistance R and bandwidth Δf. The expression (8.34) is valid for frequencies $f \ll kT/h$. For instance, kT/h amounts to about 6 THz at the triple point of water TPW.

$$\left(U^2 \right) = 4kTR\Delta f. \tag{8.34}$$

Relative uncertainty u$_r$ in temperature T is given as

$$u_r(T) \approx 2.5\sqrt{(t\Delta v)}. \tag{8.35}$$

Here, t is the time and Δv is the frequency bandwidth.

Keeping in view the statistical nature of the measured quantity, long measuring time t is required.

One of the main problems is the accurate measurement of the very small voltages avoiding extraneous sources of noise and maintaining a constant bandwidth and gain of the amplifiers [44].

Bandwidth and gain are usually not determined directly. Rather, a calibration is performed using a resistor at a known temperature or a voltage standard. Only in the latter case can (voltage standard) the Boltzmann constant is directly determined from the ratio of two macroscopic quantities $(U^2)/R$ if the temperature T is known.

The noise thermometry did not do better than those of gas-based techniques due to limitations from the non-ideal performance of electronic detection systems. In the past, in the high-temperature range, the uncertainties of noise thermometry have been larger than obtained from other gas technologies. By using four-wire system and using two amplifier chains, the noise generated by the wires which connect the sensor to the amplifiers has to be eliminated. The most successful technique to date is the switched-input digital correlator pioneered by Brixy and others [44, 45]. The correlator is implemented by digitizing the signals from the two channels and carrying out the multiplication and averaging function by software. This eliminates the amplifier and transmission line noise superimposed on the thermal noise signal. In use, the thermometer switches between a reference and the thermal noise source at the temperature T. The switching also removes the effects of drift on the gain and bandwidth of the amplifiers and filters. NIST developed a new approach using the perfect quantization of voltages from the Josephson effect [46]. This approach keeps the proven elements of the switched correlator but separates the roles of the temperature reference and the voltage reference. The sensing resistor in the reference arm of the comparator is replaced by a quantum-voltage noise source Vr. A block diagram is shown in Fig. 8.3.

The measurement of the Boltzmann constant by quantum-voltage noise method is quite different from gas-based measurement techniques, as the method has a purely electronic approach that links the kelvin to quantum-based electrical measurements. The quantum-voltage noise source, which is a low-voltage realization of the superconducting Josephson arbitrary waveform synthesizer, is programmed to produce multi-tonne pseudo-noise voltage waveforms with small amplitudes ($<1\,\mu$V peak). The voltage pulses have time-integrated areas perfectly quantized in integer values of $h/2e$, where e is the elementary charge. The synthesized voltage is intrinsically accurate because it is exactly determined from the known sequence of pulses, the clock frequency and fundamental physical constants. The resistance R_{el} of the thermal resistor is determined traceable to the quantum hall effect. With this new approach, NIST determined the Boltzmann constant to be $k = 1.380\ 652 \times 10^{-23}$ J K^{-1} [47]. It was NIST's first measurement of k with this electronic technique, and the first noise thermometry measurement to achieve a relative uncertainty of 12 parts in 10^6.

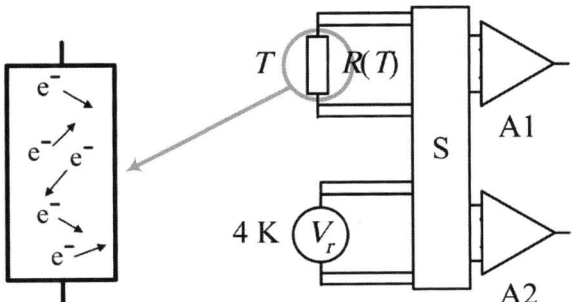

Fig. 8.3 Noise thermometry

An advanced system for a more efficient measurement is being developed at NIST, USA: The two-channel system will be replaced by a four-channel system in a very compact setting with a four-channel ADC readout. The bandwidth of the system will be increased by switching to amplifiers with increased bandwidth, lower or comparable noise and higher linearity. In the most recent measurements, NIST used a 200 Ω sensing resistor that reduced the statistical uncertainty by 25% in the same measurement period compared to that of a 100 Ω sensing resistor. However, the measurements of the 200 Ω sensing resistor show differences of -10×10^{-6} and $+27 \times 10^{-6}$ between the measured and CODATA values of k for the waveforms of the 800 Hz and 100 Hz tone spacing, respectively. For both sets of data, the statistical uncertainty is 16×10^{-6}. The larger correlated current noise of this 200 Ω measurement appears not to affect the measurement of k, probably because all associated effects are removed by fitting, as are the other quadratic effects [49]. Experiments are ongoing at NIST to understand especially the sources of spectral aberrations. The workshop on methods for new determinations of the Boltzmann constant k held on 21 January 2005, at PTB, Germany [50]. Moldover analysed the state-of-the-art measurement techniques and claimed that a relative uncertainty of k of one part in 10^6 (1 ppm) could be obtained.

8.8   Realization of K (Hierarchy of Temperature)

Formulae employed in various methods, discussed above, are given in Table 8.2. Either of the methods can be used to realize kelvin symbol K from Boltzmann constant k, with kelvin symbol K.

Here,

u_0 = speed of sound, $\gamma = Cp/C_V$ adiabatic exponent, R molar gas constant, T thermodynamic temperature, M molar mass, p pressure, k Boltzmann constant, ε dielectric constant (permittivity), ε_0 electric constant, α_0 static electric dipole polarizability, n refractive index, $\langle U^2 \rangle$ mean square noise voltage, R_{el} is resistance independent of frequency, Δf bandwidth, Δ_{VD} Doppler width, v_0 absorption frequency, m atomic mass and c_0 speed of light.

The defining constant k is related to the triple point of water (*TWP*) when determining the Boltzmann constant k by any of the methods mentioned in Table 8.2.

Table 8.2 Formulae used in primary thermometry

Acoustic gas thermometry	$u_0 = \sqrt{\frac{\gamma RT}{M}}$
Dielectric-constant gas thermometry	$p = \frac{kT(\epsilon - \epsilon_0)}{a_0}$
Refractive-index gas thermometry	$p = kT \left(n^2 - 1 \right) \epsilon_0 / a_0$
Doppler-broadening thermometry	$\Delta v_D = \left(2kT/mc^2 \right)^{1/2} v_0$
John noise thermometry	$< U^2 >= 4kTR_{el}\Delta f$

All measurements are done at triple point of water. Isotopic constituents of water are known, and necessary corrections are applied if isotopic composition is different from that of Vienna mean ocean water (VSMOW). For example, considering acoustic gas thermometry AGT the Boltzmann constant k is related to other gas parameters as follows:

$$k = M \frac{u_0^2}{\gamma T} \quad \text{or } T = M \frac{u_0^2}{\gamma k}.$$

We measure velocity of sound at zero pressure in helium or argon gas and calculate the value of T (Triple point of water) for the defining value of k and thus establish experimentally the value of triple point of water.

8.8.1 Temperature Scale

For temperatures other than the triple point of water, direct measurement of thermodynamic temperature is required. For this purpose, a primary thermometer based on a well-understood physical system whose temperature may be derived from measurements of other quantities is required. In practice, primary thermometry is difficult and time-consuming and not a practical means of disseminating the kelvin.

As an alternative, a set of transition temperatures of pure elements is called as a scale. Transition temperature is the temperature at which an element changes from one state to another without any change in temperature. Every fixed melting or freezing temperature is experimentally determined and connected with each other in steps derived by *TPW*, the International Temperature Scale. Each such scale provides an internationally accepted procedure for realizing temperature in a practical way.

8.8.2 Different Temperature Scales

CIPM (International Committee on Weights and Measures) announced the first temperature scale in 1927. In this case, the CIPM acted under the authority of the General Conference on Weights and Measures (CGPM). Since 1937, CIPM started acting on the advice of its Consultative Committee for Thermometry (CCT). It has adopted a series of International Temperature Scales. Subsequent to the 1927 scale, new scales have been adopted in 1948, 1968 and 1990, with occasional minor revisions in intervening years. The present scale, the International Temperature Scale of 1990 (ITS-90) was extended downwards in temperature (below 0.65 K). In 2000, the CIPM adopted a supplemental scale for a very low range. The range of this scale, known as Provisional Low Temperature Scale, is from 0.9 mK to 1 K, and it is designated as (PLTS-2000). The ITS-90 and the PLTS-2000 define temperatures which are good approximations to thermodynamic temperature. The ITS-90 is the most recent descendant of the original International Temperature Scale of 1927 and replaced the International Practical Temperature Scale of 1968 (IPTS-68) and its extension, the 1976 Provisional 0.5 K to 30 K Temperature Scale. The ITS-90 covers the temperature range from 0.65 K to the highest temperatures that can be determined practically by radiometric means. Supplementary information is available for both the ITS-90 and approximations to the ITS-90 from BIPM.

8.8.3 Hierarchy in Temperature Measurement

It starts from the defining constant namely Boltzmann constant k, next comes the methods of connecting it with thermodynamic temperature the kelvin. These methods are enumerated in Table 8.2. Practical temperature scales are used to disseminate kelvin further for practical purposes.

Considerable research has been conducted on establishing a temperature scale extending to temperatures lower than 0.65 K; the PLTS-2000 is the resulting outcome, defining temperature from 1 K down to 0.9 mK. The PLTS-2000 is explicitly a provisional scale, recognizing that the data sets comprising the basis of the scale were somewhat inconsistent below 10 mK. In the temperature range 0.65 K to 1 K, temperature may be defined on either the ITS-90 or the PLTS-2000. Either scale is acceptable; the choice of scale typically is dictated by convenience or the attainable uncertainty of realization. In those rare cases where use of either scale is convenient, T2000 is a better approximation of thermodynamic temperature than T90 in the region of overlap. Supplementary information for the realization of the PLTS-2000 is also available.

References

1. T.J. Quinn, *Temperature (Monographs in Physical Measurement)*, 2nd edn. (Academic, London, 1990)
2. F. Pavese, G. Molinar, *Modern Gas-Based Temperature and Pressure Measurements* (Plenum, New York, 1992)
3. M.R. Moldover, J.P.M. Trusler, Accurate acoustic thermometry I: The triple point of gallium. Metrologia **25**, 165–187 (1988)
4. M.B. Ewing, J.B. Mehl, M.R. Moldover, J.P.M. Trusler, Microwave measurements of the thermal expansion of aspherical cavity. Metrologia **25**, 211–219 (1988)
5. M.R. Moldover, S.J. Boyes, C.W. Meyer, A.R.H. Goodwin, Thermodynamic temperatures of the triple points of mercury and gallium and in the interval 217 to 303 K. J. Res. Natl Inst. Stand. Technol. **104**, 11–46 (1999)
6. M.R. Moldover, S.J. Boyes, C.W. Meyer and A.R.H. Goodwin, Primary acoustic thermometry from 217 to 303 K, in *Proceedings of the TEMPMEKO '99 International Symposium*

on Temperature and Thermal Measurements in Industry and Science, vol 7, ed. by J.F. Dubbeldam, M.J. de Groot (Delft, IMEKO/NMiVan Swinden Laboratorium, 1999), pp. 412–417

7. M.R. Ewing, J.P.M. Trusler, Primary acoustic thermometry between $T = 90$ K and $T = 300$ K. J. Chem. Thermodyn. **32**, 1229–1255 (2000)

8. D.C. Ripple, D.R. Defibaugh, M.R. Moldover, G.F. Strouse, Techniques for primary acoustic thermometry to 800 K, in *Temperature: its Measurement and Control in Science and Industry*, vol. 7, ed. by D.C. Ripple (Melville, NY, AIP, 2003), pp. 25–30

9. G.F. Strouse, D.R. Defibaugh, M.R. Moldover, D.C. Ripple, Progress in primary acoustic thermometry at NIST 273–505 K, in *Temperature: its Measurement and Control in Science and Industry*, vol 7, ed. by D.C. Ripple (Melville, NY, AIP, 2003), pp. 31–36

10. G. Benedetto, R.M. Gavioso, R. Spagnolo, P. Marcarino, A. Merlone, Acoustic measurements of the thermodynamic temperature between the triple point of mercury and 380 K. Metrologia **41,** 74–98 (2004)

11. L. Pitre, M.R. Moldover, W.L. Tew, Acoustic thermometry: new results from 273–277 K and progress towards 4 K. Metrologia **43**, 142–62 (2006)

12. M.R. Moldover, J.P.M. Trusler, T.J. Edwards, J.B. Mehl, R.S. Davis, Measurement of the universal gas constant R using a spherical acoustic resonator. J. Res. Natl. Bur. Stand. **93**, 85–144 (1988)

13. M. de Podesta, R. Underwood, G. Sutton, P. Morantz, P. Harris, D.F. Mark, F.M. Stuart, G. Vargha, G. Machin, A low-uncertainty measurement of the Boltzmann constant. Metrologi **50**, 354–376 (2013)

14. L. Pitre, C. Guianvarc'h, F. Sparasci, A. Guillou, D. Truong, Y. Hermier, M.E. Himbert, An improved acoustic method for the determination of the Boltzmann Constant at LNE-INM/CNAM. C. R. Phys. **10**, 835–848 (2009)

15. L. Pitre, F. Sparasci, D. Truong, A. Guillou, L. Risegari, M.E. Himbert, Measurement of the Boltzmann constant kB using a quasi-spherical acoustic resonator. Int. J. Thermophys. **32**, 1825–1886 (2011)

16. G. Sutton, R. Underwood, L. Pitre, M. de Podesta, S. Valkiers, Acoustic resonator experiments at the triple point of water: first results for the Boltzmann constant and remaining challenges. Int. J. Thermophys. **31**, 1310–1346 (2010)

17. R.M. Gavioso, G. Benedetto, P.A. Giuliano Albo, D. Madonna Ripa, A. Merlone, C. Guianvarc'h, F. Moro, R. Cuccaro, A determination of the Boltzmann constant from speed of sound measurements in helium at a single thermodynamic state. Metrologia **47**, 387–409 (2010)

18. M. Planck, Zur Theorie des Gesetzes der Energieverteilung im Normalspektrum. Verh. Deutsch. Phys. Ges. **2**, 237–245 (1900)

19. J.E. Martin, N.P. Fox, P.J. Key, A cryogenic radiometer for absolute radiometric measurements. Metrologia **21**, 147–155 (1985)

20. T.J. Quinn, J.E. Martin, A radiometric determination of the Stefan-Boltzmann constant and thermodynamic temperatures between -40 °C and $+100$ °C. Phil. Trans. R. Soc. Lond. A **316**, 85–189 (1985)

21. H.W. Yoon, C.E. Gibson, D.W. Allen, Saunders R D, M. Litorja, S.W. Brown, G.P. Eppeldauer, K.R. Lykke, The realization and the dissemination of the detector-based kelvin, in *Proceedingsof the TEMPMEKO 2004 International Symposium on Temperature and Thermal Measurements in Industry and Science*, vol 9 ed. by D. Zvizdiʹc, L.G. Bermanec, T. Veliki, T. Stašiʹc (Zagreb, MEKO/University of Zagreb, Faculty of Mechanical Engineering and Naval Architecture, 2005), pp. 59–70

22. D.R. Taubert, J. Hartmann, J. Hollandt, J. Fischer, Investigation of the accuracy of the ITS-90 with reference to thermodynamic temperature in the range from 400 oC up to 600 oC, in *Temperature: its Measurement and Control in Science and Industry*, vol 7, ed. by D.C. Ripple (Melville, NY, AIP, 2003), pp. 7–12

23. P.J. Mohr, B.N. Taylor, CODATA recommended values of the fundamental physical constants: 2002. Rev. Mod. Phys. **77**, 1–106 (2005)
24. W. Cencek, K. Szalewicz, B. Jeziorski, Breit-Pauli anddirect perturbation theory calculations of relativistic helium polarizability. Phys. Rev. Lett. **86**, 5675–5678 (2001)
25. G. Lach, B. Jeziorski, K. Szalewicz, Radiative n corrections to the polarizability of helium. Phys. Rev. Lett. **92**, 233001-1–233001-4 (2004)
26. C. Gaiser, T. Zandt, B. Fellmuth, J. Fischer, O. Jusko, W. Sabug, Improved determination of the Boltzmann constant by dielectric-constant gas thermometry. Metrologia **50**, L7–L11 (2013)
27. L. Pitre, F. Sparasci, L. Risegari, C. Guianvarc'h, C. Martin, M.E. Himbert, M.D. Plimmer, A. Allard, B. Marty, P.A. Giuliano Albo,B. Gao, M.R. Moldover, J.B. Mehl, New measurement of the Boltzmann constant k by acoustic thermometry of helium-4 gas. Metrologia **54**, 856–879 (2017)
28. D. Gugan, G.W. Michel, Dielectric constant gas thermometry Metrologia **16**, 149–167 (1980)
29. M.P. White, D. Gugan, Direct measurements of the dielectric virial coefficients of 4 He between 3 and 18 K. Metrologia **29**, 37–57 (1992)
30. H. Luther, K. Grohmann, B. Fellmuth, Determination of thermodynamic temperature and 4 He virial coefficients between 4.2 and 27.0 K by dielectric-constant gas thermometry. Metrologia **33**, 341–352 (1996)
31. K.H. Berry, NPL-75: a low temperature gas thermometry scale from 2.6 to 27.1 K. Metrologia **15**, 89–115 (1979)
32. R.L. Rusby, R.P. Hudson, M. Durieux, K. Grohmann, H.-J. Jung, P.P.M. Steur, J.V. Nicholas, The status of thermodynamic thermometry. Metrologia **33**, 409–414 (1996)
33. A.R. Colclough, A projected refractive index thermometer for the range 2–20 K. Metrologia **10**, 73–74 (1974)
34. A.R. Colclough, A refractive index thermometer for use at low temperatures, in *Temperature: its Measurement and Control in Science and Industry*, vol. 5, ed. by J.F. Schooley (New York, AIP, 1982), pp. 89–94
35. J.A. Stone, A. Stejskal, Using helium as a standard of refractive index: correcting errors in a gas refractometer. Metrologia **41**, 189–197 (2004)
36. E.F. May, L. Pitre, J.B. Mehl, M.R. Moldover, J.W. Schmidt, Quasi-spherical cavity resonators for metrology based on the relative dielectric permittivity of gases. Rev. Sci. Instrum. **75**, 3307–3317 (2004)
37. Joachim Fischer, Progress towards a new definition of the Kelvin. Metrologia **52**, S364–S375 (2015)
38. C. Daussy, M. Guinet, A. Amy-Klein, K. Djerroud, Y. Hermier, S. Briaudeau, ChJ Borde, C. Chardonnet, Direct determination of the Boltzmann constant by an optical method. Phys. Rev. Lett. **98**, 250801 (2007)
39. C. Lemarchand, M. Triki, B. Darquie, ChJ Borde, C. Chardonnet, C. Daussy, Progress towards an accurate determination of the Boltzmann constant by Doppler spectroscopy. New J. Phys. **13**, 073028 (2011)
40. G. Casa, A. Castrillo, G. Galzerano, R. Wehr, A. Merlone, D. Di Serafino, P. Laporta, L. Gianfrani, Primary gas thermometry by means of laser-absorption spectroscopy: determination of the Boltzmann constant. Phys. Rev. Lett. **100**, 200801 (2008)
41. A. Castrillo, G. Casa, A. Merlone, G. Galzerano, P. Laporta, L. Gianfrani, On the determination of the Boltzmann constant by means of precision molecular spectroscopy in the near-infrared. C. R. Phys. **10**, 894–906 (2009)
42. B. Fellmuth, J. Fischer, C. Gaiser, N. Haft, Dielectric-constant gas thermometry and determination of the Boltzmann constant, in *Proceedings of the TEMPMEKO 2004 International Symposium on Temperature and Thermal Measurements in Industry and Science*, vol. 9, ed. by D. Zvizdi´c, L.G. Bermanec, T. Veliki, T. Staši´c (Zagreb, IMEKO/University of Zagreb, Faculty of Mechanical Engineering and Naval Architecture, 2005), pp. 73–8

43. H. Nyquist, Thermal agitation of electric charge in conductors. Phys. Rev. **32**, 110–113 (1928)
44. D.R. White et al., The status of Johnson noise thermometry. Metrologia **33**, 325–335 (1996)
45. H. Brixy, R. Hecker, J. Oehmen, K.F. Rittinghaus, W. Setiawan, E. Zimmermann, Noise thermometry for industrial and metrological applications at KFA Julich, in *Temperature Its Measurement and Control in Science and Industry*, vol. 6, ed. J.F. Schooley (New York, American Institute of Physics, 1992), pp. 993–996
46. F. Edler, M. Kuhne, E. Tegeler, Noise temperature measurements for the determination of the thermodynamic temperature of the melting point of palladium. Metrologia **41**, 47–55 (2004)
47. S.P. Benz, J.M. Martinis, S.W. Nam, W.L. Tew, D.R. White, A new approach to Johnson noise thermometry using a Josephson quantized voltage source for calibration, in *International Symposium on Temperature and Thermal Measurements in Industry and Science (TEMPMEKO)*, vol 8, ed. B. Fellmuth et al (Berlin, VDE Verlag GmbH, 2002), pp. 37–44
48. S.P. Benz, A. Pollarolo, J. Qu, H. Rogalla, C. Urano, W.L. Tew, P.D. Dresselhaus, D.R. White, An electronic measurement of the Boltzmann constant. Metrologia **48**, 142–153 (2011)
49. A. Pollarolo, T. Jeong, S.P. Benz, P.D. Dresselhaus, H. Rogalla, W.L. Tew, Johnson-noise thermometry based on a quantized-voltage noise source at NIST, in *AIP Proceedings of the Temperature Its Measurement and Control in Science and Industry*, vol. 1552, ed. C.W. Meyer (Melville, NY, American Institute of Physics, 2013), 23–8
50. B. Fellmuth, J. Fischer, C. Gaiser, W. Buck, Workshop on methods for new determinations of the Boltzmann constant, in *Working Documents of the 23rd Meeting of the Consultative Committee for Thermometry*, BIPM document CCT/05-02 (2005)

Chapter 9
Radiometry, Photometry and Realization of Candela and Mole

9.1 SI Units Used in Radiometry and Photometry

1. Radiant intensity of a point source is the power radiated per unit solid angle.
2. Irradiance is the ratio of power irradiated per unit area.
3. Radiance of a source is the power radiated in a unit solid angle per unit area.
4. Luminance is the intensity of illumination per unit area.
5. Luminous flux of a point source is the product of luminous intensity and the area of illumination.
6. Illuminance is the luminous flux per unit area.

The quantities given from Serial No. 1 to 6 are concerned with radiometry and photometry. However, all radiometric units are in terms of base units of length, mass, time and solid angle. But photometric units involve the process of vision and depend upon the sensitivity of eye to radiations of different frequencies in the visible region. The radiometry is for the entire electromagnetic radiations except for the visible region.

For photometry, the base quantity is the luminous intensity with SI unit candela, which is a certain fraction of power of a monochromatic source of certain frequency in a unit solid angle. The frequency mentioned in the definition of candela is at which eye has a maximum response, while for radiometry the starting quantity is power with unit watt. Radiant intensity is the power emitted in a unit solid angle. Its counterpart in photometry is intensity of illumination with unit candela. Other units are shown in Table 9.1.

We can see from Table 9.1 that units are given according to the specific field radiometry or photometry, depending on size of the source (Pinhole or extended) and energy per unit area or per unit solid angle to give the sense of direction.

The paragraphs given below are heavily based upon the document prepared by the Consultative Committee for Photometry and Radiometry (CCPR) of the

© Springer Nature Switzerland AG 2020

S. V. Gupta, *Units of Measurement*, Springer Series in Materials Science 122,
https://doi.org/10.1007/978-3-030-43969-9_9

Table 9.1 Units in photometry and radiometry

Quantity	Radiometry		Photometry	
	Point source			
	Quantity	Unit	Quantity	Unit
Power	Radiant power	watt W	Luminous power	lm = cd·sr
Directional power per unit solid angle	Radiant intensity	W/sr	Intensity of illumination	cd
Extended source				
Power per unit area	Radiance	W/m²	Luminance	lm/m²
Directional power per unit area and solid angle	Radiance per steradian	W/m²sr	Luminance per steradian	cd·/m²
Looking at the illuminated object				
Power/area	Irradiance	W/m²	Illuminance	lm/m² = lux

International Committee for Weights and Measures (CIPM) and formally adopted by the CIPM [1]. The author has limited to discuss only photometric units only.

9.2 Traceability and Realization of Photometric Units

9.2.1 Traceability Routes for the Practical Realization of Photometric Units

The realization of photometric units associated with the corresponding photometric quantities (e.g. luminous intensity, luminance, illuminance, luminous flux) through the use of spectral luminous efficiency functions (to provide a spectral weighting) combined with the luminous efficacy at a frequency of 540×10^{12} Hz, as given in the definition of the candela. The lowest uncertainty for the realization of photometric units is currently achieved if the traceability chain starts with an absolute detector, but in the future it could be achieved by using an absolute source or the photon counting approach.

9.2.1.1 Detector-Based Photometric Traceability

The most common method for realization of photometric units is to measure the photometric output of a standard-quality light source (described in more detail in Sect. 9.3) in the desired geometric configuration using a reference photometric detector with a spectral responsivity that matches the desired luminous efficiency function and that has been spectrally calibrated for absolute irradiance responsivity traceable to an absolute radiometer and which is equipped with a precise aperture, which has a calibrated area traceable to the SI unit of length. The realized photometric unit is then transferred to other standard-quality light sources (or, in the second step, to other photometric detectors), which become secondary standard photometric sources (or detectors) for the associated photometric quantity. In this case, the traceability to the SI is "detector-based" to SI electrical units. This method generally requires additional spectral calibration to establish the relationship (spectral mismatch) of the spectral responsivity curve of the detector to the appropriate CIE spectral luminous efficiency function. To quantify the impact of this spectral mismatch, it is also necessary to carry out a relative spectral calibration of the light source. In the case where photon-number-based quantities are experimentally measured as described in Sect. 9.3, these can be converted to the associated photometric quantity, using relevant equation, although it is more common to use a weighted integral over frequency instead of wavelength.

9.2.1.2 Source-Based Photometric Traceability

The second method realizes the photometric units directly through the use of an absolute source, whose photometric output (in the relevant geometric configuration) is calculated from first principles based upon the characteristics of the source itself. In this case, the traceability to the SI is "source-based". The most common absolute (calculable) source is a high-temperature blackbody (a cavity with high emissivity) whose output radiant flux can be predicted from the thermodynamic temperature of the cavity using Planck's radiation law. In this case, traceability is to the SI unit of temperature, the kelvin. However, at the high temperatures usually required for photometric applications, the thermodynamic temperature is generally determined by the inversion of Planck's law via a quasi-monochromatic measurement of the absolute radiant flux output of the radiator made using one or several narrowband detector(s) that have been calibrated by reference to an absolute radiometer, as outlined in Sect. 9.2.1.1. In this case, the traceability is more appropriately considered to be "detector-based" to SI electrical units.

9.3 Realizationof the Candela (Cd)

The candela (cd) is the SI base unit of luminous intensity with symbol I_v. It is most often realized using a standard lamp, whose physical design is optimized for use in a defined direction. Such a lamp provides a light source of size which is small in relation to the distance between the source and the detector's aperture. This way it provides a point source in the defined direction. In the case of a tungsten standard lamp, spectral output is adjusted close to the spectral output of Planckian radiator operating at a temperature of approximately 2856 K. This is equivalent of the CIF Standard Illuminant A. The radiant intensity is converted to the luminous intensity using the appropriate CIE spectral luminous efficiency function and the photometric constant Kcd [2].

In principle, it would be possible to realize the candela using a stable mono-chromatic reference lamp emitting at the wavelength of λ_a, corresponding to the frequency specified in the definition of the candela. The source is mounted on a photometric bench at a known distance r from the limiting aperture (area A) of an absolute radiometer that measures the radiant flux. This arrangement allows the calculation of the radiant intensity at this wavelength, $I_e(\lambda_a)$. The luminous intensity of the lamp (I_v) is then obtained using the following relation:

$$I_v = K_{cd}V(\lambda_a)I_e(\lambda_a).$$

However, such a realization would be of little use for measurements on practical broadband sources. Thus, the practical realization of the candela is predominantly carried out using one of the two methods described below.

Method A—A sufficiently small polychromatic source providing a nearly iso-tropic radiation field in the measurement direction is used. This is commonly an incandescent source which approximates the relative spectral power distribution of CIE standard illuminant A. For use as a luminous intensity reference lamp, a spectral characterization is needed. This spectral radiant intensity $I_e(\lambda)$ in a certain direction is typically measured at a sufficiently large distance using a series of calibrated reference filter radiometers of known irradiance responsivity at a few discrete wavelengths of visible region (360 nm to 830 nm). Such a source is provided by using a spectroradiometer with an appropriate irradiance input optic that has been absolutely calibrated for irradiance responsivity. For these measurements, the lamp must be set according to its specified operating conditions (lamp orientation, direction of measurement and lamp multiplied by the desired CIE spectral luminous efficiency function and spectrally integrated to give the corresponding luminous intensity).

Method B—A reference illuminance meter, which is a filtered radiometer, is used. The relative spectral responsivity has been designed to be a close match to the spectral characteristics of the desired CIE spectral luminous efficiency function. This filter radiometer is generally used together with a precision aperture and is calibrated by reference to an absolute radiometer to give a known illuminance responsivity (A lm^{-1}m^2). In most cases, this involves a calibration against the absolute radiometer to give its absolute spectral irradiance responsivity (A W^{-1} m^2 nm^{-1}) at discrete wavelengths, coupled with measurements against other reference detectors (e.g. silicon traps or PQEDs) to enable interpolation at regular intervals across the visible wavelength range. These spectral values are then converted to illuminance responsivity (for a specific source) by integration. This calibrated reference illuminance meter can then be used to calibrate a standard lamp in terms of its luminous intensity in a specified direction by means of a photometric bench, which allows the geometrical quantity of distance, r, from the source to the illuminance meter limiting aperture area, A, the alignment of the lamp, and the direction of measurement, to all be carefully controlled. A spectral calibration of the light source may also be necessary in order to correct for spectral mismatch between the illuminance meter and the required CIE spectral luminous efficiency function.

9.4   Realization of the Lumen (Lm), SI Derived Unit of Luminous Flux Φv

The lumen (lm or cd·sr) can be derived from a realization of the SI unit of luminous intensity I_v, the candela and the unit for solid angle Ω, the steradian. For a source of uniform intensity within the defined solid angle, this can be simply established using the relation

$$\Phi_v = \iint I_v(\theta, \phi) sin\theta \, d\phi d\theta.$$

For the more general case of a source whose intensity varies with direction, the luminous flux is obtained from the angular integration of the source luminous intensity distribution measured on a spherical surface according to the above relation, where θ is the polar angle and ϕ is the azimuthal angle in a spherical coordinate system; the integration is carried over $0 \le \theta \le \pi$ and $0 \le \phi \le 2\pi$. Therefore, the lumen may also be realized by measurement with a reference illuminance meter, as described in Method B. Several geometrical configurations may be utilized.

(a) The luminous flux emitted by a light source passing through an aperture of known area A may be established using the approximation of the solid angle for large distances, $\Omega = A/r^2$, and placing the aperture A at a known distance r from the known source of luminous intensity.

(b) The luminous flux emitted into a solid angle larger than that used to realize the luminous intensity for the known reference lamp may be determined using several methods of spatial integration of smaller sections. In each of these spatial integration methods, the detector used must be either a photometer with a spectral responsivity close to the desired spectral luminous efficiency function, which has been calibrated for luminous flux responsivity using configuration given in (a), or a reference illuminance meter calibrated as described in Method B. The luminous flux integration is carried out by using either of the following:

1. A goniophotometer over a defined solid angle of the source. In case the total luminous flux emitted by a light source is required, the integration is performed over the full solid angle $0 \le \theta \le \pi$ and $0 \le \phi \le 2\pi$. Note that if an illuminance meter is used that has been calibrated according to the methods in Sect. 9.4, the spatial integration of the source is performed over a solid angle that is defined by the illuminance responsivity (within a certain solid angle where the luminous intensity is expected to be constant) of the detector and the distance between the detector and the source.

2. An integrating sphere in combination with a detector, where the spectral responsivity of the sphere/detector combination is a close match to the desired spectral luminous efficiency function and that has been calibrated, for example,

by introducing a known amount of luminous flux into the sphere (measured using method (1)). The luminous flux emitted from a selected section of the source is measured by introducing only that part of the flux into the sphere. If it is desired to measure the cumulative luminous flux of the source for a solid angle of 4π sr, this total luminous flux (of the source) is then determined by placing the source entirely within the sphere. As the angular distribution of the source is generally very different from the light beam used for calibrating the sphere, the effect of the spatial non-uniformity of the sphere has to be characterized and corrected by an appropriate method. To account for spectral and spatial non-uniformities of the sphere, which influence the measurement results if different sources or geometries are compared, additional corrections must be applied. Furthermore, the linearity of the system needs to be characterized, to account for the very different flux levels that occur for the source outside and inside the sphere, respectively. Further details concerning the measurement of luminous flux may be found in [4].

9.5 Realization of the Lux (Lx), SI Derived Unit of Illuminance Ev

The lux (lx or $cd \cdot sr \cdot m^{-2}$) can be derived from a realization of the candela and the unit of length, using the relation:

$$E_v = I\,\Omega_0/r^2,$$

where r is an appropriately chosen distance from the source with luminous intensity I_v at which the illuminance E_v is produced to satisfy the condition that the area of the curved surface of the sphere (As) is approximately equal to the area of its two-dimensional projection, A, i.e. $A \cong A_S$. for more details, please see [5].

References

1. SI Brochure Appendix 2. *Mise en pratique* for the definition of the candela and associated derived units
2. Principles Governing Photometry, 2nd ed., Joint CIPM/CIE publication
3. CIE (International Commission on Illumination), Joint ISO/CIE Standard: CIE Colorimetry – Part 2: CIE Standard Illuminants for Colorimetry, ISO 11664-2:2007(E)/CIE S 014-2/E:2006
4. Y. Ohno, Photometric Standards (Chapter 3), In Handbook of Applied Photometry, Casimir DeCusatis, (pp. 55–99) American Institute of Physics Press, ISBN 1-56396-416-3, Woodbury, NY, USA. (1997)
5. CIE 210:2014 Photometry Using $V(\lambda)$-Corrected Detectors as Reference and Transfer Standards

Chapter 10
Derived Quantities and Their Units

10.1 Derived Quantities

Derived quantities are those which may be expressed in terms of base or derived quantities by means of the mathematical symbols of multiplication and division only (No addition or subtraction or any other sign). Basically, they may be divided into two categories. First group consists of derived quantities, which have proper units. Their units can be expressed in terms of units of base or derived units. Second class is of those quantities, which do not have units expressed in terms of base or derived units. These quantities, as discussed in Chap. 2, are known as dimensionless quantities or quantities of dimension 1.

10.2 Units of Derived Quantities

Units of derived quantities are known as derived units. Derived units are defined as products of powers of the base units. When the numerical factor of this product is one, the derived units are called *coherent derived units*. The base and coherent derived units of the SI form a coherent set, designated the *set of coherent SI units*. The word "coherent" here means that equations between the numerical values of quantities take exactly the same form as the equations between the quantities themselves.

The basic purpose of this book is to describe SI units. Derived units belonging to International System of units are coherent derived units in terms of base unit, coherent derived units with special names, coherent derived units expressed in terms of derived units with special names and base units, dimensionless quantities or quantities with dimension one with special names. The dimensionless quantities are simple ratios of two similar quantities, hence are pure numbers having 1 as

© Springer Nature Switzerland AG 2020

S. V. Gupta, *Units of Measurement*, Springer Series in Materials Science 122,

https://doi.org/10.1007/978-3-030-43969-9_10

their unit: units outside the SI but accepted for use with SI units, non-SI units of those quantities whose values are determined in SI units because of their importance in physics and some units which are being used for historical reasons will be discussed. Finally, non-SI units associated with CGS and CGS-Gaussian system of units will also be given.

10.3   SI Derived Units

For convenience, coherent derived units are grouped into three sections.

(1)   Derived units, which are derived from the base units only.
(2)   Derived units, which have been assigned special names and symbols.
(3)   Derived units, which are formed from the derived units with special names and base units.

10.3.1   Units Expressed in Terms of Base Units

Table 10.1 lists some coherent derived units in terms of base units using their respective definitions except the intensity of magnetization.

The word coherent has been specifically used to distinguish between the units expressed in terms of coherent base units and units expressed in terms of their multiples or sub-multiples. For example, metre is the base unit of length and not the centimetre or any multiple or sub-multiple of the metre. Hence, coherent unit of area is m^2 and not square of the centimetre.

Unit of pole strength is derived from the relation

$$\text{Force} = \mu \cdot P_1 P_2 / r^2.$$

Units of force and distance r are, respectively, newton and metre and that of μ is NA^{-2}, giving unit of pole strength as A m. The unit of magnetic moment, therefore, should be A m^2. The unit of intensity of magnetization which is magnetic moment per unit volume should be A $m^2/m^3 = A\ m^{-1}$.

The intensity of magnetization is a better nomenclature for H than the name magnetic field strength. The fact is that H is the ability to magnetize a material. After introducing the concept of permeability of free space μ_0, all formulae of magnetic and electromagnetic field will contain μ as a factor; hence, whenever the word magnetic field is occured, it will denote the magnetic flux density whose unit is tesla.

$$B = \text{Magnetic flux density} = \mu\,H.$$

Hence

$$\{B\} = NA^{-2}\,A/m = kg\,s^{-2}A^{-1},$$

Table 10.1 Examples of derived quantities and derived units in terms of base units

Derived quantity		SI coherent derived unit	
Derived unit	Symbol	Name	Symbol
Area	A	Square metre	m^2
Volume	V	Cubic metre	m^3
Speed/velocity	v	Metre per second	$m\ s^{-1}$
Acceleration	A	Metre per second square	$m\ s^{-2}$
Wave number	σ, v	Reciprocal of metre	m^{-1}
Specific volume	υ	Cubic metre per kilogram	$m^3\ kg^{-1}$
Mass density	ρ	Kilogram per metre cube	$kg\ m^{-3}$
Specific volume	v	Cubic metre cube per kilogram	$m^3\ kg^{-1}$
Area density		Kilogram per square metre	$kg\ m^{-2}$
Current density	j	Ampere per square metre	$A\ m^{-2}$
Amount concentration[a] Concentration	c	Mole per cubic metre	$mol\ m^{-3}$
Mass concentration	ρ, γ	Kilogram per metre cube	$kg\ m^{-3}$
Luminance	L_v	Candela per square metre	$Cd\ m^{-2}$
Refractive index[b]	n	One	1
Relative permeability[b]	μ_r	One	1

[a]In the field of clinical chemistry, this quantity is also called "substance concentration"
[b]These are dimensionless quantities, or quantities of dimension one, and the symbol "1" for the unit (the number "one") is generally omitted in specifying the values of dimensionless quantities
Notes Symbols of quantities are single alphabets or Greek letters and are written in italics. The following may be perused, to understand the derivation of the unit of intensity of magnetization H

Same as Tesla $=$ Weber/m^2 (Table 10.4).

10.3.2   Derived Units with Special Names

Among these names and symbols, the last four entries in Table 10.2 are of particular note since they were accepted by the 15th CGPM (1975) [1] resolutions 8 and 9, the 16th CGPM (1979) [2] and 21st CGPM 1999 [3] specifically with a view to safeguarding human health.

Relation used for arriving at the unit of each quantity has also been indicated in column 4.

A few more points need to understand.

1. Multiplication sign between the two symbols is a point (·) and is above the line midway of the height of the letter, but its use is optional.

Table 10.2 Coherent derived units with special names[a]

Quantity	Name	S	Relation used	Special names	Unit in terms of base units
Plane angle	Radian	Rad	Arc/radius of the arc	1	m/m
Solid angle	Steradian	Sr	Surface area/(radius)^2	1	
Frequency	Hertz	Hz	Inverse of time period	–	s^{-1}
Force	Newton	N	Mass acceleration	–	$m\ kg\ s^{-2}$
Pressure, stress	Pascal	H Pa	Force per unit area	$N\ m^{-2}$	$m^{-1}\ kg\ s^{-2}$
Energy of any kind Work, amount of heat	Joule	J	Force displacement	$N\ m$	$m^2\ kg\ s^{-2}$
Power, radiant flux	Watt	W	Energy per unit time	J/s	$m^2\ kg\ s^{-3}$
Electric charge amount of charge, amount of electricity	Coulomb	J C	Ampere time	–	$A\ s$
Electric potential or e.m.f	Volt	W V	Power = Voltage current	W/A	$m^2\ kg\ s^{-3}\ A^{-1}$
Capacitance	Farad	C F	Charge = Potential C capacitance	C/V	$m^{-2}\ kg^{-1}\ s^4\ A^2$
Electric resistance	Ohm	Ω	Ohms law	V/A	$m^2\ kg\ s^{-3}\ A^{-2}$
Electric conductance	Siemens	S	Inverse of resistance	A/V	$m^{-2}\ kg^{-1}\ s^3\ A^2$
Magnetic flux	Weber	Wb	dΦ/dt = voltage	V s	$m^2\ kg\ s^{-2}\ A^{-1}$
Magnetic flux density	Tesla	T	Magnetic flux per unit area	Wb/m^2	$kg\ s^{-2}\ A^{-1}$
Inductance	Henry	H	Flux = Inductance current	Wb/A	$m^2\ kg\ s^{-2}\ A^{-2}$
Celsius temperature	Degree Celsius[d]	°C	By definition	(c, d)	K
Luminous flux	Lumen	Lm	By definition	cd sr[a]	cd
Illuminance	Lux	Lx	lumen per unit area	lm/m^2	$m^{-2}\ cd$
Activity referred to radio- nuclide	Becquerel	Bq	Definition	Bq[e]	s^{-1}
Absorbed dose, kerma Specific energy imparted	Gray	Gy	Definition	J/kg	$m^2\ s^{-2}$

(continued)

Table 10.2 (continued)

Quantity	Name	S	Relation used	Special names	Unit in terms of base units
Dose equivalent, Ambient dose equivalent, directional dose equivalent, Personal dose equivalent	Sievert	Sv	Definition	J/kg	$m^2\ s^{-2}$
Catalytic activity	Katal	kat	Definition	–	$mol\ s^{-1}$

S in row and column three stands for "symbol of quantity"
[a]To honour the scientists concerned in a specific field, a unit has been assigned his/her name

2. The radian and steradian are special names for the number one that may be used to convey information about the quantity concerned. In practice, the symbols rad and sr are used where appropriate, but symbol for the derived unit 1 is generally omitted in specifying the values of dimensionless quantities.

3. In photometry, the symbols rad and sr are usually retained in expressions for other units.

4. The hertz is used only for periodic phenomena, and the becquerel is used for stochastic process in activity of radionuclide.

5. The degree Celsius is the special name for the kelvin; it used to express Celsius temperature. The degree Celsius and the kelvin are equal in magnitude, so that numerical value of a temperature difference or temperature interval is the same when expressed in degree Celsius or in kelvin.

6. The degree Celsius may be used in combination with SI prefixes, e.g. milli-degree Celsius, m °C.

7. Activity referred to a nuclide is sometimes incorrectly called radioactivity.

8. The sievert (symbol Sv) is an SI derived unit of equivalent dose or effective dose (of radiation) and so is dependent upon the biological effects of radiation as opposed to the physical aspects, characterized by the absorbed dose (measured in Gray).

9. For simplicity and because they are straight forward, the names of these units are omitted. Two examples are the unit of energy, kilogram metre squared per second squared, $kg\ m^2\ s^{-2}$; and the unit of inductance, kilogram metre squared per second squared per ampere squared, $kg\ m^2\ s^{-2}\ A^{-2}$. The order of the base units reflects the order of the base quantities in the equation that relates the derived quantity to the base quantities on which it depends.

10. Electric potential difference is also called "voltage" in many countries, as well as "electric tension" or simply "tension" in some countries.

10.3.3 Derived Units Formed from the Derived Units with Special Names

Derived units, listed in Table 10.2, have been given special names and symbols for convenience and honouring the pioneer scientists. These names and symbols may themselves be used to express other derived units. Examples of such units are given in Table 10.3. The special names and symbols are a compact form for the expression of units, which are used frequently. Relations used for arriving at the units are indicated in column 3 of Table 10.3.

1. Volume flow rate of a liquid of dynamic viscosity η in a capillary tube of radius a and length L under a pressure head P is given by Poiseuille's formula as

   $V/T = Pa^4/8\eta L$. Expressing the quantities used in terms of base units, we get $m^3/s = Pa\,m^4/(\text{unit of } \eta)\,m$, giving
   unit of $\eta = Pa\,m^3/m^3\,s^{-1} = Pa\,s$.

2. Rate of flow of heat energy in the steady state is proportional to the difference in temperature and area of the conductor divided by its length. If k is conductivity, then we may write

   Heat energy/time $=$ power $=$ k. difference in temperature. Area/length
   Expressing them in base units
   Unit of (k) $=$ W m/K m^2 $=$ W/m K.

3. Capacitance of a spherical conductor $= 4\pi\varepsilon \cdot r$, r is the radius of the spherical conductor and ε is permittivity, giving

   Unit of $(\varepsilon) =$ Farad/m.
   Unit of μ is NA^{-2}, expressing N in base units.
   Unit of $\mu = m\,kg\,s^{-2}\,A^{-2}$.
   But unit of henry is H and is given as $H = m^2\,kg\,s^{-2}\,A^{-2}$, dividing by m we get
   Unit of $\mu =$ H/m.

   Since the expression used for defining current is the gateway between mechanical and electrical quantities, hence, in view of the author, unit of μ should be expressed as NA^{-2}.

4. A single SI unit may correspond to several different quantities, for example, work and moment of a force have same unit. In the above table, which is not exhaustive, there are several examples. Thus, the joule per kelvin (J/K) is the SI

Table 10.3 SI derived units whose names and symbols include derived units with special names and symbols

Quantity	Name	Relation used	With Special names	In terms of base units
Dynamic Viscosity	Pascal second	Poiseuille's formula	Pa s	$m^{-1}\ kg\ s^{-1}$
Moment of force	Newton metre	Definition	N m	$m^2\ kg\ s^{-2}$
Angular velocity	Radian per second	Definition	rad/s	s^{-1}
Angular acceleration	Radian per second square	Definition	rad/s^2	s^{-2}
Heat flux density, Irradiance	Watt per square metre	Definition	W/m^2	$kg\ s^{-3}$
Heat capacity, entropy	Joule per kelvin	Energy required to change temperature through 1 K	J/K	$m^2\ kg\ s^{-2}\ K^{-1}$
Specific heat capacity, specific entropy	Joule per kilogram kelvin	Energy required to change unit temperature of 1 kg of substance	J/(kg K)	$m^2\ s^{-2}\ K^{-1}$
Specific energy	Joule per kilogram	Conduction formula		$m^2\ s^{-2}$
Thermal conductivity	Watt per metre kelvin	Conductivity formula	W/m K	$m\ kg\ s^{-3}\ K^{-1}$
Energy density	Joule per cubic metre	Definition	J/m^3	$m^{-1}\ kg\ s^{-2}$
Electric field strength	Volt/metre	dV/dr	V/m	$m\ kg\ s^{-3}\ A^{-1}$
Electric charge density	Coulomb per cubic metre	Definition	C/m^3	$m^{-3}\ s\ A$
Electric flux density Electric displacement, Surface charge density	Coulomb per square metre	Definition	C/m^2	$m^{-2}\ s\ A$
Surface density surface charge density coulomb per square metre C m^{-2} A s m^{-2}				
Permittivity	Farad per metre	Capacitance of a spherical conductor	F/m	$m^{-3}\ kg^{-1}\ s^4\ A^2$
Permeability	Newton per Ampere squared	NA^{-2}	H/m	$m\ kg\ s^{-2}\ A^{-2}$

(continued)

Table 10.3 (continued)

Quantity	Name	Relation used	With Special names	In terms of base units
Molar energy, Molar heat capacity	Joule per mole	Definition	J/mol	$m^2\ kg\ s^{-2}\ mol^{-1}$
Molar entropy	Joule per mole kelvin	Definition	$JK^{-1}\ mol^{-1}$	$kg\ m^2\ s^{-2}\ mol^{-1}\ K^{-1}$
Exposure (X-rays)	Coulomb per kg	Definition	C/kg	$kg^{-1}\ s\ A$
Absorbed dose rate	Gray per second	Definition	Gy/s	$m^2\ s^{-3}$
Radiant intensity	Watt per steradian	Definition	W/sr	$m^2\ kg\ s^{-3}$
Radiance	Watt per square metre. steradian	Definition	W/m^2	$kg\ s^{-3}$
Catalytic (activity)	Katal per cubic metre	Definition	kat/m^3	$m^{-3}\ s^{-1}\ mol$

Note It is important to emphasize that each physical quantity has only one coherent SI unit, even though this unit can be expressed in different forms by using some of the special names and symbols.

The converse, however, is not true, because in general several different quantities may share the same SI unit. For example, for the quantity heat capacity as well as for the quantity entropy the SI unit is joule per kelvin. Similarly, for the base quantity electric current as well as the derived quantity magnetomotive force, the SI unit is the ampere. It is therefore important not to use the unit alone to specify the quantity. This applies not only to technical texts, but also, for example, to measuring instruments (i.e. the instrument readout needs to indicate both the unit and the quantity measured).

In practice, with certain quantities, preference is given to the use of certain special unit names to facilitate the distinction between different quantities having the same dimension. When using this freedom, one may recall the process by which this quantity is defined. For example, the quantity torque is the cross product of distance and force, suggesting the unit newton metre, even though it has the same dimension as energy and could be expressed using the unit joule.

Special care must be taken when expressing temperatures or temperature differences, respectively. A temperature difference of 1 K equals that of 1 °C, but for an absolute temperature the difference of 273.15 K must be taken into account. The unit degree Celsius is only coherent when expressing temperature differences.

unit for the quantity heat capacity as well as for the quantity entropy; also the ampere (A) is the SI unit for the base quantity electric current as well as for the derived quantity magnetomotive force. It is therefore important not to use the unit alone to specify the quantity. This rule applies not only to scientific and technical texts but also, for example, to measuring instruments (i.e. an instrument should indicate both the unit and the quantity measured).

5. A derived unit can often be expressed in different ways by combining the names of basic units with special names of derived units. This, however, is an algebraic freedom to be governed by common-sense physical considerations. Joule, for

example, may be written as newton metre or kilogram metre per square second, but in a given situation some forms may be more helpful than others.

6. In practice, with certain quantities, preference is given to the use of certain special unit names, to facilitate the distinction between different quantities having the same dimension. When using this freedom, one may recall the process by which this quantity is defined. For example, the quantity torque may be thought of as the cross product of force and distance, suggesting the unit newton metre, or it may be thought of as energy per angle, suggesting the unit joule per radian.

7. The SI unit of frequency is given as the hertz, implying the unit cycles per second; the SI unit of angular velocity is given as the radian per second; and the SI unit of activity is designated the becquerel, implying the unit counts per second. Although it would be formally correct to write all three of these units as the reciprocal second, the use of the different names emphasizes the different nature of the quantities concerned. Using the unit radian per second for angular velocity, and hertz for frequency, also emphasizes that the numerical value of the angular velocity in radians per second is 2π times the corresponding frequency in hertz.

8. In the field of ionizing radiation, the SI unit is designated the becquerel rather than the reciprocal second, and the SI units of absorbed dose and dose equivalent are designated the gray and the sievert, respectively, rather than the joule per kilogram. The special names becquerel, gray and sievert were specifically introduced because of the dangers to human health that might arise from mistakes involving the units reciprocal second and joule per kilogram, in case the latter units were incorrectly taken to identify quantities involved.

10.3.4 Derived Quantities of Dimension 1

The quantities of dimension 1 or dimensionless quantities may be any one of the following types:

1. The ratios of two quantities of the same kind. Examples of such quantities are angle, solid angle, refractive index, relative permeability, friction factor, Neper and decibel.

2. Those are defined as a complex product of simpler quantities in such a way that when each simpler quantity is expressed in terms of the base units, then algebraic sum of exponents of each base unit becomes zero; hence, the quantity is dimensionless or of dimension 1 depending upon the convention followed. For example, the Reynolds number (R_e) is defined as

$$R_e = \rho \upsilon I / \eta$$

$$[Re] = ML^{-3}\,LT^{-1}L/M\,L^{-1}T^{-1} = M^0L^0T^0 = 1.$$

Table 10.4 Quantities of dimension 1

Derived quantity	Name of unit	Symbol	Ratio of two quantities
Plane angle	Radian	rad	m/m
Solid angle	Steradian	sr	m^2/m^2
Ratio of permeability in the medium and vacuum	Relative permeability	μ_r	NA^{-2}/NA^{-2}
Ratio of velocity of light in medium and vacuum	Refractive index	μ, n	ms^{-1}/ms^{-1}
Logarithmic ratio of two quantities of same kind example sound pressure	Bel	B	Log_{10} (Pa/Pa)
	Neper	Np	Log_e (Pa/Pa)
	Decibel	dB	B/10
Percentage ratio of solutes in solutions	Brix	°B	% of sugar by mass in cane sugar solution
	Alcoholic degree	°A	% of pure alcohol by volume in water

[a]For better understanding, the name steradian and the symbol sr are usually retained in expressions for units representing photometric units.

[b]The neper or bel is used to express values of such logarithmic quantities as field level, power level, sound pressure level and logarithmic decrement. Natural logarithms are used to obtain the numerical values of quantities expressed in nepers and logarithms to the base 10 are expressed in Bel. The neper is coherent with the SI, but not yet adopted by the CGPM as an SI unit. For further information, one may see ISO 31.

3. Yet, there is another class of quantities, which represent a count, such as a number of molecules, degeneracy (number of energy levels) and partition function in statistical thermodynamics; these are also called quantities of dimension 1 or dimensionless quantities.

All of the quantities of dimension have the coherent SI unit 1. Their values are simply expressed as numbers and, in general, the unit 1 is not explicitly shown. In a few cases, however, special names are given to such units, mainly to avoid confusion between some compound derived units involving such quantities. Examples of such units are the radian, steradian and refractive index. Examples of such quantities are given in Table 10.4.

10.4   Units Outside the SI

The CIPM (1969) recognized that users would wish to employ the SI with certain units, which are not part of it but are important and widely used. So the CIPM listed such units in three classes, namely, class I units to be maintained as it is; (2) may be tolerated temporarily for some time; and (3) to be avoided. Standards of Weights and Measures (National Standard) Rules 1988 framed under the Standards of Weights and Measures Act, 1976 [4] followed these CIPM decisions in regard to non-SI units.

However, on reviewing this categorization, the CIPM (1996) agreed to a new classification of non-SI units: units accepted for use with the SI, units accepted for use with the SI whose values are obtained experimentally and other units currently accepted for use with the SI to satisfy the needs of special interests.

The CIPM (2004) has revised the classification of non-SI units again.

1. Non-SI units that are accepted for use with the International System by the CIPM, because they are widely used with the SI in matters of everyday life. These are given in Table 10.5. Their use is expected to continue indefinitely, and each has an exact definition in terms of an SI unit.
2. Non-SI units, which are related to fundamental constants, are given in Table 10.6, and their values, from time to time, have to be determined experimentally.
3. Some non-SI units have exactly defined values in terms of SI units and are used in particular circumstances to satisfy the needs of commercial, legal or specialized scientific interests. These are given in Table 10.7. It is likely that these units will continue to be used for many years.
4. Non-SI units are important for the interpretation of older scientific texts and are given in Table 10.8.
5. Non-SI units found in old literature are given in Table 10.9.

In draft SI Brochure 2018, only non-SI units given in Table 10.5 are accepted. The non-SI units described in Tables 10.6, 10.7, 10.8 and 10.9 are not indicated. However, acceptance of non-SI units is quasi-legal and falls under the ambit of Legal Metrology Departments. India has not changed the rules pertaining to the subject, so it will be the case of many countries. The author, therefore, felt prudent to give other non-SI units. Precautions have been taken so that nothing contradicts the provisions of the redefining of SI base units.

10.4.1   Units Accepted for Use with the SI

Table 10.5 lists non-SI units, which are accepted for use with the SI. It includes units, which are in continuous everyday use, in particular, the traditional units of time and of angle, together with a few other units, which have assumed increasing technical importance. It also contains the hectare, the litre and the tonne, which are common in everyday use throughout the world, and which differ from the corresponding coherent SI unit by an integral power of ten. The SI prefixes are used with several of these units, but not with the units of time.

Table 10.5 Non-SI units accepted for use with the International System

Quantity	Name	Symbol	Value in SI units
Time	minute	min	$1\ \text{min} = 60\ \text{s}$
	hour[a]	h	$1\ \text{h} = 60\ \text{min} = 3600\ \text{s}$
	day	d	$1\ \text{d} = 24\ \text{h} = 86\,400\ \text{s}$
Plane angle	Degree[b, c]	°	$1° = (\pi/180)\ \text{rad}$
	Minute	′	$1' = (1/60)° = (\pi/10\,800)\ \text{rad}$
	second[d]	″	$1'' = (1/60)' = (\pi/648\,000)\ \text{rad}$
Area	Are	a	$1\text{dam}^2 = 100\ \text{m}^2$
	Hectare[e]	ha	$1\ \text{hm}^2 = (100\ \text{m})^2 = 10^4\ \text{m}^2$
Volume	Litre[f]	l, L	$1\ \text{l} = 1\ \text{dm}^3 = 10^{-3}\ \text{m}^3$
Mass	Tonne[g]	tT	$1\ \text{t} = 10^3\ \text{kg}$
	Dalton[h]	Da	$1\ \text{Da} = 1.660\,538\,86$ $(28) \times 10^{-27}\ \text{kg}$
Energy	Electronvolt[i]	eV	$1\ \text{eV} = 1.602\,176\,634 \times 10^{-19}\ \text{J}$

[a]The symbol of this unit was included in Resolution 7 of the 9th CGPM (1948; CR, 70)

[b]ISO 31 recommends that the degree be subdivided decimally rather than using the minute and second. However, for navigation and surveying, the minute has the advantage that one minute of latitude on the surface of the Earth corresponds to approximately one nautical mile

[c]The gon (or grad, where grad is an alternative name for the gon) is an alternative unit of plane angle to the degree, defined as $(\pi/200)$ rad. Thus there are 100 gon in a right angle. The advantage of the gon in navigation is that one kilometre on the surface of the Earth subtends an angle of one centigon at the centre of the Earth. This is because of the fact that the distance from the pole to the equator of the Earth is approximately 10 000 km; however, the gon is rarely used

[d]For applications in astronomy, small angles are measured in arcseconds (i.e. seconds of plane angle) and denoted as ″. Its sub-multiples like milliarcseconds, microarcseconds and picoarcseconds are denoted as mas, μas and pas, respectively. The arcsecond is an alternative name for second of plane angle

[e]The unit hectare and its symbol ha were adopted by the CIPM in 1879 (PV, 1879, 41). The hectare is used to express land area

[f]The litre and its symbol l were adopted by 3rd CGPM 1901 as a unit of volume of 1 kg mass of water at the temperature of its maximum density. The 12th CGPM (1964) by Resolution 6 abrogated the name litre as the unit of volume. However, the 16th CGPM (1979) adopted the use of litre with symbols l or L as another name of decimeter cube. The alternative symbol L was adopted in order to avoid the risk of confusion between the letter l (el) and the numeral 1 (one). For details, see reference Metrologia [2]

[g]The tonne and its symbol t were adopted by the CIPM in 1879 (PV, 1879, 41). In English-speaking countries, this unit is sometimes called "metric tonne"

[h]The dalton (Da) and the unified atomic mass unit (u) are alternative names (and symbols) for the same unit, equal to 1/12 of the mass of a free carbon 12 atom, at rest and in its ground state

[i]The electronvolt is the kinetic energy acquired by an electron in passing through a potential difference of one volt in vacuum. The electronvolt is often combined with the SI prefixes

In using these units, it is important that the nature of the quantity be specified and that any reference value used be specified

Table 10.6 Non-SI units whose values in SI units must be obtained experimentally

Quantity	Name of unit	Symbol for unit	Value in SI units[a]
Units accepted for use with the SI			
Length	astronomical unit[d]	ua	1 ua $= 1.495\,978\,707$ 00×10^{11} m
Natural units (n.u.)			
mass	n.u. of mass (electron mass)	m_e	$9.109\,383\,56(11) \times 10^{-31}$ kg
time	n.u. of time	$\hbar/(m_e c_0^2)$	$1.288\,088\,667\,12\,(58) \times 10^{-21}$ s
Atomic units (a.u.)			
mass	a.u. of mass	m_e	$9.109\,383\,56(11) \times 10^{-31}$ kg
Length	a.u. of length, bohr	a_0	$0.529\,177\,210\,67\,(23) \times 10^{-10}$ m
Energy	a.u. of energy, hartree	E_h	$4.359\,744\,650(54) \times 10^{-18}$ J
Time	a.u. of time	$\hbar/E_h$	$2.418884326505(16) \times 10^{-17}$ s

[a] The values in SI units of all units in this table, except the astronomical unit, are taken from the 2014 CODATA set of recommended values of the fundamental physical constants [5]. The combined standard uncertainty in the last two digits is given in parenthesis

[b] The electronvolt is the kinetic energy acquired by an electron in passing through a potential difference of one volt in vacuum. The electronvolt is often combined with the SI prefixes

[c] The dalton (Da) and the unified atomic mass unit (u) are alternative names (and symbols) for the same unit, which is equal to 1/12th the mass of a free carbon 12 atom, at rest and in its ground state. The dalton is often combined with SI prefixes, for example, to express the masses of large molecules in kilodaltons, kDa, or megadaltons, MDa, or to express the values of small mass differences of atoms or molecules in nanodaltons, nDa, or even picodaltons, pDa

[d] The astronomical unit is approximately equal to the mean of the distances between Earth and Sun. It is the radius of an unperturbed circular Newtonian orbit about the Sun of a particle having infinitesimal mass, moving with a mean motion of 0.017 202 098 95 radians per day (known as the Gaussian constant). The value given for the astronomical unit is quoted from the IERS Conventions 2003 [6]. The value of the astronomical unit in metres comes from the JPL ephemerides DE403 [7]

[e] The values in SI units of all units in this table, except the astronomical unit, are taken from the 2002 CODATA set of recommended values of the fundamental physical constants [5]. The combined standard uncertainty in the last two digits is given in parenthesis

[f] The electronvolt is the kinetic energy acquired by an electron in passing through a potential difference of one volt in vacuum. The electronvolt is often combined with the SI prefixes

[g] The dalton (Da) and the unified atomic mass unit (u) are alternative names (and symbols) for the same unit, which is equal to 1/12 times the mass of a free carbon 12 atom, at rest and in its ground state. The dalton is often combined with SI prefixes, for example, to express the masses of large molecules in kilodaltons, kDa, or megadaltons, MDa, or to express the values of small mass differences of atoms or molecules in nanodaltons, nDa, or even picodaltons, pDa

[h] The astronomical unit is approximately equal to the mean of the distances between Earth and Sun. It is the radius of an unperturbed circular Newtonian orbit about the Sun of a particle having infinitesimal mass, moving with a mean motion of 0.017 202 098 95 radians per day (known as the Gaussian constant). The value given for the astronomical unit is quoted from the IERS Conventions 2003 [6]. The value of the astronomical unit in metres comes from the JPL ephemerides DE403 [7]

Table 10.7 Non-SI units

Quantity	Name	Symbol	Value in SI units
Distance	Nautical mile[a]	M	1 M = 1852 m
Speed	Knot	Kn	1 kn = (1852/3600) m/s
Pressure	Bar[b]	bar[c]	1 bar = 0.1 MPa = 10^5 Pa
	Millimetres of Mercury[c]	mmHg	1 mmHg = 133.322 Pa
Length	Angstrom[d]	Å	1 Å = 0.1 nm = 10^{-10} m
Area	barn[e]	b	1 b = 100 fm^2 = 10^{-28} m^2
Logarithmic ratio sound pressure	Neper[f]	(Np)	Logarithmic ratio to the base e
	Bel[g]	B	Logarithmic ratio to the base 10
	Decible	dB	1 dB = (1/10)B

Decible, Bel and neper are the units of dimension 1 so to be avoided from this table

[a]The nautical mile is a special unit employed for marine and aerial navigation to express distances. The first International Extraordinary Hydrographic Conference, Monaco, 1929, adopted the value given above under the name "International nautical mile". As yet there is no internationally agreed symbol. This unit was originally chosen because one nautical mile on the surface of the Earth subtends approximately one minute of angle at its centre. As yet there is no internationally agreed symbol, but the symbols M, NM, Nm and nmi are all used. The unit was originally chosen and continues to be used, because one nautical mile on the surface of the Earth subtends approximately one minute of angle at the centre of the Earth, which is convenient when latitude and longitude are measured in degrees and minutes of angle

[b]The bar and its symbol are included in Resolution 7 of the 9th CGPM (1948; CR, 70). Since 1982, one bar has been used as the standard pressure for tabulating all thermodynamic data. Prior to 1982 the standard pressure used to be the standard atmosphere, equal to 1.013 25 bar, or 101 325 Pa

[c]The millimetre of mercury is a legal unit for the measurement of blood pressure in some countries

[d]The ångström is widely used by X-ray crystallographers and structural chemists because all chemical bonds lie in the range 1 to 3 ångströms. However, it has no official sanction from the CIPM or the CGPM

[e]The barn is a special unit employed in nuclear physics to express effective cross section

[f]The neper is used to express values of such logarithmic quantities as field level, power level, sound pressure level and logarithmic decrement. Natural logarithms are used to obtain the numerical values of quantities expressed in nepers. The neper is coherent with the SI, but not yet adopted by the CGPM as an SI unit. For further information, one may see ISO 31

[g]The bel is used to express values of such logarithmic quantities as field level, power level, sound pressure level and attenuation. Logarithms to base ten are used to obtain the numerical values of quantities expressed in bels. The sub-multiple decibel, dB, is commonly used. For further information, one may see ISO 31

[h]Np is enclosed in parentheses because, although the neper is coherent with the SI, it has not yet been adopted by the CGPM

[i]In using these units, it is particularly important that the quantity be specified. The unit must not be used to imply the quantity

Table 10.8 Non-SI units for the interpretation of older scientific CGS derived units with special names

Quantity	Name	Symbol	Value in SI units
Energy	Energy[a]	erg	$1 \text{ erg} = 10^{-7} \text{ J}$
Force	Force[a]	dyn	$1 \text{ dyn} = 10^{-5} \text{ N}$
Dynamic viscosity	Poise[a]	P	$1 \text{ P} = 1 \text{ dyn·s/cm}^2 = 0.1 \text{ Pa·s}$
Kinematic viscosity	Stokes	St	$1 \text{ St} = 1 \text{ cm}^2/\text{s} = 10^{-4} \text{ m}^2/\text{s}$
Luminance	Stilb[a]	sb	$1 \text{ sb} = 1 \text{ cdcm}^{-2} = 10^4 \text{ cdm}^{-2}$
Illuminance	Phot	ph	$1\text{ph} = 1 \text{ cd sr cm}^{-2} = 10^4 \text{ lx}$
Acceleration	gal[b]	Gal	$1 \text{ Gal} = 1 \text{ cm/s}^2 = 10^{-2} \text{ m/s}^2$
Magnetic flux	Maxwell[c]	Mx	$1 \text{ Mx} \wedge 1 \, 0{-}8 \text{ W b}$
Magnetic flux density	Gauss[c]	G	$1 \text{ G} \wedge 10^{-4} \text{ T}$
Magnetic field	Oersted[c, d]	Oe	$1 \text{ Oe} \wedge (1000/4\pi) \text{ A/m}$

[a]This unit and its symbol were approved by the 9th CGPM (1948)
[b]The gal is a special unit employed in geodesy and geophysics to express acceleration due to gravity
[c]This unit is part of the so-called "electromagnetic" three-dimensional CGS system and cannot strictly be compared with the corresponding unit of the International System, which has four dimensions when only mechanical and electric quantities are considered. For this reason, all such units are linked to its corresponding SI through the symbol ($\wedge$), which stands for the words "corresponds to"
[d]These units are part of the so-called "electromagnetic" three-dimensional CGS system based on un-rationalized quantity equations and must be compared with care to the corresponding unit of the International System which is based on rationalized equations involving four dimensions and four quantities for electromagnetic theory. The magnetic flux, Φ, and the magnetic flux density, B, are defined by similar equations in the CGS system and the SI, so that the corresponding units can be related as in the table. However, the un-rationalized magnetic field, H (un-rationalized) $= 4\pi \times H$ (rationalized). The equivalence symbol ($\wedge$) is used to indicate that when H (un-rationalized) $= 1$ Oe, H (rationalized) $= (10^3/4\pi)$ A m^{-1}

10.4.2 Non-SI Units with Experimentally Obtained Values

Non-SI units indicated in Table 10.6 are also accepted for use with the SI, whose values in SI units have been obtained by experiment and are therefore not known exactly. Their values are given with their combined standard uncertainties, which apply to the last two digits, shown in parentheses. These units are in common use in certain specialized fields.

Table 10.9 Examples of other non-SI units

Name	Symbol	Value in SI units
curie[a]	Ci	$1 \text{ Ci} = 3.7 \times 10^{10}$ Bq
röntgen[b]	R	$1 \text{ R} = 2.58 \times 10^{-4}$ C/k g
rad[c, f]	rad	$1 \text{ rad} = 1 \text{ cGy} = 10^{-2}$ Gy
rem[d, f]	rem	$1 \text{ rem} = 1 \text{ cSv} = 10^{-2}$ S v
X unit[e]	–	$1 \times \text{ unit} \approx 1.002 \times 10^{-4}$ nm
gamma[f]	γ	$1 \gamma = 1 \text{ nT} = 10^{-9}$ T
jansky	Jy	$1 \text{ Jy} = 1 0^{-26} \text{ W·m}^{-2}\text{·Hz}^{-1}$
fermi[f]	–	$1 \text{ fermi} = 1 \text{ fm} = 10^{-15}$ m
metric carat[g]	–	$1 \text{ metric carat} = 200 \text{ mg} = 2 \cdot 10^{-4}$ kg
torr	Torr	$1 \text{ Torr} = (101\,325/760)$ Pa
standard atmosphere	atm[8]	$1 \text{ atm} = 101\,325$ Pa
calorie	cal[9]	
micron[f]	μ[10]	$1 \mu = 10^{-3} \text{ mm} = 10^{-6}$ m

[a]The curie is a special unit employed in nuclear physics to express activity of radionuclide as retained by 12th CGPM in 1964

[b]The röntgen is a special unit employed to express exposure to X or γ radiation

[c]The rad is a special unit employed to express absorbed dose of ionizing radiation. When there is risk of confusion with the symbol for radian, rd may be used as the symbol for rad

[d]The rem is a special unit used in radioprotection to express dose equivalent

[e]The X unit was employed to express the wavelengths of X-rays. Its relationship with the SI unit is an approximate one

[f]These non-SI units are exactly equivalent to some sub-multiple of the corresponding SI unit

[g]The metric carat was adopted by the 4th CGPM in 1907 for commercial dealings in diamonds, pearls and precious stones. In India, carat is still being extensively used in diamonds and precious stone industry as a unit of mass

[h]The designation "standard atmosphere" for a reference pressure of 101 325 Pa as approved by 10th CGPM in 1954 was acceptable till 1982

[i]There are several "calories" in use

(a) a calorie labelled "at 15 °C": 1 cal 15 = 4.1855 J value adopted by the CIPM in 1950 [8]

(b) a calorie labelled "IT" (International Table): 1 cal IT = 4.1868 J [9]

(c) a calorie labelled "thermo-chemical": 1 cal th = 4.184 J

[j] The micron and its symbol, adopted by the CIPM in 1879 (PV, 1879, 41) and repeated in Resolution 7 of the 9th CGPM (1948;) were abolished by the 13th CGPM (1967–1968)

The units described under n. u, namely, speed of light c, action (h/π) and elementary charge e, have been taken as defining constants have been removed from this table.

10.4.3 Non-SI Units Used by Special Groups

To allow freedom to people working in special fields who see an advantage to express their viewpoints in specific units, units given in Table 10.7 are allowed to be used. Since, however, SI units are the international meeting ground in terms of which all other units are defined, those who use units from Tables 10.7 and or 10.8 should always give the definition of the units they use in terms of SI units.

10.4.4   Other Non-SI Units with Special Names

The quantities and their units given in Table 6.8 deal with the relationship between CGS units and the SI, and CGS units that were assigned special names are also given in 6.8. In the field of mechanics, the CGS system of units was built upon three quantities of length, mass and time with corresponding base units of centimetre, gram and second. In the field of electricity and magnetism, units were expressed in terms of these three base units. Because this can be done in different ways, it led to the establishment of several different systems, like the CGS electrostatic system, the CGS electromagnetic system and the CGS Gaussian system. In these three last-mentioned systems, the system of quantities and the corresponding system of equations differ from those used with SI units.

10.4.5   Other Non-SI Units Found in Old Literature

The units, given in Table 10.9, are normally found in older literature. In the present context, it should be noted that if these units were continued to be used, the advantages of the SI would be lost. The relation of these units to the SI should be specified in every document in which they are used. In India, through Weights and Measures Regulations, some of these units have been declared as prohibited units. In fact, there are too many non-SI units, which are in use by some countries still using fps system, or in some specific fields. However, it will be useful to know their conversion factors in terms of SI units. These ones can be found on the BIPM website.

References

1. J. Terrien, BIPM news. Metrologia **11**(179–183), 180 (1975)
2. P. Giacomo, BIPM news. Metrologia **16**(55–61) (1980)
3. T.J. Quinn, International report: news from the BIPM. Metrologia **37**, 87–99
4. S.V. Gupta, *A treatise on Standards of Weights and Measures* (Commercial Law Publishers, Delhi, 2005)
5. P.J. Mohr, D.B. Newell, B.N. Taylor, Rev. Mod. Phys. **2016**(88), 1–69 (2016)
6. D DMcCarthy, G. Petit (eds), IERS Technical Note 32, Frankfurt am Main: Verlag des Bundesamts für Kartographie und Geodäsie, 12 (2004)
7. E.M. Standish, *Report of the IAU WGAS Sub-Group on Numerical Standards, Highlights of Astronomy*, Appenzeller edn. (Kluwer Academic Publishers, Dordrecht, 1995), pp. 180–184
8. BIPM, Proc. Verb. Com. Int. Poids et Mesure **22**, 79–80 (l950)
9. 5th International Conference on the Properties of Steam (London, 1956)

Chapter 11
Expressing SI Units

11.1 Introduction

We have discussed evolution of International System of units, base units, coherent derived units and non-SI units in the last few chapters. Continuing the subject, in this chapter, we are going to discuss the SI prefixes, their use, methods to express the quantities with proper numerals and units. Specific advantage of the International System of Units (SI) will also be discussed.

11.2 SI Prefixes

The 11th CGPM (1960) [1] adopted a series of prefixes and their symbols to form the names and symbols of the decimal multiples and sub-multiples of SI units ranging from 10^{12} to 10^{-12}. Prefixes for 10^{-15} and 10^{-18} were added by the 12th CGPM (1964) [2], for 10^{15} and 10^{18} by the 15th CGPM (1975) [3, 4], and for 10^{21}, 10^{24}, 10^{-21} and 10^{-24} by the 19th CGPM (1991) [5, 6]. All prefixes and their respective symbols, approved till date, are given in Table 11.1.

These SI prefixes refer strictly to powers of 10. They should not be used to indicate powers of 2 (for example, one kilobit represents 1000 bits and not 1024 bits).

11.2.1 Rules for Using SI Prefixes

In accord with the general principles adopted by the ISO (ISO 31), the CIPM recommended the following rules to be observed when using the SI prefixes:

© Springer Nature Switzerland AG 2020
S. V. Gupta, *Units of Measurement*, Springer Series in Materials Science 122,
https://doi.org/10.1007/978-3-030-43969-9_11

Table 11.1 SI prefixes

Factor	Name	Symbol	Factor	Name	Symbol
10^{24}	Yotta	Y	10^{-1}	Deci	d
10^{21}	Zetta	Z	10^{-2}	Centi	c
10^{18}	Exa	E	10^{-3}	Milli	m
10^{15}	Peta	P	10^{-6}	Micro	μ
10^{12}	Tera	T	10^{-9}	Nano	n
10^{9}	Giga	G	10^{-12}	Pico	p
10^{6}	Mega	M	10^{-15}	Femto	f
10^{3}	Kilo	k	10^{-18}	Atto	a
10^{2}	Hecto	ha	10^{-21}	Zepto	z
10^{1}	Deca	da	10^{-24}	Yocto	y

1. Regardless of the type used in the surrounding text, all prefix symbols are printed in roman (upright) type and are attached to unit symbols with no space between the prefix symbol and the unit symbol.
2. Similarly, prefix names are also inseparable from the unit names to which they are attached. Thus, for example, millimetre, micropascal and meganewton are single words.
3. With the exception of da (deca), h (hecto) and k (kilo), all multiple prefix symbols are in capital (uppercase) letters, and all sub-multiple prefix symbols are in lowercase letters.
4. All prefix names are printed in lowercase letters, except at the beginning of a sentence.
5. The grouping formed by the prefix symbol attached to the unit symbol constitutes a new inseparable symbol (of a multiple or sub-multiple of the unit concerned), which can be raised to a positive or negative power and combined with other unit symbols to form compound unit symbols.
   For example,

$$1\,\text{cm}^3 = \left(10^{-2}\text{m}\right)^3 = 10^{-6}\text{m}^3$$
$$1\,\mu\text{s}^{-1} = \left(10^{-6}\text{s}\right)^{-1} = 10^{6}\text{s}^{-1}$$
$$1\,\text{V/cm} = (1\text{V})/\left(10^{-2}\text{m}\right) = 10^{2}\text{V/m}$$
$$1\,\text{cm}^{-1} = \left(10^{-2}\text{m}\right)^{-1} = 10^{2}\text{m}^{-1}.$$

6. Compound prefixes, i.e. prefixes formed by the juxtaposition of two or more SI prefixes, are not permitted. This rule also applies to compound prefix names. For 1 nm do not write as 1 mμm. Similarly, microcentimetre with symbol μcm is also not allowed.
7. Prefix symbols can neither stand alone nor be attached to the number 1, the symbol for the unit one. Similarly, prefix names cannot be attached to the name of the unit one, that is, to the word "one". We cannot call mega men for one million men.

8. Prefix names and symbols are used with a number of non-SI units, but they are never used with the units of time like minute (min), hour (h) and day (d). However, astronomers use milliarcsecond, which they denote as **mas**, and microarcsecond, **μas**, which they use as units for measuring very small angles.

11.2.2 *Prefix About the Kilogram*

Among the base units of the International System, the kilogram is the only one whose name and symbol, for historical reasons, include a prefix. Names and symbols for decimal multiples and sub-multiples of the unit of mass are, therefore, formed by attaching prefix names to the unit name "gram", and prefix symbols to the unit symbol "g" [7, 8].

11.3 Writing of SI Unit Symbols

11.3.1 *Unit Symbols and Their Combinations*

1. Every symbol of a unit is written in Roman upright form. In general, unit symbols are written in lowercase, but, if the name of the unit is derived from the proper name of a person, the first letter of the symbol is a capital. When the name of a unit is expressed in full, it is always written in lowercase, except for the name "degree Celsius" or when a sentence starts with the name of the unit.
2. The 16th CGPM (1979, Resolution 6) permitted the use of either capital L or lowercase l for the litre. This was done in order to avoid possible confusion between the numeral 1 (one) and the lowercase letter l (el).
3. A multiple or sub-multiple prefix, if used, is part of the unit and precedes the unit symbol without a separator. A prefix is never used in isolation, and compound prefixes are never used.
4. Unit symbols are mathematical entities and not abbreviations. Therefore, they are not followed by a period except at the end of a sentence.
   One may right a rod is 5.6 cm long is correct, but not a rod is 5.6 cm long. As cm is an abrivationof centimetre.
5. Unit symbols are not to be changed in the plural.
   For example, one should write 100 kg but not 100 kgs.
   Unit symbols and unit names are not to be mixed within one expression, since names are not mathematical entities.
   For example, for writing the unit of mass density, use either kgm^{-3}, kg/m^3 or kilogram per metre cubed but not kilogram per m^3 or kg per metre cube.
6. In forming products and quotients of unit symbols, the normal rules of algebraic multiplication or division apply. Multiplication must be indicated by

a space or a half-high (centred) dot (·), since otherwise some prefixes could be misinterpreted as a unit symbol. Indicate division by a horizontal line, by a solidus (oblique stroke, /) or by negative exponents. When several unit symbols are combined, care should be taken to avoid ambiguities, for example, by using brackets or negative exponents. A solidus must not be used more than once in a given expression without brackets to remove ambiguities.

For example, one may write

$$\text{m/s or ms}^{-1} \text{ for m/s.}$$

Write ms for millisecond and m s for metre times second; the same may be written as ms. Expressions like m kg/(s^3 A) or m kg s^{-3} A^{-1} are permitted but not m kg/s^3/A, nor m kg/s^3 A.

Work done in joules is expressed, as m^2 kgs^{-2} and permeability as m kg s^{-2} A^{-2} are some examples for expressing quantities involving many units.

7. It is not permissible to use abbreviations for unit symbols or unit names, such as:
   - sec for either s or second,
   - sq. mm for either mm^2 or square millimetre,
   - cc for either cm^3 or cubic centimetre and
   - mps for either m/s or metre per second.

The use of the correct symbols for SI units, and for units in general, as listed in the book, is mandatory. In this way, ambiguities and misunderstandings in the values of quantities are avoided.

11.3.2 Names of Units

1. Unit names are normally printed in roman (upright) type, and they are treated like ordinary nouns. In English, the names of units start with a lowercase letter (even when the symbol for the unit begins with a capital letter), except at the beginning of a sentence or in capitalized material such as a title. In keeping with this rule, the correct spelling of the name of the unit with the symbol °C is "degree Celsius" (the unit degree begins with a lowercase d and the modifier Celsius begins with an uppercase C because it is a proper name).
   Other examples are joule symbol J, hertz symbol Hz, second symbol s, ampere symbol A and watt symbol W.
2. Although the values of quantities are normally expressed using symbols for numbers and symbols for units, if for some reason the unit name is more appropriate than the unit symbol, the unit name should be spelled out in full.
   For example, we may write 5.9 N or 5.9 newtons; no abbreviation for the name of the unit can be used.
3. When the name of a unit is combined with the name of a multiple or sub-multiple prefix, no space or hyphen is used between the prefix name and

the unit name. The combination of prefix name plus unit name is a single word, like millimetre and not milli-metre. One should write kilopascal rather than kilo-pascal.
4. In both English and French, however, when the name of a derived unit is formed from the names of individual units by multiplication, then either a space or a hyphen is used to separate the names of the individual units.
5. In both English and French qualifiers, such as "squared" or "cubed" are used in the names of units raised to powers, and they are placed after the unit name. However, in the case of area or volume, as an alternative the qualifiers "square" or "cubic" may be used, and these modifiers are placed before the unit name, but this applies only in English.

The rules enumerated in sections and subsections of Sects. 11.2 and 11.3 are enforced through Legal Metrology (National Standard) Rules 2011 [12]. The rules are in continuation of Standards of Weight and Measures (National Standards) Rules 1988.

11.3.3 Quantity Calculus

11.3.3.1 Value of Quantity

The value of a quantity is expressed as the product of a number and a unit. The number multiplying the unit is the numerical value of the quantity expressed in that unit.

11.3.3.2 Numerical Value of a Given Quantity

The numerical value of a given quantity depends on the choice of unit. Though the value of a given quantity is independent of the choice of unit, its numerical value will be different when expressed in different units. For example, the statements that distance between the two given lines on the International Prototype of metre is 1 m, 100 cm or 1000 mm are all correct. Numerical values are 1, 100 and 1000. Units are m, cm and mm. The same distance may be expressed as 1.093 613 3 yards.

11.3.3.3 Formatting the Value of a Quantity

1. The numerical value of the magnitude of the quantity always precedes the unit
2. A space is always used to separate the unit from the number.
3. The space is regarded as a multiplication sign. Thus, the value of the quantity is the product of the number and the unit.

4. The exceptions to above rule 2 are for degree symbol ° and its sub-multiples, viz., minute and second when representing plane angle.
5. Degree symbol ° just precedes Celsius symbol C when temperature is expressed in degree Celsius. However, a gap is always kept in between the symbol (degree Celsius) °C and the numerical value of the temperature, when expressed in degree Celsius. Say, for example, write 27.5 °C.
6. The symbols for degree minute and second for plane angle, respectively, are °, ' and ", for which no space is left between the numerical value and the unit symbol. Correct way of expressing a plane angle is 54° 33′ 44″.
7. Even when the value of a quantity is used as an adjective, a space is left between the numerical value and the unit symbol. Only when the name of the unit is spelled out would the ordinary rules of grammar apply, so that in English a hyphen would be used to separate the number from the unit. For example, write 15 kΩ resistor and 30 cm—ruler.
8. It is preferable to use only one unit rather than the units and its sub-multiples. For example, to express a long-distance quite accurately, express its numerical value in decimal up to the desired places. Express a distance as 10.532 m rather than 10 m, 5 dm, 3 cm and 2 mm.

For plane angles, it is generally preferable to divide the degree decimally. Thus, it is advisable to write 22.20° rather than 22° 12′.

Historically, in fields of navigation, cartography, astronomy and in the measurement of very small angles, minutes and seconds are used as subdivision of degrees expressing plane angles.

11.3.3.4 Symbols of Quantities

Symbols for quantities are generally single letter set in an italic font, although they may be qualified by further information in subscripts or superscripts or in brackets. Thus, C is the recommended symbol for heat capacity, C_m for molar heat capacity, $C_{m,p}$ for molar heat capacity at constant pressure and $C_{m,v}$ for molar heat capacity at constant volume.

For further details for symbols of quantities, one may see standard references like [9–11]. However, one must remember that symbols for quantities are only recommendations; one may or may not use them. But in contrast the symbols for units are mandatory and are to be used in a prescribed form. In particular circumstances, authors may wish to use a symbol of their own choice for a quantity, for example, in order to avoid a conflict arising from the use of the same symbol for two different quantities. Invariably, the meaning of each symbol of the quantities used is clearly stated.

Symbols for units are treated as mathematical entities. In expressing the value of a quantity as the product of a numerical value and a unit, both the numerical value and the unit may be treated by the ordinary rules of algebra. This procedure is described as the use of quantity calculus, or the algebra of quantities. For example, the equation $m = 1.235$ kg may equally be written $m/\text{kg} = 1.235$. For the heading of a column in a table, it is often convenient to write the quotient of a quantity and its unit, so that the entries in the table are all simply numbers.

11.3.3.5 Quantity Symbols and Unit Symbols

Just as the quantity symbol does not imply any particular choice of unit, the symbol of a unit should not be used to provide specific information about the quantity. The unit used should never be the sole source of information on the quantity.

For example, if L is the symbol for the load on a balance, then L may be written as

$$L = 1.675 \, \text{kg}$$

and L_{max} as the capacity of the balance should be written as

$$L_{max} = 20 \, \text{kg}.$$

But never write the capacity of the balance as

$$L = 20 \, \text{kg}_{max}.$$

It means the symbol of a unit should never be qualified for further information about the nature of the quantity. Any extra information on the nature of the quantity should be attached to the quantity symbol and not to the unit symbol.

For example, if maximum voltage across two points is 1000 V and U is symbol for voltage, then write

$$U_{max} = 1000 \, \text{V}.$$

But never write

$$U = 1000 \, \text{V}_{max}.$$

Taking w as a symbol of mass fraction, you may write the mass fraction of copper in the sample of silicon as

$$w(\text{Cu}) = 1.3 \times 10^{-6}$$

$$\text{but not } 1.3 \times 10^{-6} \, \text{w/w}.$$

11.3.4 Stating Values of Quantities of Dimension One

The coherent SI unit of quantities of dimension one, also termed dimensionless quantities, is the number one, symbol 1. Values of such quantities are expressed simply as numbers. The unit symbol 1 or unit name "one" is not explicitly shown. In some special cases, the unit symbol 1 is given specific name. Such as

- For the quantity plane angle, the unit one is given the special name radian, symbol rad.
- For the quantity solid angle, the unit one is given the special name steradian, symbol sr.
- For the logarithmic ratio quantities, the special names neper, symbol Np, bel, symbol B, and decibel, symbol dB, are used.

Because SI prefix symbols can neither be attached to the symbol 1 nor to the name "one", powers of 10 are used to express the values of particularly large or small quantities of dimension one. Do not write mega books for one million books.

11.3.4.1 Use of Symbol %

In mathematical expressions, the internationally recognized symbol % (percent) may be used with the SI to represent the number 0.01. Thus, it can be used to express the values of dimensionless quantities. When it is used, a space separates the number and the symbol %. In expressing the values of dimensionless quantities in this way, the symbol % should be used rather than the name "percent".

In written text, however, the symbol % generally takes the meaning of "parts per hundred". Phrases such as "percentage by mass", "percentage by volume" or "percentage by amount of substance" should not be used; the extra information on the quantity should instead be conveyed in the name and symbol for the quantity. For example, $Q = 3.6\%$ is correct but to write $Q = 3.6\%$ *V/V* is not correct. To express the last expression, one should define the Q by writing it as Q_V and write $Q_V = 3.6\%$.

In expressing, the values of dimensionless fractions (e.g. mass fraction, volume fraction and relative uncertainties), the use of a ratio of two units of the same kind is sometimes useful. For example, molar concentration of B symbol X_B instead of writing

$$X_B = 2.5 \times 10^{-3}.$$

It is better to write

$$X_B = 2.5 \text{ mmol/mol}.$$

The term "ppm", meaning 10^{-6} relative value, or 1 in 10^6, or parts per million, is also used. This is analogous to the meaning of percent as parts per hundred. The terms "parts per billion" and "parts per trillion", and their respective abbreviations "ppb" and "ppt", are also used, but their meanings are language dependent. For this reason, the terms ppb and ppt should best be avoided. The reason is the ambiguity in the values of words billion and trillion.

- In English-speaking countries, a billion is generally taken to be 10^9 and a trillion to be 10^{12};
- In French-speaking countries, a billion is interpreted as 10^{12} and a trillion as 10^{18}.
- The abbreviation ppt is also sometimes read as parts per thousand, adding further confusion.

When any of the terms %, ppm, etc., are used, it is important to state the dimensionless quantity whose value is being specified.

11.4 Expression of Numbers

In India, the Legal Metrology (Numeration) Rules, 2011 [13], deals with the numeration and expressing any number including large numbers and fractions. The rules are in accordance with international practices and are the same as prescribed in the international system of units—SI.

SI rules governing the expression of numbers are as follows:

(1) Every numeration shall be made in accordance with decimal system.
(2) Every number shall be represented on base 10.
(3) In representing any number in digits, the international form of Indian numerals, namely, 0, 1, 2, 3, 4, 5, 6, 7, 8 and 9 are to be used. Quite often these digits are called as International form of Arabic numerals.
(4) The symbol for the decimal marker (to separate the integral part of numbers from the decimal part) shall be either the point on the line or the comma on the line (22nd CGPM 2003). In India, we adopted the point on the line to represent decimal marker.
(5) In any number in digits exceeding three, the decimal point is taken as the starting point; and the digits, whether to left or to right of it, are divided in groups of three; each group is separated by a space. No comma or full stop is to be inserted in the spaces between such groups (CGPM, 1948, reconfirmed by 22nd CGPM in 2003). However, when there are only four digits before or after the decimal marker, it is customary not to use a space to isolate a single digit.
    Note: The practice of grouping digits in this way is a matter of choice; it is not always followed in certain specialized applications such as engineering drawings, financial statements and scripts to be read by a computer.
(6) For numbers in a table, the format used should not vary within one column.
(7) If the number is between +1 and −1, then the decimal marker is always preceded by a zero.

11.4.1 Formatting Numbers and the Decimal Marker

The symbol used to separate the integral part of a number from its decimal part is called the decimal marker.

Following the decision of the CIPM made at its 86th meeting (1997), the BIPM now uses the following:

1. The dot (point on the line) as the decimal marker in all the English language versions of its publications.
2. A comma (on the line) is used for the decimal marker in all of its French language publications.

However, some international bodies including some international standards organizations use the comma on the line as the decimal marker in all languages including English.

Use of the comma on the line or the point on the line as decimal marker varies from country to country. In some countries, symbol for decimal marker varies from one native language to other. To cater to the need of every section of the Society the CGPM in its 22nd meeting held in 2003, vide resolution 10, decided that the decimal marker "shall be either the point on the line or the comma on the line". Hence, decimal marker should be recognized in context of the language and the country.

11.4.2 Expressing the Measurement Uncertainty

The uncertainty that is associated with the estimated value of a quantity should be evaluated and expressed in accordance with the Guide to the Expression of Uncertainty in Measurement [ISO, 1995] [14]. The standard uncertainty associated with a quantity x is denoted by u(x). It is the estimated standard deviation with coverage factor $k = 1$. A convenient way to represent the uncertainty is given in the following example:

$$m_n = 1.674\,927\,28\,(29) \times 10^{-27}\,\text{kg},$$

where m_n is the symbol for the quantity (in this case the mass of a neutron), and the number in parenthesis is the numerical value of the combined standard uncertainty of the estimated value of m_n referred to the last two digits of the quoted value.

In this case $u(m_n) = 0.000\,000\,29 \times 10^{-27}\,\text{kg}$.

In literature, normally standard uncertainty is cited. However, some calibration laboratories give combined expanded uncertainty with a coverage factor k of 2 or 3 depending upon if the stated results are at 96% or 99.7% confidence level. Expanded uncertainty is k times the combined standard uncertainty. However, if any coverage factor, k, different from one, is used, this factor must be stated.

11.5 Advantages of SI Units

11.5.1 Harmonization of Units

Before the adoption of SI units, there were different units for the same quantity in different areas of measurements. For example, in the field of electrical measurements, there were different sets of units, for electrostatic, electromagnetic and Gaussian measurements. These sets used to be called as electrostatic, electromagnetic and practical units. Same was the case of energy; there were separate units for mechanical, electrical, heat and optical energies.

To make the units of the given quantity same in all areas of electrical measurements, the following steps are taken:

1. Introduced permittivity and permeability are the constants of proportionality in the Coulombs law for force of attraction/repulsion between the free charges and the corresponding formula for free magnetic poles, respectively.
2. As both formulae are valid in space 4π, the constant of spherical symmetry was introduced in the denominator.
3. The electric current is now defined as the coulomb per second, so the permeability of free space is not exactly equal to $4\pi \times 10^{-7}$ N A^{-2} but different only by a negligible value.
4. Using Maxwell theory, the permittivity of free space is derived from the formula that product of permittivity and permeability is an inverse of the square of the velocity of light.

An example is given below.
Coulombs formula is modified as

$$F = (1/\varepsilon_0 4\pi)\, Q_1 Q_2/r^2. \tag{11.1}$$

Here, ε_0 is the permittivity of free space.
From above, the unit of charge is defined as follows:
If two equal and opposite charges placed in vacuum at a distance of 1 m apart and each experiences a force equal to $1/\varepsilon_0 4\pi$ newtons, then each is a unit charge.

Similarly, the force (F) experienced per unit length between the two parallel wires of infinite length and negligible cross section in vacuum was modified to

$$F \text{ per unit length} = (\mu_0/2\pi)\, I_1 I_2/r, \tag{11.2}$$

where μ_0 is the permeability of free space.
Using Maxwell relation

$$\varepsilon_0 \mu_0 = c^{-2} \tag{11.3}$$

$$\text{SI unit of } c^{-2} = s^2/m^2,$$

or

$$\{\varepsilon_0 \mu_0\} = s^2/m^2. \tag{11.4}$$

If each charge is one coulomb, then from (11.1) we get the following:
Denoting unit charge by C

$$1 \text{ newton} = (1/\varepsilon_o 4\pi)C^2/m^2. \tag{11.5}$$

Similarly if $I_1 = I_2 = 1$ A and $r = 1$ m, then from (11.2)

$$\text{newton per metre} = (\mu_o/4\pi)A^2/m,$$

giving

$$1 \text{ newton} = (\mu_o/4\pi)A^2. \tag{11.6}$$

Equating (11.5) and (11.6) we get

$$(1/\varepsilon_o 4\pi) \times C^2/m^2 = (\mu_o/4\pi)A^2,$$

or

$$C^2/m^2 = A^2 \cdot \{\varepsilon_o\mu_o\}.$$

But

$$\{\varepsilon_o\mu_o\} = s^2/m^2, \tag{11.7}$$

giving

$$C^2/m^2 = A^2 \cdot s^2/m^2,$$

giving us

$$\mathbf{C} = \mathbf{A} \cdot \mathbf{s}. \tag{11.8}$$

This means that unit of charge in electrostatic is ampere · second. The unit of charge using electromagnetic field is also A · s. **Hence, unit of charge becomes same in the two fields**.

11.5.1.1 SI Unit of Magnetic Pole Strength

Force between two poles of strength P_1 and P_2 placed r metres apart experience a force F in newtons given by

$$F = \mu_0 P_1 P_2/4\pi r^2.$$

Writing unit equation we get

$$N = NA^{-2}\{P\}^2/m^2$$

$$\{P\}^2 = A^2 m^2,$$

giving us

$$\{P\} = A.m.$$

SI unit of Pole strength P is A·m.

11.5.2   Expressing the Values of μ_O and ε_O in Terms of SI Units

Using the relation between the force acting on the wires per unit length, between the two parallel wires of infinite length and negligible cross section carrying currents as

$$\text{Force/length} = (\mu_o/4\pi)I_1 I_2/\text{distance between the wires.}$$

For equal currents

$$\text{Force} = (\mu_o/4\pi)(\text{Current})^2,$$

giving unit equation as

$$N = \{\mu_o\}A^2$$
$$\{\mu_o\} = N/A^2 \tag{11.9}$$
$$\{\mu_o\} = m \cdot kg \cdot s^{-2}A^{-2}.$$

But from Table 10.2, the henry H the unit of inductance can be expressed in terms of base units as

$$H = m^2 \cdot kg \cdot s^{-2} \cdot A^{-2}$$

or

$$H/m = m \cdot kg \cdot s^{-2} \cdot A^{-2}.$$

So from (11.9), we get unit of μ_o

$$\{\mu_o\} = H/m. \tag{11.10}$$

Therefore, unit of permeability may also be taken as henry per metre with symbol H/m.

Using (11.13), unit of ε_o is given by

$$\{\varepsilon_o\} = 1/\{\mu_o c^2\}$$
$$= m^{-1} \cdot kg^{-1} \cdot s^2 \cdot A^2 . m^{-2} \cdot s^2$$
$$= m^{-3} \cdot kg^{-1} \cdot s^4 \cdot A^2.$$

But using Table 10.2, unit farad symbol F is expressed in terms of base units as $m^{-2} \cdot kg^{-1} \cdot s^4 \cdot A^2$, giving us

$$\{\varepsilon_o\} = F/m. \tag{11.11}$$

Therefore, the unit of permittivity is expressed in Faraday per metre.

11.5.3   Magnetic Flux Density/Magnetizing Force

The magnetic flux density and magnetizing force are two quantities, which are quite often misunderstood. In SI units in all the relations where magnetic field is used, it is magnetic flux density, which represents intensity of a magnetic field. One way of defining the quantity of magnetic flux density is as follows:

A charge q moving with a velocity v in a field of magnetic flux density B experiences a force F normal to the plane containing v and B given by the following relation:

$$F = q(v \cdot B \cdot sin\,\theta), \qquad (11.12)$$

where θ is the angle between the velocity of the moving charge q with the direction of magnetic flux density B.

Putting each of q and v equal to one and taking θ as $90°$ in (11.12), we get

$$F = B. \qquad (11.13)$$

Hence, magnetic flux density or intensity of magnetic induction is the force acting on a unit positive charge moving with unit velocity at right angles to the magnetic field B, and its unit has a special name, i.e. tesla.

Writing quantity equation of magnetic flux density from (11.12), we get

$$B = F/v \cdot q,$$

giving unit equation of B as

$$\begin{aligned}
\{B\} &= \{F\}/\{v\}\{q\} \\
&= N/(m \cdot s^{-1} \cdot C) \\
&= N/(m \cdot (C \cdot s^{-1})) \\
&= N/(A \cdot m).
\end{aligned} \qquad (11.14)$$

On the other hand, magnetizing force or intensity of magnetization H is the degree to which a magnetic field can magnetize a material. For example, a toroidal solenoid having n turns per unit length wound over a circular ring of magnetic material and carrying a steady current I produces a magnetic field B, given by the relation

$$B = \mu \cdot n \cdot I. \qquad (11.15)$$

The product nI is called the magnetizing force or magnetic intensity H given by

$$H = n \cdot I.$$

Hence, the magnitude of magnetizing force is defined as the product of current (in amperes) and number of turns of a solenoid wound around the unit length of toroidal solenoid. So its unit is ampere per metre with symbol A/m.

If inside the toroidal solenoid there is a free space, then magnetic induction is

$$B = \mu_0 H. \qquad (11.16)$$

Here, μ_0 is the magnetic permeability of free space. So SI unit of H is given by

$$\text{Unit of } H = \left(\text{Wb} \cdot \text{m}^{-2}\right)/\text{N} \cdot \text{A}^{-2}.$$

Expressing in base units, we get

$$\text{Unit of } H = \text{m}^2 \cdot \text{kg} \cdot \text{s}^{-2} \cdot \text{A}^{-1} \cdot \text{m}^{-2}/\text{m} \cdot \text{kg} \cdot \text{s}^{-2} \cdot \text{A}^{-2}$$

$$\textbf{Unit of } \boldsymbol{H} = \textbf{A/m}. \tag{11.17}$$

11.5.4 Intensity of Magnetization

Intensity of magnetization represents the ability to magnetize, same as magnetizing force. Numerically, it is equal to the magnetic moment per unit volume of the material, i.e. the intensity of magnetization H is given by

$$H = \text{Magnetic moment/Volume of the material.} \tag{11.18}$$

Hence,
the unit of intensity of magnetisation $=$ ampere·metre^2/metre^3 $=$ ampere/metre

$$\textbf{Unit of } \boldsymbol{H} = \textbf{A/m}.$$

For example, for a rectangular solid bar of uniform cross section of area a and length $2\,l$, if P is the pole strength developed in it, then by (11.18)

$$H = \text{Magnetic moment per unit Volume.}$$

Here, magnetic moment is $P \cdot 2\,l$ and volume of the magnet is $a \cdot 2\,l$, giving us

$$H = P \cdot 2l/a \cdot l = P/a.$$

So

$$\textbf{Unit of } \boldsymbol{H} - \textbf{the intensity of magnetisation} = \textbf{A} \cdot \textbf{m/m}^2 = \textbf{A/m}. \tag{11.19}$$

Coming to the field of magnetism, there is another term—the strength of a magnetic field—let us denote this by I. Strength of magnetic field due to a pole of strength P at a point distance r from it is the force experienced by a unit positive pole at that point given by the relation

$$I = \mu_o P/r^2. \tag{11.20}$$

Expressing each quantity of the above equation in SI units, SI unit of I is given by

$$\{I\} = \left(\text{NA}^{-2}\right)(\text{A} \cdot \text{m})/\text{m}^2$$
$$= \text{N}/(\text{A} \cdot \text{m}). \tag{11.21}$$

This expression is same as that of magnetic induction or flux density.

Hence, magnetic induction, magnetic flux density and strength of the magnetic field are one and the same quantity. Wherever the term magnetic field occurs, the tesla should be taken as its unit. Referring to last item of Table 10.1 of Chap. 10, the term intensity of magnetization having the unit-ampere per metre should be preferable over the term magnetic field.

11.5.5   Homogenizing of Units of Energy in Heat

Prior to adoption of SI units, the units of mechanical energy, heat energy and electrical energy remained different, as all were independently defined. The erg—unit of mechanical energy—was a dot product of two vectors, namely, force and displacement. The calorie was the heat exchanged by 1 g of water through a change of one degree centigrade. While electrical energy was the product of current, potential difference and time. The current was taken in ampere, potential difference in volts and time in seconds.

To solve this problem, mechanical energy was expressed in terms of base units of mass, length and time. Watt unit of power is obtained from mechanical energy, electromotive force or potential difference is obtained by dividing watt by electrical current, so making energy units same in mechanical and electrical fields. To bring out homogeneity in the area of heat, unit of energy is taken as joule and corresponding changes have been made in the specific heat capacity of water, which roughly comes out 4200 J/**kg**-K, instead of 1 cal/g °C.

11.5.6   Coherent System

Any system of measurements is said to be coherent if all derived units from base units have no numerical multiplier other than one. In this system, as seen in Chap. 10, all derived units are expressed in terms of base units having one only as the multiplier. Every derived unit is expressed as a product or division of relevant base or derived unit with special names but all the time has unity as coefficient. So it is a coherent system.

11.5.7   Coherent Derived Unit

Coherent derived unit, for a given system of quantities and for a chosen set of base units, is a product of powers of base units with no other proportionality factor than one.

It may be noted that

1. A power of base unit is the base unit raised to an exponent.
2. Coherence can be determined only with respect to a particular system of quantities and a given set of base units.
   Examples
   If the metre, the second and the mole are base units, the metre per second is the coherent derived unit of velocity when velocity is defined by the **quantity equation** $v = d\boldsymbol{r}/dt$, and the mole per cubic metre is the coherent derived unit of amount-of-substance concentration when amount of substance concentration is defined by the quantity equation $c = n/V$. The kilometre per hour and the knot, given as examples of derived units in chapter 10, are not coherent derived units in SI.
3. A derived unit can be coherent with respect to one system of quantities, but not to another.
   Example: The centimetre per second is the coherent derived unit of speed in the CGS system of units but is not a coherent derived unit in the SI.
4. The coherent derived unit for every derived quantity of dimension one, in a given system of units, is the number one, symbol 1. Name and symbol of the measurement unit one are generally not indicated.

11.5.8   Well-Defined Units

All the base units are very precisely defined and are understandable.

11.6   Expressing Electrostatic and Electromagnetic Quantities in SI Units

By redefining the electric current in terms of elementary charge, though the value of μ_0 is no more exact and equal to $4\pi \times 10^{-7}$, difference is almost negligible; similarly, the value of c, speed of light, in vacuums may be taken as 3×10^8 m·s^{-1} for the purposes of finding ratios of electrostatic and electromagnetic units with the corresponding SI unit. Now using the fact that

$$\mu_0 \times \varepsilon_0 = 1/c^2, \tag{11.22}$$

giving

$$4\pi \times 10^{-7} \times \varepsilon_0 = 1/9 \times 10^{16} \tag{11.23}$$

$$4\pi\varepsilon_0 = 1/9 \times 10^9. \tag{11.24}$$

11.6.1   *Charge and Current*

11.6.1.1   Esu of Charge

Coulomb's law in SI units

$$F \text{ newtons} = Q_1 O_2 / 4 \pi \varepsilon_0 r^2$$
$$\text{Unit equation } N = C^2 / \{\varepsilon_0\} m^2 \tag{11.25}$$

giving unit of ε_0

$$\text{as } \{\varepsilon_0\} = C^2 N^{-1} m^2. \tag{11.26}$$

Putting $Q_1 = Q_2 = 1$ C and $r = 1$ m in (11.24) and using (11.24), we get

$$1 (\text{coulomb})^2 / 1 \text{ m}^2 = 9.10^9 \text{ newtons}. \tag{11.27}$$

The law defines the unit of charge as follows:

Two equal charges are placed in vacuum and at one metre apart; if they experience a force of $9 \cdot 10^9$ newtons, then each is one coulomb of charge.

Coulombs law in CGS units is written as

$$\text{Force in dynes} = Q_1 O_2 / r^2.$$

Force in dynes, charge in electrostatic units and r in centimetres giving

$$1 \text{ dyne} = (\text{esu})^2 / 1 \text{ cm}^2 = 10^4 (\text{esu})^2 / 1 \text{ m}^2. \tag{11.28}$$

Multiplying each side by 10^5, we get

$$10^5 \text{ dynes} = 1 \text{ newton} = 10^9 (\text{esu})^2 / 1 \text{ m}^2.$$

Multiplying each side by $9 \cdot 10^9$, we get

$$9 \cdot 10^9 \text{ newtons} = 9 \times 10^{18} (\text{esu})^2 / 1 \text{ m}^2.$$

But from (11.26)

$$9.10^9 \text{ newtons} = 1 (\text{coulomb})^2 / 1 \text{ m}^2.$$

So

$$(\text{coulomb})^2 = 9 \times 10^{18} (\text{esu})^2$$
$$1 \text{ coulomb} = 3 \times 10^9 \text{esu of charge}$$
$$\mathbf{1 \text{ esu of charge} = \left(10^{-9} / 3\right) \quad \text{coulomb}}. \tag{11.29}$$

11.6.1.2   Emu of Current and Charge

Electromagnetic unit of charge is derived from the emu of current, whose unit is abampere. By definition, if 1 abampere of steady current is passing through two parallel infinite wires of negligibly small cross section placed at one cm apart, then each wire experiences a force of one dyne per cm length of wire. Relation used is F per unit length$= I_1 I_2/r$)

$$1 \, dyn/cm = 1(abampere)^2/1 \, cm$$

$$1 \, dyne = (1 \, abampere)^2.$$

In SI units when 1 A current is flowing through aforesaid wires and placed 1 m apart, then force acting is $2 \cdot 10^{-7}$ N/m, giving us

$$10^{-7} \, N/m = (ampere)^2/m$$

or

$$10^{-2} \, dyn = (ampere)^2$$

$$1 \, dyne = 100 \, (ampere)^2$$

giving us

$$1 \, dyne = (abampere)^2 = 100(ampere)^2$$

$$\mathbf{1 \, abampere = 10 \, ampere}. \tag{11.30}$$

It may be mentioned that initial definition of ampere comes from the fact that ampere was taken as one-tenth of abampere—the electromagnetic unit current.
Further

$$1 \, coulomb = 1 \, second.1 \, Ampere = 1 \, second \cdot 0.1 \, abampere$$

or 1 second.1 abampere = 1 emu of charge

$$\mathbf{1 \, emu \, of \, charge = 10 \, coulomb}. \tag{11.31}$$

11.6.2   Potential

11.6.2.1   esu Potential

By definition, potential at a point is work done on unit positive charge in bringing it from infinity to that point. Hence, unit of potential in SI units may be written as 1 J/1 C and is given a special name volt. Similarly, unit of potential in electrostatic field will be 1.erg/1. esu of charge

$$1 \, volt = 1 \, joule/1 \, coulomb$$

$$= 10^7 \, ergs/3 \cdot 10^9 esu \, of \, charge$$

$$= (1/300) \, (erg/esu \, of \, charge)$$

$$= (1/300) \, esu \, of \, potential$$

giving

$$\textbf{1 esu of potential} = \textbf{300 volts}. \tag{11.32}$$

11.6.2.2 Emu Potential

$$1 \text{ coulomb} = 3 \times 10^9 \text{ esu of charge} = 0.1 \text{ emu of charge}$$
$$1 \text{ emu of charge} = 3 \times 10^9 \text{ esu of charge}.$$

But

$$300 \text{ volt} = 1 \text{ esu of potential} = 1 \text{ erg/esu of charge} = 3 \cdot 10^{10} \text{ erg/emu of charge}$$

$$300 \text{ volt} = 3 \cdot 10^{10} \text{ emu of potential}$$

$$\textbf{emu of potential} = \textbf{10}^{-8} \textbf{ volt}. \tag{11.33}$$

11.6.3 Electrical Resistance

11.6.3.1 Esu of Resistance

In the field of electrostatics, there is no motion and concept of resistance is against motion so as such there should be no concept of resistance in the field of electrostatics; however, there is potential, so charge has a capacity to move; moreover, in the field of electromagnetic, there is current with unit abampere, so we may proceed as follows:

Potential/current = resistsnce,

$$1 \text{ ohm} = 1 \text{ volt/1 ampere} = (1/300) \text{ esu potential/0.1 abampere}$$
$$\textbf{1 ohm} = \textbf{1/30 esu of potential per abampere}.$$

Abampere is chosen, as in electrostatic the current has no meaning.

If we wish to express resistance in esu, we will replace abampere by $3 \cdot 10^{10}$ esu of current, giving

$$1 \text{ ohm} = (1/9) \cdot 10^{-11} \text{esu of resistance}$$

giving

$$\textbf{1 esu of resistance} = \textbf{9} \cdot \textbf{10}^{11} \textbf{ohms}. \tag{11.34}$$

11.6.3.2 Emu of Resistance

$$1 \text{ ohm} = 10^8 \text{ emu/0.1 abampere}$$

$$1 \text{ ohm} = 10^9 \text{ emu of resistance}$$

$$\textbf{1 emu of resistance} = \textbf{10}^{-9} \textbf{ ohm}. \tag{11.35}$$

11.6.4 *Electrical Capacitance*

11.6.4.1 Esu of Capacitance

$$\text{farad} = 1\,\text{C}/1\,\text{V} = 3 \cdot 10^9 \text{ esu of charge}/(1/300) \text{ of esu potential}$$

$$1\,\text{farad} = 9 \cdot 10^{11} \text{ unit of capacity in esu}$$

$$\mathbf{1\,esu\ of\ capacity = \left(10^{-11}/9\right)\,farad.} \qquad (11.36)$$

11.6.4.2 Emu of Capacitance

$$1\,\text{farad} = 1\,\text{C}/1\,\text{V} = 10^{-1} \text{ emu of charge}/10^8) \text{ emu of potential}$$
$$10^{-9} \text{ emu of capacitance}$$

giving us

$$\mathbf{1\,emu\ of\ capacity = 10^9\,farad.} \qquad (11.37)$$

11.6.5 *Emu of Magnetic Flux*

The unit of flux in SI is weber with symbol Wb. We know

$$1\,\text{weber} = 1\,\text{volt} \cdot 1\,\text{second}$$

giving

$$\text{weber} = 10^8 \text{ emu of potential} \cdot 1 \text{ second.}$$

But unit of emu of flux has been given the name maxwell with symbol Mx, hence

$$1\,\text{weber} = 10^8\,\text{Mx}$$

$$\mathbf{1\,Mx = 10^{-8}\,Wb.} \qquad (11.38)$$

11.6.6 *Magnetic Field Strength (Flux Density)*

Magnetic flux density = magnetic flux per square metre

$$1\,\text{tesla} = 1\,\text{weber}/\text{m}^2$$
$$= 10^8\,\text{Mx}/10^4\,\text{cm}^2$$
$$= 10^4\,\text{Mx}/\text{cm}^2.$$

But unit of emu of magnetic field strength has been given the name gauss with symbol G; hence,

$$1\ \text{tesla} = 10^4\ \text{gauss}$$

or

$$\textbf{1 gauss} = \mathbf{10^{-4}}\ \textbf{tesla.} \tag{11.39}$$

11.6.7 Electric Field

$$1\ \text{V}/1\text{m} = (1/300)\ \text{esu of potential}/100\text{cm}$$

$$1\ \text{V/m} = (1/3) \cdot 10^{-4}\ \text{esu of electric field}$$

$$\textbf{1 esu of electric field} = \mathbf{3 \cdot 10^4}\ \textbf{V/m.} \tag{11.40}$$

11.6.8 Inductance

Unit of inductance is henry $= d\Phi/di$, where Φ is flux and i is current

$$1\ \text{H} = 10^8\ \text{emu of flux}/0.1\ \text{emu of current}$$

$$1\ \text{H} = 10^9\ \text{emu of inductance}$$

$$\textbf{1 emu of inductance} = \mathbf{10^{-9}}\textbf{H.} \tag{11.41}$$

11.6.9 Oerested

The CGS unit of H is oerested and that of B is gauss. So from (11.25)

$$\text{Gauss/oerested} = \mu_0 = 4\pi 10^{-7}\text{N} \cdot \text{A}^{-2}.$$

So

$$\text{oersted} = 10^{-4}\text{T}/\left(4\pi \cdot 10^{-7}\text{N} \cdot \text{A}^{-2}\right)$$
$$= \left(10^3/4\pi\right) \cdot \text{Wb} \cdot \text{m}^{-2} \cdot \text{N}^{-1} \cdot \text{A}^2.$$

Expressing in SI base units, we get

$$1\ \text{Oersted} = (10^3/4\pi) \cdot \text{V} \cdot \text{s} \cdot \text{m}^{-2} \cdot \text{m}^{-1} \cdot \text{kg}^{-1} \cdot \text{A}^{-2}.$$

Substituting the SI units for V the volt, we get

$$(10^3/4\pi) \cdot m^2 \cdot kg \cdot s^{-3} \cdot A^{-1} \cdot s \cdot m^{-3} \cdot kg^{-1} \cdot s^2 \cdot A^2$$

$$\mathbf{1\,Oersted} = \left(\mathbf{10^3/4\,\pi}\right)\mathbf{A/m}. \tag{11.42}$$

Giorgi G. L. T [15], in 1904, some 30 years after the Metre Treaty, suggested that (if permeability of free space μ_o is taken as $4\pi \cdot 10^{-7}$) in definition of current, the units of the same quantities in electromagnetic and electrostatic will become the same.

References

1. CIPM, 1960, Comptes Rendus R, resolution 7, 87
2. CIPM, 1964, Comptes Rendus, resolution 8, 94
3. CIPM 1975, Comptes Rendus resolution 10, 106
4. Terrien J, 1975 BIPM News, Metrologia **11**, 180–181
5. CGPM, 1991 Comptes Rendus, resolution 4, 185
6. Quinn T.J, 1992, BIPM News, Metrologia **29**, 3
7. CIPM, Recommendation 2 of CIPM. Proces-Verbaux **35**, 29 (1967)
8. J Terrien, 1968, BIPM News, Metrologia, **4**, 45
9. ISO Standard 31 Quantities and Units
10. IUPAP SUNAMCO Red Book, Symbols, Units and Nomenclature in Physics
11. IUPAC Green Book Quantities, Units and Symbols in Physical Chemistry
12. Gupta S V, 2019, A Treatise on Legal Metrology Act 2009, (National Standard) Rules,2011, Commercial Law Publishers New Delhi
13. Gupta S V, 2019, A Treatise on Legal Metrology Act 2009, (Numeration) Rules,2011, Commercial Law Publishers New Delhi
14. ISO/IEC Guide 98–3:2008 - Uncertainty of measurement – Part-3
15. G. Giorgi, "Unita razionali di elettromagnetismo", Atti Assoc. Elettroteen **5**, 402–418 (1901)

Chapter 12
Past Efforts in Redefining of SI Units

12.1 In Terms of Physical Constants

In the previous chapters, we have seen a number of sets of physical constants to define a system of units. All through the efforts are being to find out a set of physical constants, which can describe all units of measurement.

12.1.1 Basis of SI Units

The SI—the International System of Units—was based, till recently, on the following values of fundamental constants [1]:

Velocity of light	$299\,792\,458\ \mathrm{ms}^{-1}$ for defining metre
Transition Periods of caesium atom 133	$9\,192\,631\,770$ for defining second
Triple point of water	273.16 for defining temperature
Permeability of free space	$4\pi \times 10^{-7}$ for defining unit of electric current

But this is not the only set of constants, which we can use for defining system of units. In fact using the same constants, one can arrive at several other sets of base units. For example, instead of using μ_0—the permeability of free space for defining electric current—we can use it and velocity of light c to define impedance of the free space. This will make ohm as base unit instead of electric current. We know $c \cdot \mu_0$ has the unit of resistance defining:

$$1\,\Omega = c \cdot \mu_0/376.731\,119\,44 \tag{12.1}$$

As $c \cdot \mu_0 = 376.731\,119\,44$, because of the presence of π in μ_0, the value of $c \cdot \mu_0$ may be taken to large number of decimal places; hence, this value is not unique. Petley [2] suggested this definition of ohm in 1990.

© Springer Nature Switzerland AG 2020
S. V. Gupta, *Units of Measurement*, Springer Series in Materials Science 122,
https://doi.org/10.1007/978-3-030-43969-9_12

12.2   From a Single Source

From above we see that we are using different elements or compounds and sources to arrive at a certain set of fundamental constants. Let us consider the possibility to define base units including that of the kilogram in terms of fundamental constants obtained from single source.

12.2.1   In Terms of Hydrogen Atom

Prof Kose et al. [3], in 2003, suggested that among many possibilities one possibility is to consider hydrogen for defining base units, say kilogram in terms of nucleus of the atom, second in terms of period of hydrogen atom in the ground state. Keep the definition of metre unchanged as it is already defined in terms velocity of light c, a fundamental constant. Other units are defined as follows:

Time: Second—the unit of time—is defined as the duration of 466 8xx xxx xxx xxx periods of the radiation corresponding to the transitions between the levels $2S_{1/2}$ and $3P_{1/2}$ of hydrogen atom. As the radiation transitions in hydrogen atom are measured eight times more accurately than the hyperfine structure in caesium atom, it will prove to be a better option.

Mass: The kilogram—the unit of mass—is $5.973\ 386\ xxx\ 10^{26}$ hydrogen atoms.

Electric current: The ampere—the unit of electric current—corresponds to $6.241\ 509\ 484 \times 10^{18}$ of elementary charges (charge on electron) per second.

Thermodynamic Temperature: The kelvin—the unit of temperature—is the fraction 1/13.80xx of the triple point of hydrogen.

Amount of substance: The mole—the unit of substance—is the amount of substance in a system, which contains $6.022141xxx\ 10^{25}$ elementary entities [4].

Definitions of metre and luminous intensity remain the same as metre is already defined in terms of velocity of light in a fundamental constant and second. We know that luminous intensity in SI is only a derived unit.

Please note that xxx after decimal places indicate that specific numerals will be substituted according to the latest internationally accepted values of physical constants involved.

Please remember that the second, the kilogram and the kelvin are independent base units, whereas other four units are metrologically dependent, like metre depends upon velocity of light, candela is a derived unit from the mechanical units like watt and frequency, etc. (Fig. 12.1).

Here, T_H represents the triple point of hydrogen, and a^{-1} is numerically equal to T_H. The symbols c, e, m_H and N_A are, respectively, velocity of light, charge on the electron, rest mass of hydrogen atom and the Avogadro constant. The fundamental constants within square brackets represent the numerical values in SI units.

Fig. 12.1 SI units in terms
of hydrogen atom

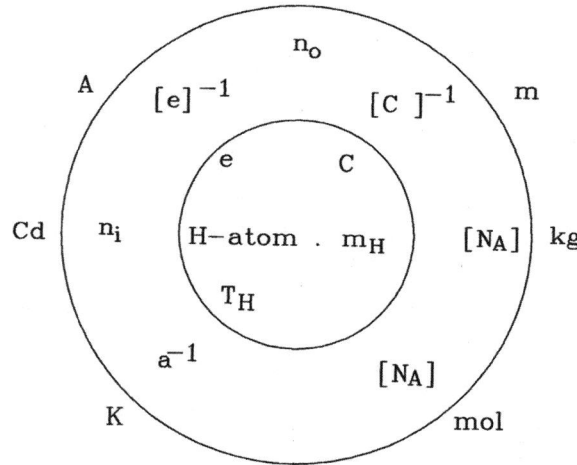

The values, in SI units, of the constants used are shown in the ring with hydrogen, and its constants are inside the inner circle. Corresponding SI symbols are indicated on outer periphery of the two circles.

12.2.2   In Terms of Only One Standard (Frequency)

Another approach may be taking frequency as the base standard and expressing all other base units in terms of frequency and other fundamental constants like Planck's constant, Boltzmann constant, velocity of light and the electronic charge. The basic reason for this proposal is the fact that frequency can be measured with uncertainty several orders of magnitude better than any other base unit.

12.2.3   In Terms of Fundamental Constants Using Maxwell Equations

Using Maxwell equations and permeability of free space μ_0 and velocity of light c in vacuum, we may find permittivity of free space. It gives electrical quantities. Use of velocity of light defines metre, the unit of length. Josephson constant (h/2e) gives voltage and then kilogram may be obtained in terms of voltage through voltage balance. The system may not be so good, as to get the kilogram from volt, the realizable uncertainty is 2×10^{-6} only, whereas two mass standards of the same material can be compared with an uncertainty of 5×10^{-9}. The relationships with various units are diagrammatically shown in Fig. 10.2 (Fig. 12.2).

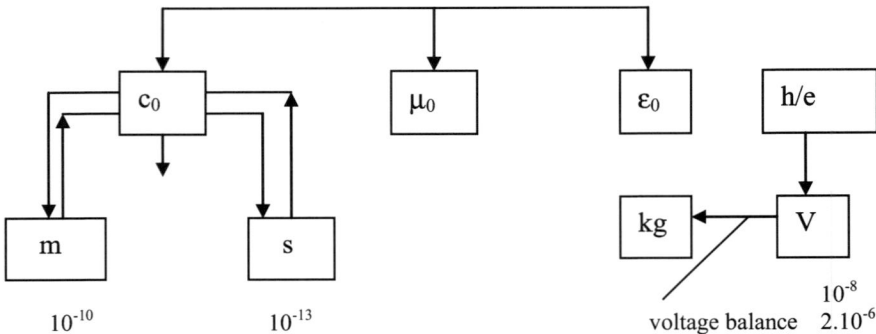

Fig. 12.2 Maxwell equations

12.2.4 A Consistent Set of Fundamental Constants by BIPM

BIPM [5] has given, another way to link base units in SI with the fundamental physical and atomic constants. The relationship with physical constants (shown in boxes) with base units is represented in Fig. 12.3. In the figure, it is shown that the base units of the SI are linked to measurable quantities through the unchanging and universal constants of physics.

In Fig. 12.3, the surrounding boxes, lines and uncertainties represent measurable quantities. The numbers marked next to the base units are estimates of the standard uncertainties of their best practical realizations; the fraction shown next to the fundamental constants represents the uncertainty of our knowledge of these constants [6]. The less-dark boxes reflect the unknown long-term stability of the kilogram artefact and its consequent effects on the practical realization of the definitions of the ampere, mole and candela.

The definition of the ampere, for example, involves the kilogram, but an alternative link is the Josephson constant (K_{J-90}) and von Klitzing's quantum-Hall resistance (R_{J-90}), both of which are given fixed conventional values in 1990.

For further reading, references at [7, 8] may be seen.

12.3 CIPM Recommendation 1 (CI-2005)

On the direction of 21st CGPM, 1999, the International Committee for Weights and Measures (CIPM) holds its meeting on 7 October 2005. The CIPM, in this meeting, in consultation with CCU, CCM, CCEM, CCQM and CCT suggested

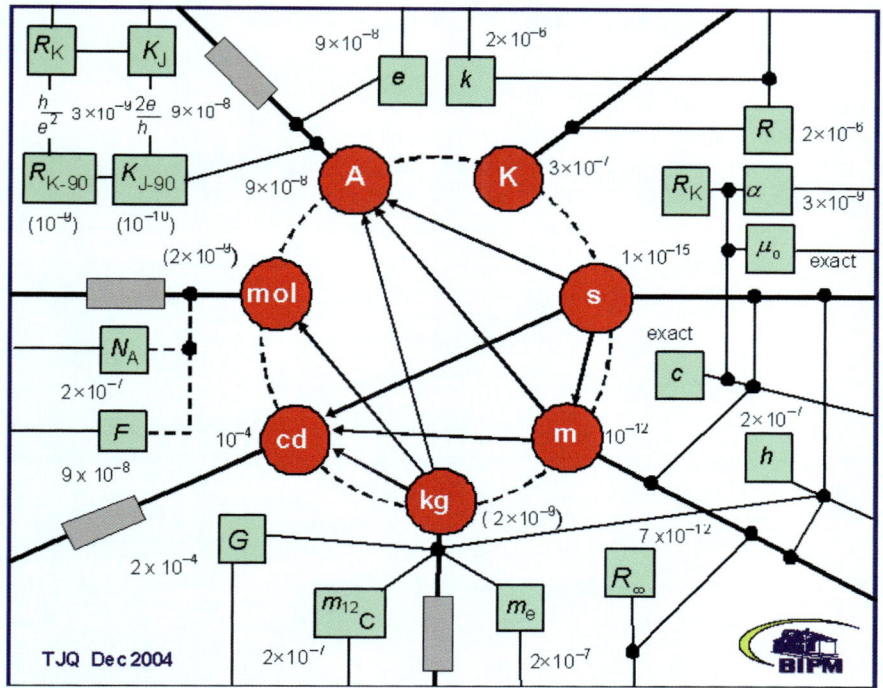

Fig. 12.3 A consistent set of fundamental constants by BIPM

preparing the new definitions and practical methods to realize (*mises en pratique*) for each unit, namely, kilogram, ampere, kelvin and mole.

If the results of experimental measurements over the next few years are indeed acceptable by all and agreed by the various Consultative Committees and other relevant bodies, then the CIPM should

1. Prepare proposals well in time, for possible adoption by the 24th CGPM in 2011;
2. Urge member states for funding National Metrology Institutes to pursue continued relevant research in order to facilitate the changes suggested here and improve knowledge of the relevant fundamental constants, with a view to further improvement in the SI;
3. Explore the possibility of redefining, at the same time, the mole in terms of a fixed value of the Avogadro constant; and
4. Invite all Consultative Committees particularly the CCM, CCEM, CCQM and CCT, to consider the implications of changing the definitions of the above-mentioned base units of the SI, and to submit a report to the CIPM not later than June 2007.

12.4   A Proposal to Redefine Kilogram, Ampere, Kelvin and Mole

Following the aforesaid recommendations of the CIPM 2005, a paper about the proposed definitions of kilogram, ampere, kelvin and mole appeared in 2006 of Metrologia. The paper contains at least two ways of defining each unit.

12.4.1   Kilogram

The kilogram may be defined as one of the following ways:

1   The kilogram is the mass of a body whose equivalent energy is equal to that of a number of photons whose frequencies sum to exactly [(299 792 458)^2/662 606 93] × 10^{41} Hz or 1.356 313 8 × 10^{50} Hz.
2.   The kilogram is the mass of a body whose de Broglie–Compton frequency is equal to exactly [(299 792 458)^2/(6.626 069 3 × 10^{-34})] Hz or 1.356 313 8 × 10^{50} Hz.
3.   The kilogram, unit of mass, is such that the Planck constant is exactly 6. 626 069 3 × 10^{-34} J s.

12.4.2   Ampere

1.   The ampere is the electric current in the direction of the flow of exactly 1/(1.602 176 53 × 10^{-19}) = 6.241 509 48 × 10^{18} elementary charges in one second.
2.   The ampere, unit of electric current, is such that the elementary charge is exactly 1.602 176 53 × 10^{-19} C.

12.4.3   Kelvin

1.   The kelvin is the change of thermodynamic temperature that results in a change of thermal energy kT by exactly 1. 380 650 5 × 10^{-23} J.
2.   The kelvin, unit of thermodynamic temperature, is such that the Boltzmann constant is exactly 1. 380 650 5 × 10^{-23} J/K.

12.4.4   Mole

(1)   The mole is the amount of substance of a system that contains exactly 6.022 141 5 × 10^{23} specified elementary entities, which may be atoms, molecules, ions, electrons, other particles or specified groups of such particles.

(2)   The mole, unit of amount of substance of a specified elementary entity, which may be an atom, molecule, ion, electron, any other particle or a specified group of such particles, is such that the Avogadro constant is exactly 6.022 141 5 × 10²³ mol⁻¹.

12.5   The Values of *h*, e, k and N$_A$

The kilogram, ampere, kelvin and mole link to the exact values of the Planck constant h, elementary charge e, Boltzmann constant k and Avogadro constant N$_A$, respectively. However, only the values of Planck constant h and molar gas constant R will be taken from the adjusted values of CODATA 2000 or will be taken from the latest CODATA values; all other three values, namely, of elementary charge e, Boltzmann constant k and Avogadro constant N$_A$ will be derived from the following formulae:

$$e = (2\alpha h/\mu_0 c)^{1/2}$$
$$k = R/N_A$$
$$N_A = cA_r(e)M_u\alpha^2/2R_\infty h,$$

where $\mu_0 = 4\pi \times 10^{-7}$ N·A⁻² is the magnetic constant (permeability of vacuum), $M_u = 10^{-3}$ kg mol⁻¹ is the molar mass constant and α, $A_r(e)$ and R_∞ are the fine structure constant, relative atomic mass of the electron and the Rydberg constant, respectively. These are also adjusted constants.

The respective relative uncertainties u of the 2002 recommended values of R, the Rydberg constant, fine structure constant and relative atomic mass is

$$u_r(R) = 1.7 \times 10^{-6},$$
$$u_r(R_\infty) == 6.6 \times 10^{-12}.$$
$$u_r(\alpha) == 3.3 \times 10^{-9} \text{ and}$$
$$u_r[A_r(e)] = 4.4 \times 10^{-10}.$$

The values of *h*, *e*, *k* and N$_A$, derived from above formulae of e, k and N$_A$, are as follows:

$$h = 6.626\,0693(11) \times 10^{-34} \text{ Js } \left[1.7 \times 10^{-7}\right]$$
$$e = 1.602\,176\,53\,(14) \times 10^{-19} \text{ C } \left[8.5 \times 10^{-8}\right]$$
$$k = 1.380\,6505\,(24) \times 10^{-23} \text{ JK}^{-1} \left[1.8 \times 10^{-6}\right]$$
$$N_A = 6.022\,1415\,10 \times 10^{23} \text{ mol}^{-1} \left[1.7 \times 10^{-7}\right],$$

where as usual the number in parentheses is the numerical value of the standard uncertainty referred to the last two digits of the quoted value. Relative standard uncertainties are indicated within square brackets.

12.5.1   Observations

Thus, the uncertainty of h plays the dominant role by far in determining the uncertainty of e and N_A, while the uncertainty of R (Gas constant) plays a similar role in determining the value of k.

Here, one may observe that the measurement capability of each base unit is better than with which these constants are known. The advantage of taking these constants as fixed with zero uncertainty is that the uncertainty of the host of fundamental constants involving these constants will be considerably reduced.

12.6   Practical Standards to Realize Kilogram

The kilogram, the unit of mass in SI, may be realized by either of the following method:

1. The present international prototype kilogram may be used, after cleaning as per BIPM procedure with an uncertainty of

$$\left[\left(1 \times 10^{-9}\right)^2 + \left(< 5 \times 10^{-9}\right)^2\right]^{1/2} \approx 5 \times 10^{-9}.$$

2. The electron volt as given in the SI Brochure by BIPM [9].
3. The unified atomic mass unit u.
4. The plank constant h or h/c^2, which may be inserted in the forthcoming SI Brochure. It may also be advisable to include realization of h through Josephson and von Klitzing effects, with designation h_{s-90}, given by the relation

$$h_{s-90}/c^2 = 4/\left[k_{j-90}^2 \times R_{k-90} \times c^2\right].$$

This will avoid disruption to the disseminated representations of electrical units and will also provide a stable mass reference for the moving-coil watt realizations and a method to inter-compare with each other.

12.6.1   Other Methods of Redefining Kilogram

- Through Avogadro's constant,
- Levitation of pure diamagnetic bodies in the superconducting state,

- Ion collection of heavy metals like Bismuth or Gold,
- Voltage balance and
- Watt balance.

References

1. BIPM (2006) International System of units SI, 8th edn, BIPM, Severes, France
2. W.B. Petley, Metrology, the key to progress in the past and future. Phys. Scr. **41**, 707–711 (1990)
3. V. Kose, B.R. Siebert, W. Woger, General principle for the definition of the base units of SI. Metrogia **40**, 146–153 (2003)
4. V.S. Tuninsky, Unit system based on the fundamental constants (1999)
5. http://www1.bipm.org/en/si/si_constants.html
6. P.J. Mohr, B.N. Taylor, CODATA, recommended values of the fundamental physical constants. Rev. Mod. Phys. **72**, 351–495 (2000)
7. D. Kind, T.J. Quinn, Metrology: Quo Vadis? Physics Today, August 98 1998
8. B.N. Taylor, P.J. Mohr, The role of fundamental constants in the International System of Units (SI) present and future IEEE Trans. Instrum. Meas. **50**, 563–567 (2001)
9. T.J. Quinn, Base units of the Système international d'unités, their accuracy, dissemination and international traceability. Metrolgia **31**, 515–527 (1995)
10. I.M. Mills, P.J. Mohr, T.J. Quinn, B.N. Taylor, E.R. Williams Redefinition of the kilogram, ampere, kelvin and mole. Metrologia **43** (2006)

Chapter 13
Scientists Associated with Units of Measurements

It is interesting to know about the life and work of the scientists who worked throughout their life in the field of measurement. To honour some of such eminent scientists, some of the base and derived units have been assigned to their respective names.

Among the base units, the units of electric current (Ampere), thermodynamic temperature (Kelvin) and temperature difference (Celsius) have been, respectively, named after Andre Marie Ampere, Lord Kelvin and Anders Celsius. Max Planck and Boltzmann are, respectively, associated with the SI base unit of mass and thermodynamic temperature.

13.1 Scientists Associated with Base Units

13.1.1 Anders Celsius

Anders Celsius
1701 –1744

© Springer Nature Switzerland AG 2020
S. V. Gupta, *Units of Measurement*, Springer Series in Materials Science 122,
https://doi.org/10.1007/978-3-030-43969-9_13

A child was born on 27 January 1701 in Uppsala, Sweden. This child became famous as Anders Celsius. After his education time in his town north of Stockholm, he became professor for astronomy in 1730. At that time, there was no larger observatory anywhere in Sweden. Therefore, Celsius made a round trip to some of the famous European astronomy sites from 1732 to 1734.

Director of the Paris observatory, founded in 1672, was Jaques Cassini (1677–1756) son of Jean-Dominique Cassini (1625–1712). At this time, there was a dispute between English and French astronomers about the actual shape of the Earth. To find the true answer to this question, expeditions had to be sent to the "ends" of the world to measure exactly the local positions. The expedition to the north was commissioned to Pierre Louis de Maupertuis (1696–1759), where Celsius joined as an assistant. The journey to Lapland, the very northern part of Sweden, lasted from 1736 to 1737. After all the measurements, it confirmed the theory of Newton about the flattening of the Earth at poles in 1744.

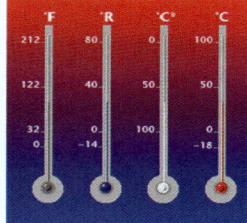

Originally, Celsius defined its temperature scale is third from the left.

After the expedition, Celsius returned to Uppsala and worked on the erection of an observatory, which was finished in 1740. Celsius was one of the first to examine the changes of the Earth magnetic field at the time of a Northern light. He was also one of the first measuring the brightness of stars with measurement tools. After the first Swedish observatory was completed, he was made the director of it. Celsius became famous for his recommendation in 1742 to divide the temperature scale of a mercury thermometer at air pressure of 760 mm of mercury into 100°, where 100 was taken as the freezing point and 0 the boiling point of water. Because of the detailed fixation of the measuring environment and methods, this definition was considered more exact than those given by Gabriel Daniel Fahrenheit (1686–1736) and the aristocrat and biologist René-Antoine Ferchault de Réaumur (1683–1757). Later, the reversion of the Celsius scale with 0 as the freezing point and 100 as the boiling point of water was introduced with this modification it became widely accepted.

Celsius was an active supporter of the introduction of the Gregorian calendar, which was accepted in Sweden in 1753 just 9 years after his death. The unit of temperature interval "degree Celsius" has been named to honour this great scientist.

13.1.2   Andre Marie Ampere

The ampere—unit of electric current—is named in the honour of Andre Marie Ampere.

Andre Marie Ampere
1775–1836

He was born on 20 January 1775 near Lyon, France. He enjoyed a happy youth only until the age of 17, when his father died by the guillotine.

He worked systematically on topics in mathematics, chemistry, optics and metaphysics, always aiming at an orderly taxonomy of knowledge and the reduction of observations to rational principles.

In 1820, Oersted announced his discovery of the magnetic effect of an electric current. Ampère performed his experiments more thoroughly than Oersted could manage. For all that Maxwell called him "the Newton of electricity". It was only through the framework developed by Faraday, Weber and Maxwell himself that the merits of Ampère's obsessive devotion could be appreciated. He died on 10 June 1836 in Marseille and buried in the Cimetière de Montmartre, Paris. France. The practical international ampere defined with the help of electrolysis of silver nitrate is 0.999 85 A.

13.1.3   Avogadro

Amedeo Avogadro, full name Lorenzo Romano Amedeo Carlo Avogadro, conte di Quaregna e Cerreto, was born on 9 August 1776, Turin, in the Kingdom of Sardinia and Piedmont, Italy. Avogadro married to Felicita Mazzé in 1818 when he was 42. They had six sons. Avogadro was the son of Filippo Avogadro, conte di Quaregna e Cerreto, a distinguished lawyer and senator in the Piedmont region of northern Italy. Avogadro graduated in jurisprudence in 1792 but did not practice law until after receiving his doctorate in ecclesiastical law 4 years later. In 1801, he became secretary to the prefecture of Eridano. Beginning in 1800, Avogadro privately pursued studies in mathematics and physics, and he focused his early research on electricity.

Amedeo Avogadro
1776-1856

In 1820, he accepted the first chair of mathematical physics at the University of Turin. Due to civil disturbances in the Piedmont, the university was closed and Avogadro lost his chair in July 1822. Avogadro was reappointed in 1833 and remained in this post until, at the age of 74, he retired in 1850.

Avogadro is chiefly remembered for his molecular hypothesis, first stated in 1811, in which he claimed that equal volumes of all gases at the same temperature and pressure contain the same number of molecules.

His hypothesis is now regarded as a law, and the value known as Avogadro's number is $6.022140857 \times 10^{23}$; the number of molecules in a gram molecule, or mole, of any substance, has become a fundamental constant of physical science. In tribute to him, the number of elementary entities (atoms, molecules, ions or other particles) in 1 mol of a substance, $6.022140857(74) \times 10^{23}$, is known as the Avogadro constant, one of the seven SI base units and represented by N_A.

Between 1837 and 1841, Avogadro published four weighty volumes looking in detail at the physics of matter. Avogadro's findings were almost completely ignored until Stanislao Cannizarro presented them at the Karlsruhe Conference in 1860, 4 years after his death. This conference had been called to remedy the scientific confusion that existed about atoms, molecules and their masses.

In 1803, in cooperation with his brother Felice, Avogadro published his first scientific paper, which looked at the electrical behaviour of salt solutions. This was state-of-the-art science: only 3 years earlier, Avogadro's fellow Italian Alessandro Volta had invented the electric battery.

He died on 9 July 1856 in Turin.

13.1.4 Boltzmann Ludwig Eduard

Ludwig Aduard Boltzmann was born on 20 February 1844. His father, Ludwig Georg Boltzmann, was a tax official. He was the eldest of three children and his mother, Katharina Pauernfeind, was from a wealthy family. Ludwig was initially educated by a private tutor and he then attended the local gymnasium in Linz where he showed great aptitude in mathematics and science.

Ludwig learnt to play the piano and played throughout his life. His father died when he was just 15. At the age of 19, Ludwig Boltzmann enrolled at the University of Vienna, studying mathematics and physics. He earned his Ph.D. degree 3 years later in 1866.

Boltzmann taught mathematics, experimental physics and theoretical physics at several universities, but theoretical physics was his main passion. He wrote his famous travelogue "Reise eines deutschen Professors ins Eldorado" (Journey of a German professor to the Eldorado) during this time.

Ludwig Boltzmann
1844-1906

He obtained his first professorship in 1869 as professor of mathematical physics at the University of Graz. Later on, he moved to the University of Vienna as professor of mathematics in 1873. In 1876, Boltzmann returned to Graz to take up the chair of experimental physics and the same year he married mathematics teacher Henriette von Aigentler. They had three daughters and two sons.

Boltzmann was appointed to the Chair of Theoretical Physics at the University of Munich in Bavaria in 1890, returning to the University of Vienna as Professor of Theoretical Physics in 1894.

Apart from a short spell at the University of Leipzig from 1900 to 1902, Boltzmann returned to Vienna to teach physics and natural philosophy until his death.

Boltzmann's scientific approach was to attack the problem. He explained the second law of thermodynamics in the early 1870s on the basis of the atomic theory of matter. The Second Law of Thermodynamics states that the state of entropy of the entire universe, as an isolated system, will always increase over time. The second law also states that the changes in the entropy in the universe can never be negative.

He demonstrated that the second law could be interpreted by blending the laws of mechanics, applied to the motions of the atoms, with the theory of probability. He clarified that the second law is an essentially statistical law. He formulated most of the structure of statistical mechanics, which was later researched by the mathematical physicist Josiah Willard Gibbs.

In addition to his contributions to statistical mechanics, Boltzmann made detailed calculations in the kinetic theory of gases. He was one of the first people to understand the significance of James Clerk Maxwell's theory of electromagnetism, on which he wrote a two-volume treatise.

Boltzmann also worked on a derivation for blackbody radiation based on Stefan's law, which was later termed by Hendrik Antoon Lorentz as "a true pearl of theoretical physics".

His work in statistical mechanics was vocally criticized by Wilhelm Ostwald and the energy scientist, who disregarded atoms and based physical science exclusively on energy conditions. They were unable to understand the statistical nature of Boltzmann's logic.

His ideas were supported by the later discoveries in atomic physics in early 1900, for instance, Brownian motion, which can only be explained by statistical mechanics.

Ludwig Boltzmann was greatly demoralized due to the harsh criticism of his work. He committed suicide on 5 September 1906 at Duino, Italy by hanging himself. He was 62 years old.

Boltzmann constant is now the redefining constant for thermodynamic temperature kelvin with symbol K.

13.1.5   Lord Kelvin

Lord Kelvin
1824 -1907

The real name of Lord Kelvin was William Thomson. He was born on 26 June 1824 at Belfast Ireland. He was an outstanding leader in the physical sciences of the nineteenth century. He did important work in the mathematical analysis of electricity and thermodynamics, and did much to unify the emerging discipline of physics in its modern form. He also enjoyed a second career as a telegraph engineer and inventor, a career that propelled him into the public eye and ensured his fame and honour.

He was the first Baron Kelvin; his barony was named after the river Kelvin which runs through the University of Glasgow. He was awarded many meritorious awards like GCVO, OM, PC and PRS. He died on 17 December 1907 in Largs, Ayrshire, Scotland.

The unit of thermodynamic temperature kelvin has been named to honour this great mathematician, physicist and engineer.

13.1.6 Planck, Karl Ernst Ludwig Marx (Max)

Birth and Education
Planck was born in Kiel, Holstein, to Johann Julius Wilhelm Planck and his second wife, Emma Patzig on 23 April 1858. He was baptized with the name of Karl Ernst Ludwig Marx Planck. Planck came from a traditional, intellectual family. His paternal great-grandfather and grandfather were both theology professors in Göttingen; his father was a law professor at the University of Kiel and Munich. One of his uncles was also a judge.

Before coming to physics, Planck was interested in music. He took singing lessons and played piano, organ and cello, and composed songs and operas.

Planck studied at the Universities of Munich and Berlin, where his teachers included Kirchhoff and Helmholtz, and received his doctorate of philosophy at Munich in 1879. He was Privatdozent in Munich from 1880 to 1885, and then Associate Professor of Theoretical Physics at Kiel until 1889. He succeeded Kirchhoff as Professor at Berlin University the same year (1889). He remained there until his retirement in 1926. Afterwards, he became President of the Kaiser Wilhelm Society for the Promotion of Science, a post he held until 1937. The Prussian Academy of Sciences appointed him a member in 1894 and Permanent Secretary in 1912.

Planck as a young man, 1878

Max Planck
1858-1947

Plank earliest work was on the subject of thermodynamics, an interest he acquired from his studies under Kirchhoff.

In 1894, Planck turned his attention to the problem of blackbody radiation. Plank first proposed solution to the problem in 1899 followed from what Planck called the "principle of elementary disorder", which allowed him to derive Wien's law from a number of assumptions about the entropy of an ideal oscillator, creating what was referred to as the Wien–Planck law. Soon, it was found that experimental evidence did not confirm the new law at all, to Plank frustration.

Quantization of electromagnetic energy
The central assumption behind his new derivation, presented to the DPG on 14 December 1900 was the supposition, now known as the Planck postulate, that electromagnetic energy could be emitted only in quantized form, in other words, the energy could only be a multiple of an elementary unit:

$$E = h\nu.$$

Here, h is Planck constant, also known as Plank action quantum (introduced already in 1899), and ν is the frequency of the radiation. Physicists now call these quanta photons, and a photon of frequency ν will have its own specific and unique energy.

Planck was among the few who immediately recognized the importance of three papers published in Annalen Physik by Albert Einstein in 1905 on Special Theory of Relativity.

Planck Constant and quantum theory
In 1900, Max Planck discovered the quantum of action, now known as Plank constant, h, in 1900. This work laid the foundation for quantum theory, which won him the Nobel Prize for Physics in 1918. Planck died on 4 October 1947.

The Planck constant is now the defining constant for the kilogram.

Important Publications

- Planck, M. (1900a). "Über eine Verbesserung der Wienschen Spektralgleichung". Verhandlungen der Deutschen Physikalischen Gesellschaft. **2**: 202–204. Translated in ter Haar, D. (1967). "On an Improvement of Wien's Equation for the

Spectrum" The Old Quantum Theory (PDF), Pergamon Press. pp. 79–81. LCCN 66029628

- Planck, M. (1900b). "Zur Theorie des Gesetzes der Energieverteilung im Normalspectrum". Verhandlungen der Deutschen Physikalischen Gesellschaft. **2**: 237. Translated in ter Haar, D. (1967). "On the Theory of the Energy Distribution Law of the Normal Spectrum". The Old Quantum Theory (PDF). Pergamon Press. p. 82, LCCN 66029628.
- Planck, M. (1900c). "Entropie und Temperatur strahlender Wärme" [Entropy and Temperature of Radiant Heat]. Annalen der Physik. **306** (4): 719–737. Bibcode:1900AnP...306..719P. https://doi.org/10.1002/andp.19003060410.
- Planck, M. (1900d). "Über irreversible Strahlungsvorgänge" [On Irreversible Radiation Processes]. Annalen der Physik. **306** (1): 69–122. Bibcode:1900AnP...306...69P. https://doi.org/10.1002/andp.19003060105.
- Planck, M. (1901). "Über das Gesetz der Energieverteilung im Normalspektrum". Annalen der Physik. **309** (3): 553–563 Bibcode: 1901 AnP 309..553P. https://doi.org/10.1002/andp.19013090310. Translated in Ando, K. "On the Law of Distribution of Energy in the Normal Spectrum" (PDF). Archived from the original (PDF) on 6 October 2011. Retrieved 13 October 2011.
- Planck M, (1903). Treatise on Thermodynamics. Ogg, A. (transl.). London: Longmans, Green & Co. OL 7246691 M.
- Planck, M. (1906). Vorlesungen über die Theorie der Wärmestrahlung. Leipzig: J.A. Barth. LCCN 07004527.
- Planck, M. (1914). The Theory of Heat Radiation. Masius, M. (transl.) (2nd ed.), P Blakiston's Son & Co. OL 7154661 M.
- Planck, M. (1915). Eight Lectures on Theoretical Physics. Wills, A. P. (transl.). Dover Publications. ISBN 0-486-69730-4.
- Planck, M. (1943). "Zur Geschichte der Auffindung des physikalischen Wirkungsquantums". Naturwissenschaften. **31** (14–15): 153–159 Bibcode: 1943NW.....31..153P. https://doi.org/10.1007/bf01475738.

13.2   Scientists Associated with Derived Units

It will be also interesting to know a little more about the work of the scientists, who have been honoured by assigning their names to some SI derived units.

13.2.1   Sir Isaac Newton

The unit of force has been named after the name of this great scientist Sir Isaac Newton. The unit of force is newton with symbol N.

Isaac Newton
(1642 - 1727)

Isaac Newton was born in Lincolnshire, near Grantham, on 25 December 1642. Newton was the contemporary and friend of Wallis Huygens. He was educated at Trinity College, Cambridge, and lived there from 1661 till 1696, during which time he produced the bulk of his work in mathematics. Though most of his mathematical work was done between the years 1665 and 1686, the bulk of it was not printed till some years later.

And the development of mathematics in Great Britain was, for a century, entirely in the hands of the Newtonian school.

In October 1669, Barrow resigned the Lucasian chair in favour of Newton. Newton laid down the foundation of differential and integral calculus. Around 1696, he discovered the binomial theorem. His work in gravitation and optics made him one of the greatest scientists, the world has ever known.

He died at Kensington, London, on 20 March 1727.

13.2.2   *Heinrich Rudolf Hertz*

Heinrich Hertz
1857- 1894

Heinrich Rudolf Hertz was born on 22 February 1857, in Hamburg, Germany. In 1888, he was the first to experimentally prove the existence of electromagnetic waves. His apparatus consisted of a wire connected to an induction coil to produce the waves and a small loop of wire with a spark gap to detect them. When currents were induced in the detection loop, the induced current produced a spark across the gap. He further showed, with the help of mirrors, prisms and metal gratings, that his electromagnetic waves do have analogous properties as light. In the process of his investigation, he discovered the photoelectric effect also but could not recognize it.

In 1892, he published an important paper "Investigations on the Propagation of Electric Force". Through this work, he reformulated Maxwell's complicated field equations into a symmetric and compact form. He criticized Maxwell's definition of electric charge and concept of displacement current, which he replaced with a mathematical formalism. Hertz's simplification of Maxwell's theory to a mathematical formalism led to its widespread acceptance. He died on 1 January 1894.

13.2.3 Blaise Pascal

Blaise Pascal
(1623 – 1662)

Blaise Pascal was born on 19 June 1623 at Clemont, France. He died at the young age of 39 years on 19 August 1662. His father Etienne Pascal had unorthodox views regarding education and decided to teach his son himself and removed all books on mathematics from the house. This raised a curiosity in Blaise, and he studied geometry of his own and discovered that sum of the angles of a triangle is two right angles. His first work, Essay on Conic Sections, was published in February 1640. He invented the first digital calculator to help his father with his work of collecting taxes. He worked on it for 3 years between 1642 and 1645. The device, called the Pascaline, resembled a mechanical calculator of the 1940s.

From about this time, Pascal began a series of experiments on atmospheric pressure. By 1647, he had proved to his satisfaction that a vacuum existed to which Descartes a great scientist of that time discarded his idea and wrote a sarcastic letter to Huygens, another big name of that time, "Pascal has too much vacuum in his head".

In August 1648, Pascal observed that the pressure of the atmosphere decreases with height and deduced that a vacuum existed above the atmosphere. In October 1647, Pascal wrote "New Experiments Concerning Vacuums". From May 1653, Pascal worked on mathematics and physics writing Treatise on the Equilibrium of Liquids (1653) in which he explains Pascal's law of pressure.

Blaise Pascal was a very influential French mathematician and philosopher who contributed in many areas of mathematics. He worked on conic sections and projective geometry and in correspondence with Fermat he laid the foundations for the theory of probability.

The pascal—the unit of pressure—has been named to honour this great man.

13.2.4   James Prescott Joule

James Joule
1818–1889

He was born on 24 December 1818 in Salford near Manchester, UK. He studied the nature of heat and discovered its relationship to mechanical energy. This led to the theory of conservation of energy (the First Law of Thermodynamics). He worked with Lord Kelvin to develop the absolute scale of temperature and made observations on magnetostriction. Magnetostriction is a property of ferromagnetic materials that causes them to change their shape when subjected to a magnetic field. Joule was first to identify it in 1842 while observing a sample of nickel. He found the relationship between the flow of current through a resistance and the heat dissipated, now called Joule's law.

The SI unit of energy—the joule—is named after him and is pronounced to rhyme with "tool".

13.2.5   *James Watt*

James Watt
1736—1819

James was born on 19 January 1736 in Greenock, Scotland. He was the son of a ship's chandler. His father set him up in his workshop with his own bench and tools and there, the young James made models and became familiar with instruments used in ships.

In 1755, he decided to be a maker of scientific instruments so he took up an apprenticeship in London and got a job making instruments at Glasgow University. He did not confine himself to scientific instruments only but made violas, guitars, fiddles, flutes and organs also.

In 1763, when asked to repair a steam Newcomen engine, Watt realized that the efficiency of the machine could be greatly improved by having a separate, but linked, condenser. This invention of Watt saved between two-thirds and three-quarters of the coal consumed by the older type of engine. In 1781, he patented five methods of converting the reciprocating motion of a steam engine's piston into continuous rotary motion.

In 1782, he patented the double-acting steam engine, in which steam is admitted alternately at either end of the cylinder. In 1784, he patented the parallel motion, an arrangement of connected rods which he described as "one of the most ingenious, simple pieces of mechanism I have contrived". Then, in 1788, again at Matthew Boulton's urging, he designed the centrifugal governor for controlling the speed of an engine. He also invented a gauge for measuring steam pressure and a revolution counter.

He helped Joseph Priestley with his investigations into gases; he experimented on the strength of materials, a subject of acute interest to his manufacturer friends. He further developed accurate means of measuring dimensions, furnace temperatures and the like, again vital to the advancement of manufacturing processes. In 1780, he had patented what was probably the earliest form of copier, a press copier that he marketed through his own company, James Watt & Co. The process involved writing with ink mixed with Arabic gum. When a sheet of damp tissue paper was pressed against the manuscript, some of the ink stuck to it, creating a mirror image of the original on the tissue paper. By turning the copy over it could then be read through the tissue paper. He died on 25 August 1819 in Heathfield, England.

The **watt** (symbol: W) is the SI unit of power that is named in honour of the physicist.

13.2.6   Charles Augustin Coulomb

Charles Coulomb
1736–1806

The **coulomb** (symbol: C), the SI unit of electric charge, is named after Charles-Augustin de Coulomb. Coulomb was a French physicist. He was born in Angoulême on 14 June 1736, France in a well to do family. He chose the profession of military engineer and spent 3 years; till decisive injury to his health, he was forced to leave military service. Upon his return, he was employed at La Rochelle, the Isle of Aix and Cherbourg. He discovered an inverse relationship on the force between charges and the square of its distance, later named after him as Coulomb's law.

In 1781, he was stationed permanently in Paris. In 1784, he published his work on theory and practice on torsional forces on metallic strip. In 1785, he published his three reports on Electricity and Magnetism in the Royal Academy of Sciences on

1. The construction and use of electric (torsion) balance and experimentally verified the laws of force of attraction or repulsion between two charged bodies.
2. The laws according to which both the magnetic and the electric fluids act, either by repulsion or by attraction.
3. On the quantity of electricity that isolated body losses in a certain time period either by contact with less humid air.

Coulomb explained the laws of attraction and repulsion between electric charges and magnetic poles, although he did not find any relationship between the two phenomena. He thought that the attraction and repulsion were due to different kinds of fluids.

On the outbreak of the Revolution in 1789, he resigned his post and retired to a small estate, which he possessed at Blois. He was recalled to Paris in order to take part in the new determination of weights and measures, which had been decreed by the revolutionary government. He was one of the first members of the National Institute; and he was appointed inspector of public instruction in 1802. But his health became very feeble, and 4 years later he died on 23 August 1806 in Paris.

13.2.7   Alessandro Volta

Alessandro Volt
1745–1827

The **volt** (symbol: V), the SI derived unit of electric potential difference, is named in honour of the Italian physicist Alessandro Volta, who invented the voltaic pile, the first chemical battery. He was born on 18 February 1745 and died on 3 March 1827 near Como, Lombardy, Italy.

In 1800, Alessandro Volta built the voltaic pile and discovered the first practical method of generating electricity. The voltaic pile comprised of alternating discs of zinc and copper, with pieces of cardboard soaked in brine between the metals. It produced electrical current. The metallic conducting arc was used to carry the electricity over a greater distance. Alessandro Volta's voltaic pile was the first battery that produced a reliable, steady current of electricity.

One contemporary of Volta was Luigi Galvani; in fact, it was Volta's disagreement with Galvani's theory of galvanic responses (animal tissue contained a form of electricity) that led Volta to build the voltaic pile to prove that electricity did not come from the animal tissue but was generated by the contact of different metals, brass and iron, in a moist environment. Ironically, both scientists were right. He also worked on chemistry of gases and also discovered methane.

13.2.8   Michael Faraday

Michael
1791 – 1867

The SI unit Farad is named after the English chemist and physicist Michael Faraday. He was born on 22 September 1791, in Newington, Surrey, near London. He is known for his pioneering experiments in electricity and magnetism. Many consider him the greatest experimentalist who ever lived. Several concepts that he derived directly from experiments, such as lines of magnetic force, have become common ideas in modern physics.

He received little more than a primary education, and at the age of 14 he was apprenticed to a bookbinder. There he became interested in the physical and chemical works of the time. After hearing a lecture by the famous chemist Humphry Davy, he sent Davy the notes he had made of his lectures. As a result, Faraday was appointed, at the age of 21, assistant to Davy in the laboratory of the Royal Institution in London.

During the initial years of his scientific work, Faraday occupied himself mainly with chemical problems. He discovered two new chlorides of carbon and succeeded in liquefying chlorine and other gases. He isolated benzene in 1825, the year in which he was appointed director of the laboratory.

Davy, who had the greatest influence on Faraday's thinking, had shown in 1807 that the metals sodium and potassium could be precipitated from their compounds by an electric current. He called this process as electrolysis. Faraday's vigorous pursuit of these experiments led in 1834 to what became known as Faraday's laws of electrolysis.

He demonstrated the principle of electromagnetic induction in 1831. Faraday expressed the electric current induced in the wire in terms of the number of lines of force that are cut by the wire. The principle of induction was a landmark in applied science, for it made possible the dynamo, or generator, which produces electricity by mechanical means.

Faraday's discovery (1845) that an intense magnetic field can rotate the plane of polarized light is known today as the Faraday effect. The phenomenon has been used to elucidate molecular structure and has yielded information about galactic magnetic fields.

Faraday described his numerous experiments in electricity and electromagnetism in three volumes entitled Experimental Researches in Electricity (1839, 1844 and 1855); his chemical work was chronicled in Experimental Researches in Chemistry and Physics (1858). Faraday ceased research work in 1855 because of declining mental powers, but he continued as a lecturer until 1861. A series of six children's lectures published in 1860 as The Chemical History of a Candle has become a classic of science literature. He died on 25 August 1867.

13.2.9 Wilhelm Eduard Weber

Wilhelm Weber
1804 – 1891

Wilhelm Weber was born on 24 October 1804 in Wittenberg, Germany and died on 23 June 1891. The weber, the unit of magnetic flux, is named in the honour of German Scientist Wilhelm Eduard Weber. One weber is equal to 108 maxwells.

He joined the University of Halle in 1822 and wrote his doctoral dissertation in 1826. After that, he taught at Halle. In 1831, Weber was appointed to the chair of physics at Göttingen and there followed 6 years of close friendship and collaboration with Gauss. Weber developed sensitive magnetometers and other magnetic instruments during this time.

When Victoria became Queen of Britain in 1837 her uncle became ruler of Hanover and revoked the liberal constitution. Weber was one of the seven professors at Göttingen to sign a protest and all were dismissed. He remained at Göttingen without a position until 1843 when he became professor of physics at Leipzig.

In 1848, he returned to his old position in Göttingen and, in 1855, he became temporary directors of the astronomical observatory there. His work on the ratio between the electrodynamic and electrostatic units of charge in 1855 proved extremely important and was crucial to Maxwell in his electromagnetic theory of light. Weber found that the ratio was 3.1074×10^8 m/s but failed to take any notice of the fact that this was close to the speed of light.

Weber's later years at Göttingen were devoted to work in electrodynamics and the electrical structure of matter. He was described by Thomas Hirst in the following way:

> He speaks and stutters on unceasingly, one has nothing to do but listen. Sometimes he laughs for no earthly reason, and one feels sorry at being not able to join him.

13.2.10   Nickola Tesla

Nickola Tesla
1856 - 1943

Nickola Tesla was born in Croatia (then part of Austria-Hungary) on 9 July 1856. He was the electrical engineer who invented the alternating current (AC) induction motor, which made the universal transmission and distribution of electricity possible. Tesla began his studies in physics and mathematics at Graz Polytechnic, and then took philosophy at the University of Prague. He worked as an electrical engineer in Budapest, Hungary and subsequently in France and Germany. In 1888, his discovery that a magnetic field could be made to rotate if two coils at right angles are supplied with AC current $90°$ out of phase made possible the invention of the AC induction motor. The major advantage of this motor is its brushless operation, which many at the time believed was impossible.

Tesla moved to the United States in 1884, where he worked for Thomas Edison who quickly became a rival Edison being an advocate of the inferior DC power transmission system. During this time, Tesla was commissioned with the design of the AC generators installed at Niagara Falls. George Westinghouse purchased the patents to his induction motor and made it the basis of the Westinghouse power system, which still underlies the modern electrical power industry today. He also did notable research on high-voltage electricity, at one point creating an earthquake, which shook the ground for several miles around his New York laboratory. He also devised a system, which anticipated worldwide wireless communication: fax machines, radar, radio-guided missiles and aircraft. He died on 7 January 1943.

13.2.11   Joseph Henry

Joseph Henry
1797-1878

Joseph Henry, physicist and scientific administrator, was born on 17 December 1797. Although he was largely self-educated, Henry studied at the NY Academy, Albany from 1819 to 1822. Henry began teaching at the Academy in Albany in 1826 where he remained until 1832 when he accepted a position at the College of New Jersey (now Princeton University).

He is widely considered the foremost American scientist of the nineteenth century. Although Henry at an early age appeared to be headed for a career in the theatre, a chance encountered with a book of lectures on scientific topics turned his interest to science. Henry's early investigations concerned electromagnetic phenomena, and his discovery of electromagnetic self-induction in 1831 established his reputation in America. Henry appears to have discovered the principle of electromagnetic induction independently of British scientist Michael Faraday, but because Faraday published his results before Henry, he is credited with the discovery. In 1846, Henry was named first Secretary of the newly established Smithsonian Institution, a position he held until his death. In 1868, he was elected President of the Academy; this position, too, he held until his death. He died on 13 May 1878. The henry, unit of inductance, has been named in the honour of this American scientist known as Joseph Henry.

13.2.12   *Antoine Henri Becquerel*

Antoine Bacquerel
1852–1908

Antoine Henri Becquerel was born on 15 December 1852 in the family of scientists, Paris, France. He was the son of Alexandre Becquerel, who studied light and phosphorescence and invented the phosphoroscope, and grandson of Antoine César Becquerel, one of the founders of electrochemistry. His son also became a great scientist later on.

In 1892, he became the third in his family to occupy the physics chair at the National Natural History Museum, France. In 1894, he became chief engineer in the Department of Bridges and Highways.

In 1896, Becquerel accidentally discovered radioactivity while investigating phosphorescence in uranium salts. This discovery led Becquerel to investigate the spontaneous emission of nuclear radiation. In 1903, he shared the Nobel Prize in Physics with Pierre and Marie Curie "in recognition of the extraordinary services he has rendered by his discovery of spontaneous radioactivity".

In 1908, the year of his death, he was elected permanent secretary of the Académie des Sciences. He died at the age of 55 on 25 August 1908 in Le Croisic.

The SI unit for radioactivity, the becquerel (Bq), is named after him. Also, the craters on the Moon and Marsh are named as Becquerels in his honour.

13.2.13   Louis Harold Gray

Henry Gray
1905 - 1965

Louis Harold Gray was Born on 10 November 1905 and died on 9 July 1965. He obtained his Ph.D. at the Cavendish Laboratory under Rutherford at a time when the laboratory was a world centre for fundamental research in nuclear physics. Although W H Bragg had stated the principle in 1912, Gray worked out the consequences in far greater detail. In 1936, he developed the Bragg-Gray principle, which provides the basis for the cavity ionization method for measuring gamma-ray energy.

Gray was interested in the biological effects of neutrons. Realizing that more powerful sources were required, Gray, together with John Read and technician J G Wyatt, constructed a neutron generator at the Mount Vernon Hospital, where Gray had been hospital physicist since 1933. With this tool, Gray and his colleagues made important contributions to understanding the relative biological effectiveness (RBE) of neutrons, discovering that it depended on dose, dose rate and level of biological damage.

In a 1940 paper, Gray and Read employed their energy unit, "that amount of neutron radiation which produces an increment of energy in unit volume of tissue equal to the increment of energy produced in unit volume of water by one röntgen of radiation".

After World War II, Gray joined the new radio-therapeutic research unit at Hammersmith where a cyclotron for radiobiology research and radioisotope production was built. As Deputy Director, he oversaw important research on radiobiology and DNA.

Leaving the Hammersmith group, Gray constructed a laboratory at the Mount Vernon Hospital, the nucleus of the present Gray Laboratory, which attracted many important researchers. The unit became known as a centre for radiation chemistry, and studies were carried on the irradiation of bacteria and of tumours. Gray himself worked with Eleanor Deschner on the oxygen effect and with Dewey developed the Hersch cell for the measurement of oxygen.

Gray was Vice Chairman of the International Commission on Radiation Units and Measurements (ICRU) from 1956 to 1962 and assisted in the formation of the IARR. He received many awards for his work, notably the Betrner Medal in 1964. He was elected Fellow of the Royal Society (FRS) in 1961.

13.2.14　Rolf M. Sievert

Rolf M Sievert
1896-1966

Rolf Maximilian Sievert was born in Stockholm on 6 May 1896. His dissertation for Ph.D. was on measuring methods on röntgen, radium and ultraviolet. The same year he became associate professor in medical physics at Stockholm University.

Between 1924 and 1937, he was head of the physics laboratory at Radiumhemmet. In 1937, he was appointed as the head of the department of radiation physics at Karolinska Institute and in 1941 professor in radiation physics at Karolinska Institute.

After his retirement in 1965 and to his death on 3 October 1966, he continued to take a very active part in the national and international cooperation in his particular field of interest, radiation dose measurement and radiation protection. He had played a pioneering role in his area of activities.

Already in 1919 Rolf Sievert took contact with radiologists, physicians using ionizing radiation in their work, and offered them his cooperation in the attempt to solve the physical problems linked with the usage of radiation for diagnosis and therapy. His unremunerated cooperation continued until 1924, when the Cancer Society in Sweden decided to remunerate Sievert as head of the physics laboratorium of Radiumhemmet, which he had organized and financed on his own. Under the leadership of Sievert, the laboratory was developed into a worldwide known centre for radiation physics. In 1938, he moved to the Karolinska Hospital and was named Head Department of Radiation Physics.

During the early part of the 1920s, no standardization of patient doses for different hospitals was performed. For that reason, Sievert started an organization in 1925, which was made responsible for the continuous control of dosage levels at all clinics in the country performing radiation treatment. The control programme was extended as time went by and eventually included control of all work with radiation, medical as well as industrial. On the initiative of Rolf Sievert, the government passed Sweden's first radiation protection law in 1941. The law gave the Department of Radiation Physics the task to supervise all such activities.

During the years 1920–1940, Rolf Sievert gave his most important contributions to the field of clinical physics. He developed the basics on how to calculate the absorbed dose to tumours; he developed new devices for patient irradiation and pointed out the importance of the contribution of secondary radiation. Furthermore, he invented a number of ingenious instruments for dose measurements, among other the worldwide known Sievert chamber.

During the 1930s, Sievert worked primarily with the biological effects of ionizing radiation, and particularly the effects of the low doses received by radiologists in their daily work, and for comparison, the effects caused by unavoidable natural radiation background that we all are exposed to. Several years before the question of radioactive fallout was raised, Sievert studied the matter by gathering available data on the spreading of aches in the atmosphere after volcano eruptions.

During the last 20 year of his life, Sievert spent most of his time working with radiation protection issues and made the plans for what was to become the Swedish Radiation Protection Institute, SSI.

To honour Rolf Sievert, the CGPM conference of 1979 accepted sievert (Symbol Sv), as the unit for dose equivalent for ionizing radiation. This unit is a part of the SI system for units.

$$1\,Sv = 1J/kg.$$

He was the pioneer in the field of radiation protection, one of the main initiators of both ICRP and ICRU, 19213. He remained Chairman of ICRP 1956–1962, UNSCEAR 1958–1960 and Professor at the Department of Medical Radiation Physics in Stockholm 1941–1965. He died in Stockholm on 3 December 1966.

Sievert Chamber

In its most usual form, the Sievert chamber is a sphere or cylinder of a magnesium alloy (electron metal) placed in the centre of a hollow sphere of the same material. The inner electrode is fixed in its position by amber isolators. Through an opening in the outer sphere, they could be charged to a well-known potential. The opening is the closed with a lid equipped with a staff acting as a holder of the chamber. If the chamber is exposed to ionizing radiation, the air in the cavity between the inner and the outer sphere becomes conducting through the ion pairs formed, and the charge of the chamber is reduced by the leakage current formed. The charged reduction can then easily be measured on a separate instrument at some other location. The reduction of the charge is a measure of the radiation dose received by the chamber. Such a chamber can be transported long distances without affecting the readout. The diameter of the chamber can be as small as a few millimetres.

13.2.15   Georg Simon Ohm

Georg Simon Ohm
1787-1854

Georg Simon Ohm was born on 16 March 1787 in Erlangen Germany. He was a German physicist who was best known for his research in electrical currents. He was educated at the University of Erlangen. Unfortunately, when Ohm published his finding in 1827, that current flowing in a given resistor was proportional to the voltage applied across it, his colleagues dismissed his ideas. Ohm was forced to resign from his high-school teaching position and he lived in poverty and shame until he accepted a position at Nuremberg in 1833.

From 1833 to 1849, he was Director of the Polytechnic Institute of Nuremberg, and from 1852 until his death he was professor of experimental physics at the University of Munich. His formulation of the relationship between current, electromotive force and resistance, known as Ohm's law, is the basic law of current flow.

In 1841, the Royal Society in London recognized the significance of his discovery and awarded him the Copley medal. The following year, they admitted him as a member. In 1849, just 5 years before his death, Ohm's lifelong dream was realized when he was given a professorship of experimental physics at the University of Munich. On 7 July 1854, he passed away in Munich, at the age of 65.

Electricity was not the only topic on which Ohm undertook research and not the only topic in which he ended up in controversy. In 1843, he stated the fundamental principle of physiological acoustics, concerned with the way in which one hears combination tones. However, the assumptions, which he made in his mathematical derivation, were not totally justified and this resulted in a bitter dispute with the physicist August Seebeck. He succeeded in discrediting Ohm's hypothesis and Ohm had to acknowledge his error.

The ohm with symbol Ω, the unit of electrical resistance has been named in his honour.

13.2.16   *Werner Von Siemens*

Werner von Siemens
1816-1892

Ernst Werner von Siemens was a German inventor and industrialist and was known as Werner von Siemens.

Werner Siemens was born in Lenthe, near Hanover, Germany on 13 December 1816. He was the fourth child out of fourteen children of a tenant farmer. He left school without finishing his education but joined the army to undertake training in engineering.

Siemens invented a telegraph that used a needle to point to the right letter, instead of using Morse code. Based on this invention, he founded the company Telegraphen-Bauanstalt von Siemens and Halske on 1 October 1847, with the company taking occupation of its workshop on 12 October.

Soon after founding the company, it was internationalized. One brother of Werner represented him in England (Sir William Siemens) and another in St. Petersburg, Russia (Carl von Siemens), each earning separate recognition in their own right. Following his industrial career, he was ennobled in 1888, becoming Werner von Siemens. He retired from his company in 1890 and died on 6 December 1892.

The company, reorganized as Siemens and Halske AG, Siemens-Schuckertwerke and—since 1966—Siemens AG, has later been led by his brothers, his three sons

Arnold, Wilhelm and Carl Friedrich and his nephews Hermann, Ernst and Peter von Siemens. Siemens AG is still one of the largest electro-technological firms in the world.

Apart from the pointer telegraph, Siemens made several contributions to the development of electrical engineering and is therefore known as the founding father of the discipline in Germany. On 14 December 1877, he received German patent No. 2355 for an electromechanical "dynamic" or moving-coil transducer, which was adapted by A. L. Thuras and E. C. Wente for the Bell System in the late 1920s for use as a loudspeaker. Wente's adaptation was issued US patent 1,707,545 in 1929. Siemens is also the father of the trolleybus, which he initially tried and tested with his "Elektromote" on 29 April 1882.

The name Siemens has been adopted for the SI unit of electrical conductance.

13.3   Some Units Not Named After Any Scientist

It may be informed that derived units katal, lumen and lux are not after the name of any scientist. Lumen is a Latin word for light or window, and lux is the Latin word for light.

Index